**Photography
and
English text
by**

GREG LAWSON

Published by

First Choice

THANK YOU

Thank you Ralph Cernuda for the lending of your many skills to this work, as well as for your constant encouragement.

Thank you Janine Builder, Evelyne Berkmuller and Matthew Mendenhall for your time and talents used in the translation of the English text.

I also appreciate the assistance recieved from various departments of the City and County of Santa Barbara, the University of California and the Santa Barbara Chamber of Commerce.

To the many others, including my family, who have helped in many ways, Thank you.

G.L.

ENGLISH · ESPAÑOL · FRANÇAIS · DEUTSCH

BEAUTY SPOT
SANTA BARBARA

BEAUTY SPOT—SANTA BARBARA

Published in the United States by

First Choice

P.O. Box 1680
Ramona, California 92065

Second Printing 1988
©Copyright 1981 by Greg Lawson. All rights reserved.

Library of Congress Catalog Card Number 81-68211
ISBN 9-9606 704-0-8 Hardcover
ISBN 0-9606 704-1-6 Softcover

Artwork and book design by
RALPH CERNUDA

English text translated into Spanish, French and German by Matthew Mendenhall, Janine Builder and Evelyne Berkmuller respectively.

Typography by Friedrich Typography
Printed in Singapore

Cover photo taken at El Paseo

CONTENTS

FOREWORD

Santa Barbara is beautiful! Protected on the north by California's east-west Santa Ynez Mountains, and on the south by the Pacific Ocean's Channel Islands, the sheltered city enjoys a salubrious climate considered by many to be paradisiac. Over 350 species of trees from around the world flourish here. Sightings of more than 400 species of birds have been recorded in the area. Flowers are in bloom each month of the year.

Centuries ago, when the only human inhabitants of the area were the amicable Chumash Indians, Spanish explorers claimed the region for Spain. Later the Mexican government held dominion over Santa Barbara and, of course, now it is an American city; but today, in many ways the city chooses to reflect its Spanish heritage. Its architectural style, its red tile roofs, many of its parks and street names are distinctly Spanish, distinctively Santa Barbara.

Just over the Santa Ynez Mountains lies a beautiful valley. Farms, ranches, orchards, vineyards, lakes, rivers, parks, rolling hills and colorful communities — the splendor of the Santa Ynez Valley is seen at every turn.

People from around the world agree, the Santa Barbara area is one of earth's foremost beauty spots.

PREFACIO

¡Santa Bárbara es bella! Protegida al norte por la Cordillera Santa Inés de California, y al sur por las Islas del Canal de Santa Bárbara, la ciudad amparada disfruta de un clima salubre que muchos consideran paradisíaco. Más de 350 especies de árboles de todo el mundo medran aquí. Se han observado y anotado más de 400 especies de pájaros en la región. Brotan flores todos los meses del año.

Hace siglos, cuando los únicos habitantes humanos del área eran los amistosos indios Chumash, exploradores españoles se adueñaron de la región en el nombre de España. Más tarde el gobierno mexicano tuvo dominio sobre Santa Bárbara, y por supuesto, ahora es una ciudad estadounidense; pero hoy en día, en muchas maneras la ciudad prefiere reflejar su herencia española. Su estilo arquitectural, sus techos de tejas rojas y muchos de los nombres de sus parques y calles son característicamente españoles, distintamente Santa Bárbara.

Al otro lado de la Cordillera Santa Inés yace un valle hermoso. Granjas, ranchos, huertos, viñas, lagos, ríos, parques, colinas onduladas y comunidades pintorescas—a cada paso se nota el esplendor del Valle de Santa Inés.

Personas de todas partes del mundo convienen en que la región de Santa Bárbara es una de las más hermosas de la tierra.

AVANT-PROPOS

Santa Barbara est belle! Elle est protégée au nord par les montagnes californiennes de Santa Ynez, qui s'étendent de l'est à l'ouest, et au sud par les îles "Channel" de l'Océan Pacifique. Cette ville abritée jouit d'un climat sain que beaucoup de gens estiment paradisiaque. Plus de 350 espèces d'arbres provenant du monde entier fleurissent la ville, et l'on peut voir plus de 400 espèces d'oiseaux dans la région. Des fleurs s'épanouissent toute l'année.

Il y a des siècles, à une époque oú les indiens amicaux de la tribu Chumash étaient les seuls habitants de l'endroit, les explorateurs espagnols ont réclamé le territoire pour l'Espagne. Plus tard, le gouvernement mexicain a dominé Santa Barbara et ses environs. C'est maintenant une ville américaine; pourtant, on aperçoit le reflet de son héritage mexicain dans beaucoup de choses. Son architecture, ses toits aux tuiles d'argile rouge, beaucoup de ses parcs et de ses noms de rues réflètent un style purement espagnol, purement "Santa Barbara".

Juste de l'autre côté des montagnes de Santa Ynez s'étend une belle vallée avec des fermes, des ranches, des vergers, des vignobles, des lacs, des rivières, des parcs, des collines ondulantes et des communautés pittoresques — la splendeur de la vallée de Santa Ynez se révèle à tout moment.

Les gens du monde entier reconnaissent que la région de Santa Barbara est l'un des plus beaux endroits du monde.

VORWORT

Santa Barbara ist eine schöne Stadt! Eingebettet zwischen Kaliforniens südwestlichen Santa Ynez Bergen im Norden und den Channel Islands des Pazifischen Ozeans im Süden, erfreut sich diese Stadt eines überaus angenehmen Klimas, das von vielen als paradiesisch bezeichnet wird. Über 350 Baumsorten aus aller Welt gedeihen hier. Mehr als 400 verschiedene Vogelarten kann man in dieser Umgebung beobachten und die exotischsten Blumen blühen zu jeder Jahreszeit.

Vor Jahrhunderten, als die friedlichen Chumash Indianer noch die einzigen menschlichen Bewohner dieser Gegend waren, nahmen spanische Entdecker dieses Gebiet für Spanien in Anspruch. Später befand sich Santa Barbara unter mexikanischer Herrschaft. Jetzt ist es natürlich eine amerikanische Stadt, die aber in vieler Hinsicht auch heute noch ganz bewußt ihr spanisches Erbe widerspiegelt. Die Architektur, die roten Ziegeldächer, die Namen von vielen Parks und Straßen sind ausgesprochen spanisch und im Stil — eben Santa Barbara.

Gleich hinter den Santa Ynez Bergen liegt ein herrliches Tal mit Farmen, Ranches, Obstplantagen, Weingärten, Seen, Flüssen, Naturschutzgebieten, sanften Hügeln und malerischen Orten — die ganze Pracht des Santa Ynez Tals entfaltet sich an jeder Wegbiegung aufs neue.

Besucher aus allen Teilen der Welt sind sich einig, daß Santa Barbara und Umgebung zu den schönsten Plätzen der Welt zählt.

1 A bird's eye view of Santa Barbara, California.

Santa Bárbara, California fotografiada a vista de pájaro.

Vue générale de Santa Barbara, Californie.

Santa Barbara, Kalifornien aus der Vogelperspektive.

2 Observed from atop one of Santa Barbara's coastal cliffs, dainty
flowers add color to a cypress frame of the Pacific Ocean.

Flores delicadas prestan color a una vista del Océano Pacífico,
observada a través de un marco de cipreses desde uno de los riscos
costaneros de Santa Bárbara.

Vues d'une falaise de Santa Barbara, de petites fleurs ajoutent de la
couleur à des cyprès qui encadrent l'Océan Pacifique.

Aussicht von einer der Klippen an Santa Barbaras Küste: Blumen als
Farbtupfer und Zypressen als Rahmen für das Meer.

3 Pacific waters roll ashore near Gaviota.

Las aguas del Pacífico llegan a la orilla cerca de Gaviota.

Les eaux de l'Océan Pacifique baignent la côte près de Gaviota.

Wogen des Pazifik bei Gaviota.

4 Vivid sunsets frequent South Coast skies.

Vívidas puestas del sol frecuentan los cielos de la Costa del Sur.

Les cieux de la côte sud sont éclaboussés par les couchers de soleil magnifiques.

Farbenprächtige Sonnenuntergänge sind keine Seltenheit an der Südküste Kaliforniens.

6 Arroyo Burro Beach is a favorite of many locals and visitors in search of sun and surf.

La Playa Arroyo Burro es una de las predilectas de muchos residentes y visitantes en busca del sol y oleaje.

La plage Arroyo Burro est l'endroit préféré de ceux qui cherchent le soleil et les vagues.

Arroyo Burro Beach—ein beliebter Strand bei Einheimischen und Besuchern, die Sonne und Wasser suchen.

5 The Santa Barbara Harbor provides shelter for over 1000 working and pleasure vessels.

El Puerto de Santa Bárbara ampara más de 1,000 barcos comerciales y de recreo.

Le port de Santa Barbara abrite plus de 1000 bâteaux de plaisance et bâteaux de pêche.

Im Hafen von Santa Barbara liegen über 1000 Fischerboote und Jachten.

7 High spots throughout the city afford a variety of panoramic views.

Puntos altos por toda la ciudad proporcionan una variedad de vistas panorámicas.

Les points culminants de la ville offrent une variété de vues panoramiques.

Die vielen Hügel der Stadt bieten immer wieder neue Rundblicke.

8 The architectural lines of the beautiful County Courthouse reflect the
9 city's Spanish roots. Built in the 1920s the Courthouse is covered with the
red tile characteristic of the city's roofs.

Las líneas arquitecturales de la bella Sede del Tribunal del Condado
reflejan las raíces españolas de la ciudad. Construida en los años 1920,
la Sede está techada con las tejas rojas características de los tejados
de la ciudad.

L'architecture du beau palais de justice du comté réflète l'héritage
espagnol de la ville. Construit dans les années 1920, le palais de justice
est couvert du toit aux tuiles d'argile rouge qui caractérise la ville.

Die Architektur des schönen Gerichtsgebäudes spiegelt den
spanischen Ursprung der Stadt wider. Es wurde in den zwanziger Jahren
erbaut und hat das für Santa Barbara so typische rote Ziegeldach.

10 The Riviera, a hillside residential section as seen from the clock-tower of the County Courthouse.

La Riviera, un barrio residencial en la ladera del monte, tal como se ve desde la torre del reloj de la Sede del Tribunal del Condado.

La "Riviera", secteur résidentiel sur les flancs de la côte, vue du clocher du palais de justice.

Die Riviera, ein Villenviertel am Hang, von Glockenturm des Gerichtsgebäudes aus gesehen.

11 Grey skies yield to sunlight and a heavenly spectrum.

Cielos grises ceden a la luz del sol y un espectro celestial.

Le ciel gris laisse la place au soleil et à un spectre céleste.

Ein grauer Himmel weicht der Sonne und einem Regenbogen.

12 Business sections, like residential sections, are lined with an
13 international variety of trees. Shown is the spring bloom of a Brazilian
Jacaranda tree.

En los distritos comerciales, lo mismo que en los barrios residenciales,
se encuentra una variedad internacional de árboles. Aquí se ve el
florecimiento primaveral de un jacarandá brasilero.

Les rues des secteurs commerciaux aussi bien que celles des zones résidentielles sont bordées d'une variété d'arbres. Voici la floraison printanière d'un jacaranda brésilien.

Entlang den Straßen der Geschäfts- und Wohnviertel grünen Bäume aus aller Welt. Hier eine brasilianische Jacaranda in Frühjahrsblüte.

14 Downtown buildings must by law conform to the Spanish style of
15 architecture common to old Santa Barbara. El Cuartel, or "The Guards
House", was part of the Royal Spanish Presidio, a military fortification
built in the 1780s. The office building was completed in the 1980s.

Todos los edificios del centro, según la ley, deben conformarse al estilo
arquitectural español propio de la Santa Bárbara vieja. El Cuartel, o sea,
la "Casa de los Guardias", era parte del Presidio Español Real, una
fortificación militar construida en los años 1780. El edificio de oficinas
fue completado en los años 1980.

La loi exige l'adhésion des bâtiments de centre-ville au vieux style
espagnol typique de Santa Barbara. El Cuartel, ou "le corps de garde",
faisait partie du préside espagnol, un fortification militaire construite
dans les années 1780; alors que le bâtiment administratif fut achevé
dans les années 1980.

Alle Gebäude in der Innenstadt müssen sich dem gesetzlich
vorgeschriebenen Stil des alten Santa Barbara anpassen. El Cuartel,
oder "die Wache" war ein Teil des Königlich Spanischen Präsidiums,
einer Militärfestung, die in den achtziger Jahren des achtzehnten
Jahrhunderts erbaut wurde. Das Bürogebäude wurde erst nach 1980
vollendet.

16 Whitewashed buildings are first to reflect the morning sun.

Edificios blanqueados son los primeros en reflejar el sol de la mañana.

Les âtiments badigeonnés en blanc sont les premiers à réfléchir le soleil du matin.

Weißgetünchte Häuser reflektieren die ersten Strahlen der Morgensonne.

17 A peaceful retreat from the busy downtown shopping district is nearby Alice Keck Park.

A corta distancia del bullicioso sector comercial del centro es el asilo tranquilo del Parque Alice Keck.

Le parc "Alice Keck", à côté du quartier commercial animé, sert de refuge contre l'activité de la ville.

Nach der Unruhe der geschäftigen Innenstadt, lädt der nahegelegene Alice Keck Park zu einer Ruhepause ein.

18 This courtyard fountain is on the grounds of the Santa Barbara Historical
Society Museum, one of several excellent museums in the city.

Esta fuente se encuentra en el patio del Museo de la Sociedad Histórica
de Santa Bárbara, uno de varios museos excelentes en la ciudad.

Cette fontaine se trouve dans la cour du Musée de la Société Historique de Santa Barbara, qui est parmi plusieurs excellents musées de la ville.

Dieser Brunnen befindet sich auf dem Gelände des Santa Barbara Historical Society Museums, eines der ausgezeichneten Museen der Stadt.

19 El Paseo: Offices, restaurants and shops in an old Santa Barbara setting.
20
20A El Paseo: Oficinas, restaurantes y tiendas en un ambiente propio de la Santa Bárbara vieja.

El Paseo, arcade commerciale de bureaux, restaurants et boutiques, située dans une ambiance de Santa Barbara historique.

El Paseo: Büros, Restaurants und Geschäfte im Stil des alten Santa Barbara.

21 A downtown financial structure erected in the 1920s.

Un edificio comercial del centro construido en los años 1920.

Un bâtiment commercial de centre-ville construit dans les années 1920.

Ein Finanzgebäude der Innenstadt, errichtet in den zwanziger Jahren.

22 Called a "Naked Lady", this long stemmed beauty, a member of the amaryllis family, pushes up out of the ground even before its leaves do.

Llamada "Dama desnuda", esta belleza de tallo largo, un miembro de la familia amarilis, brota del suelo aún antes de echar sus hojas.

La "belle dame", belle plante à longue tige et membre du genre amaryllis, produit sa fleur même avant que ses feuilles ne poussent.

Diese langstielige schöne Blüte, genannt "Naked Lady", gehört zu den Amaryllisgewächsen und sprießt aus der Erde noch bevor sie Blätter hat.

23 Known as the "Queen" of California's famous Missions, the Santa
24 Barbara Mission was founded in the 1780s. Pictured Mission structures
25 were for the most part completed in the 1830s. A Mission museum
contains many historical artifacts.

Conocida como la "Reina" de las famosas misiones de California, la
Misión Santa Bárbara fue fundada en los años 1780. Las estructuras que
aparecen aquí se terminaron por la mayor parte durante los años 1830.
Un museo de la misión contiene muchos artefactos históricos.

Reconnue comme "la reine" de toutes les missions célèbres de
Californie, la Mission Santa Barbara fut fondée dans les années 1780.
Les bâtiments qui figurent ici étaient achevés pour la plupart dans les
années 1830. Le musée de la mission contient beaucoup d'objets
façonnés.

Die Santa Barbara Mission wurde in den achtziger Jahren des 18.
Jahrhunderts gegründet und ist als die "Königin" von Kaliforniens
berühmten Missions bekannt. Die abgebildeten Gebäude wurden
größtenteils in den dreißiger Jahren des 19. Jahrhunderts fertiggestellt.
Ein dazugehöriges Museum enthält viele historische Gegenstände.

26 The Lobero Theatre has been designated an official Historic Landmark by the State of California.

El Teatro Lobero ha sido designado un lugar histórico oficial por el estado de California.

Le gouvernement de Californie a désigné le théâtre Lobero comme point de repère historique.

Das Lobero Theater wurde von der kalifornischen Regierung unter Denkmalsschutz gestellt.

27 The Arlington Center for the Performing Arts.
28

El Centro Arlington para las Bellas Artes.

Le Centre Arlington donne des Présentations et des Spectacles.

Das Arlington Theater—ein Center für Theateraufführungen und
Konzerte.

29 Though you may never see snow fall in Santa Barbara, it will on rare occasions lace the city's shoulders, the lovely Santa Ynez Mountains, seen here from Laguna Blanca in Hope Ranch.

Aunque nunca nieva en Santa Bárbara, a veces adorna los hombros de la ciudad, las hermosas montañas Santa Inés, vistas aquí desde Laguna Blanca en Hope Ranch.

La neige ne tombe jamais dans la ville de Santa Barbara, mais parfois les belles montagnes de Santa Ynez sont couvertes de neige, vues ici de Laguna Blanca à Hope Ranch.

Obwohl es in Santa Barbara kaum jemals schneit, können die umliegenden Santa Ynez Berge wohl manchmal weiße Spitzen haben. Man sieht sie hier von Laguna Blanca aus (in Hope Ranch).

A posted scenic route includes a drive through the lush residential sections of Hope Ranch and Montecito, adjacent to Santa Barbara.

Una ruta pintoresca marcada incluye un paseo por los lozanos barrios residenciales de Hope Ranch y Montecito, contiguos a Santa Bárbara.

Les zones résidentielles de luxe de "Hope Ranch" et de Montecito font partie d'une excursion sur une route panoramique de la régione de Santa Barbara.

Eine markierte Panoramastraße führt durch die üppig bewachsenen Villenviertel Hope Ranch und Montecito, die an Santa Barbara grenzen.

30 A Montecito residence.

Una residencia de Montecito.

Une résidence de Montecito.

Eine Villa in Montecito.

31 From high above the valley floor spring color beckons.

Desde lo alto del valle los colores primaverales convidan.

Au dessus de la vallée, les couleurs du printemps nous attirent.

Die Höhen leuchten im Frühjahr in bunten Farben.

THE SANTA YNEZ VALLEY

32 A tranquil ranch scene.

Una escena tranquila en un rancho.

Vue paisible d'un ranch.

Das friedliche Leben auf der Ranch.

33 A valley winery surrounded by summer's golden hills.

Un lagar del valle rodeado por los cerros dorados del verano.

Des collines dorées entourent un vignoble de la vallée.

Eine Weinkellerei inmitten der sommerlichen Hügel.

34 The Santa Ynez River carves its path through the Rancho San Fernando Rey.

El Río Santa Inés talla su cauce por el Rancho San Fernando Rey.

La rivière de Santa Ynez se fraye un chemin à travers le ranch San Fernando Rey.

Der Santa Ynez Fluß durchschneidet das Gebiet der San Fernando Rey Ranch.

36 Rolling hills near the valley are yellowed by spring blossom.

Cerros ondulados cerca del valle teñidos de amarillo por flores primaverales.

Les fleurs printanières font jaunir les collines ondulantes près de la vallée.

Die hügelige Landschaft gelb übersät mit Frühlingsblumen.

35 An old truck and water tower in the town of Santa Ynez.

Un camión y una torre de agua viejos en el pueblo de Santa Inés.

Un vieux camion et un château d'eau dans la ville de Santa Ynez.

Ein alter Lastwagen und der Wasserturm in dem Städtchen Santa Ynez.

37 A short walk on a forested pathway leads to graceful Nojoqui Falls,
38 sometimes a torrent, sometimes a trickle, it's worth the hike any time of
year.

Un paseo corto por una senda arbolada lleva a la Cascada Nojoqi, a
veces un torrente, a veces un hilillo, vale la pena dar la caminata durante
cualquier época del año.

Une courte promenade dans un sentier boisé nous amène aux belles
cascades de Nojoqui. S'écoulant parfois en torrents, parfois en minces
filets, cette chute d'eau mérite d'être vue à toute saison.

Ein kurzer Spaziergang auf einem Waldpfad führt zum reizvollen Nojoqui
Wasserfall, der manchmal ein Strom und manchmal nur ein Rinnsal ist.
Aber er ist zu jeder Jahreszeit eine Wanderung wert.

39 In the early 1900s some 450 of these bells were placed along the
    Mission route, "El Camino Real". This one is at Mission Santa Ines in
    Solvang.

    Hacia principios de los años 1900 unas 450 de estas campanas se
    colocaron a lo largo de la ruta entre las misiones, "El Camino Real". Esta
    se encuentra en la Misión Santa Inés, en Solvang.

    Au début des années 1900, environs 450 de ces cloches ont été
    placées le long de la route de missions, "El Camino Real". La cloche
    que l'on peut voir est à la mission de Santa Ynez à Solvang.

    Im frühen 19. Jahrhundert wurden etwa 450 dieser Glocken entlang der
    Straße der Missionsstationen, "El Camino Real", aufgestellt. Diese
    befindet sich bei Mission Santa Inez in Solvang.

40 This charming windmill house can be seen in the ever popular town of
    Solvang, a community rich in Danish culture.

    Puede verse esta encantadora casa con su molino de viento en el
    siempre-popular pueblo de Solvang, una comunidad ricamente dotada
    de cultura dinamarquesa.

    On peut voir ce charmant moulin, servant aussi de maison, dans la ville
    toujours populaire de Solvang, une communauté enrichie en culture
    danoise.

    Dieses hübsche Windmühlenhaus steht in dem allgemein beliebten
    Städtchen Solvang, einer Gemeinde, die von dänischer Kultur geprägt
    ist.

42 Lake Cachuma, the fresh water source for Santa Barbara and the Santa
    Ynez Valley, is also a fishing, boating, and camping area.

    El Lago Cachuma, la fuente del agua fresca para Santa Bárbara y el
    Valle de Santa Inés, también es un lugar para pescar, pasear en bote y
    hacer campamento.

    Le lac Cachuma, reservoir d'eau pour Santa Barbara et la ville de Santa
    Ynez, est aussi une aire de recréation.

    Cachuma, der See, der den Wasserbedarf von Santa Barbara und dem
    Santa Ynez Tal deckt, bietet zugleich auch Gelegenheit zum Fischen,
    Bootfahren und Camping.

41 A roadside bouquet.

Un ramo del borde del camino.

Un bouquet de fleurs au bord de la route.

Blumen am Straßenrand.

This map, keyed to photographic plate numbers, is not to scale.

Este mapa, que corresponde a los números de las láminas fotográficas, no está en proporción.

La carte qui figure ici, correspondant aux numéros des photographes, n'est pas dessinée à l'échelle.

Auf dieser Karte sind die Phototafeln markiert. Die Karte ist jedoch nicht maßstabsgetreu gezeichnet.

MACROBOLIC
NUTRITION

PRIMING YOUR BODY TO BUILD MUSCLE & BURN FAT

Gerard Dente
with Kevin J. Hopkins

**Basic
Health**
PUBLICATIONS, INC.

The information contained in this book is based upon the research and personal and professional experiences of the authors. It is not intended as a substitute for consulting with your physician or other healthcare provider. Any attempt to diagnose and treat an illness should be done under the direction of a healthcare professional.

The publisher does not advocate the use of any particular healthcare protocol but believes the information in this book should be available to the public. The publisher and authors are not responsible for any adverse effects or consequences resulting from the use of the suggestions, preparations, or procedures discussed in this book. Should the reader have any questions concerning the appropriateness of any procedures or preparation mentioned, the authors and the publisher strongly suggest consulting a professional healthcare advisor.

The author(s) of this book have a financial interest in some of the products recommended herein. This does not constitute an endorsement by Basic Health Publications, Inc.

Basic Health Publications, Inc.
8200 Boulevard East • North Bergen, NJ 07047 • 1-201-868-8336

Library of Congress Cataloging-in-Publication Data
Dente, Gerard, 1967–
  Macrobolic nutrition : priming your body to build muscle and burn body
fat / Gerard Dente with Kevin J. Hopkins.
     p. cm.
  Includes bibliographical references and index.
  ISBN 1-59120-131-4
  1. Bodybuilders—Nutrition. 2. Macrobiotic diet. I. Hopkins, Kevin J.,
1972– II. Title.

  TX361.B64D46   2004
  613.2'024'79641—dc22

                                                    2004003217

Editor: Carol Rosenberg
Typesetter/Book design: Gary A. Rosenberg
Cover photo: Per Bernal
Kurt Angle photo on page 143 owned by World Wrestling Entertainment, Inc.
and is reproduced with permission.

Printed in the United States of America

10   9   8   7   6   5   4   3   2

Contents

Photo by Irvin J. Gelb.

Acknowledgments

THERE ARE MANY PEOPLE I WOULD LIKE TO THANK for their help, support, and friendship, but to name them all would take pages. I have been extremely fortunate to have so many special people in my life.

I want to give a special thanks to my mom, dad, sisters, brother, and my wife, Linda, for all of their continued support and for always allowing me to pursue my ambitions and dreams.

I want to thank all of the athletes I work with, particularly those mentioned in this book. Working with and knowing each of you is an honor and a pleasure. Each one of you is a champion. I especially want to thank Dave Hawk for our friendship and Kurt Angle, a great athlete and role model, and an even greater human being.

I am fortunate to be able to work in an industry I truly love. So, along with the people I just mentioned, I want to thank all the people I work with at MHP and all those I work with on a regular basis in the nutrition industry who have given me so much support and so many opportunities. You know who you are and I want to say . . . Thank you! Without your support, I would not be able to continually pursue my passion to research and develop new products and educate myself and others on better ways to improve health and performance.

—Gerard Dente

Preface

I HAVE DEDICATED MOST OF MY LIFE to finding ways to increase muscle mass and improve physical performance. It started with my own personal quest to excel in high school football and then as a national-level competitive body-builder. I was fortunate enough to have fairly good genetics for building muscle. However, I knew that in order to compete at the top-level ranks against people with equal or better genetics, I had to compensate through a superior training and nutrition program. I know the extra knowledge of nutrition I gathered and applied toward my program helped me excel further than either I or anyone else had expected. During the time I was competing, I was able to maintain an off-season body weight of 285 to 295 pounds at only 10 percent body fat and a competition weight of 250 pounds at 4 to 5 percent body fat. This was back in 1995, an era when competing at 250 pounds was way above the norm.

For most bodybuilders, the goal is usually to win in competition, but the real motivation is to achieve the kind of personal progress that involves continually taking your body to the next level. That is what is so great about weightlifting and bodybuilding. If your focus is on your body and your external goals—the complete concept of what you want to achieve—bodybuilding can be very fulfilling and rewarding.

My personal quest to build my physique to its maximum potential through proper training and nutrition led me to an exploration of the research and development of sports-enhancing supplementation. Because I relied on nutrition to gain a competitive advantage over my competition and to help me reach my full genetic potential, I dedicated a lot of time to researching nutrition and supplementation and their effects on muscle building and performance. As I learned more, I realized that there was a lot of room for improvement and advancement in the sports supplements being offered to athletes, and this ultimately led to the creation of Maximum Human Performance, Inc., in 1997. MHP's company mission is to provide athletes with the latest advancements in sports supplementation.

In addition to deriving inspiration from making progress and improvements in my own physique, I am inspired by public speaking and by helping others to achieve their fitness goals. I have given many lectures and seminars on training and nutrition over the years. Also, when you are a bodybuilder, your body serves as your uniform and it's obvious that you work out. You become a target for questions; so, no matter where you are, someone is almost sure to ask you a question about training, diet, or supplementation. I must have fielded tens of thousands of questions over the years.

It became obvious to me, by the number and kinds of questions that most people ask, that they are completely uninformed about nutrition, and it is disheartening to see how frustrated, confused, and misled they consequently become. I've seen too many people working hard at the gym and not getting results. I've answered questions like "How do I get big?" "What should I eat?" and "What supplements should I take?" too many times. It is for this reason that I felt compelled to write *Macrobolic Nutrition*.

If you've ever asked or wondered about any of these questions . . . if you train hard and are unhappy with the results you've gotten, this book is for you! The answers and results lie within *Macrobolic Nutrition*'s 45/35/20 lean-mass equation.

I don't proclaim to be a "diet guru," nor am I going to try to take credit for any great diet revolution. In *Macrobolic Nutrition,* I present scientific truths about nutrition in a simple, logical fashion. This book will help you understand the enormous impact food has on your body. Macrobolic Nutrition can be applied to anyone who is working out and who wants to build muscle and burn body fat. Those of you who are hardcore will see that Macrobolic Nutrition is the only way to make serious gains in "lean mass" and reach your full genetic potential. Macrobolic Nutrition is not a quick fix: it is a long-term permanent solution! There are other diets and nutrition programs that may help you lose body fat, but these diets typically compromise your ability to pack on muscle. Macrobolic Nutrition will turn your body into an efficient muscle-building, fat-burning machine! I am confident that Macrobolic Nutrition will work for you as it has for me and for many others.

—Gerard Dente

WHEN GERARD DENTE APPROACHED ME to help write this book, I was skeptical. I understood that there was something missing within this industry, and basic nutrition was it. Gerard and I are on the same page when talking nutrition, but I was just a little concerned that we would be trying to appeal to the masses and not deliver the facts we know actually work. I soon found out that Gerard had in mind exactly what I felt was needed to guarantee bodybuilding success.

My background is in pharmacy and biochemistry, so naturally, the hormonal environment created in the body by foods and supplements was a vital interest of mine. For a few years, I worked with one of the largest compounding pharmacies in the country. I was exposed to hormonal replacement therapy practiced by some of the top physicians in the world during that time. The missing link for most patients was addressing their nutritional protocol. This slight oversight actually decreased the effectiveness of their therapy. As time went on, my love for bodybuilding and interest in nutrition drove me to open a health food store in 1995. The business grew and satisfied my desire to help educate people on the correct usage of vitamins, sports supplements, and herbs. Finally, I became a partner in a large fitness center and moved the entire health food store into the facility in 2003. I now had the ultimate approach for serving the bodybuilding community: a large state-of-the-art fitness center complete with all the cutting-edge supplements to enhance performance. I also began competing on the state level in the NPC as an open middleweight-class bodybuilder. My conditioning at contest time and my ability to stay ripped year-round drew a lot of attention from fellow competitors and patrons of our gym. Constantly barraged with questions, I felt it necessary to put it all in writing so the explanation would be easily followed.

I met Gerard quite some time ago, through my work with different physicians. One of his close friends was a client of the pharmacy where I worked, and I was very familiar with Gerard's lengthy list of bodybuilding accomplishments. Aware of each other, we finally met by chance at a New Jersey NPC bodybuilding competition. Gerard was there to launch a new supplement. We immediately struck up a conversation, and much to my surprise, he was very knowledgeable. My background in pharmacy and biochemistry intrigued him, and a friendship was formed instantly. I was very impressed with the fact that Gerard had a level of nutritional knowledge few bodybuilders could hope to possess. Coupled with his freaky genetics and 250-pound competition weight, this insightful look into nutrition turned him into an all-out superfreak!

Not long after our chance meeting, Gerard asked me to assist with the production of some new supplements to propel his company to the top of the industry. I agreed, and over the next few years TRAC, T-BOMB, TakeOFF, and their latest creation "The Up Your MASS" line were born. My background in pharmacy and drug-delivery systems proved to be invaluable for the invention of the enteric-coated delivery system of T-BOMB, which quickly became the number-one-selling prohormone in the country.

Now our chance meeting has evolved into my coauthoring *Macrobolic Nutrition*. I strongly encourage any and all athletes who are serious about lean muscle growth to try the Macrobolic Nutrition food plan. We address everything from protein, carbohydrates, and fats to the effects these macronutrients have on the hormones in the body. This book will be the most valuable tool in your muscle-building arsenal—just as important as the weights you lift and the recovery time you require. Macrobolic Nutrition will put you at the top of the food chain for the maximal results from your training efforts.

—Kevin J. Hopkins

You're a Bodybuilder, So Eat Like One!

YOU'RE DEDICATED AND COMMITTED to building an impressive, sculptured, muscular physique. You train four, five, or maybe even six times per week and stick to a strict diet to achieve the same look as those impressive professional bodybuilders you see in the magazines. Some of you may have been working hard at it for years, while some of you may be just getting started. For those of you who have been working at it for years, I say, "I'm sorry that you have been so dedicated and worked so hard, and still haven't figured out why you're not making serious gains and continual progress." For those of you just starting out, I say, "Congratulations—you are about to save yourself from years of hard work, trial and error, and frustration and misery." So, what is the secret of top bodybuilders? What do they know that you don't know? Why does the modern-day bodybuilder keep getting bigger and bigger and freaky ripped?

Come on; take a guess. I'll give you some clues. It's not their training, and it's something you consume every day. If you didn't figure it out, I'm going to tell you: FOOD! Yes, something as simple as food makes the whole difference. The foods you eat can have a tremendous impact on building a lean, muscular physique—even greater than your training. We all train hard yet we all can't achieve the degree of hard muscularity we desire. And don't blame your genetics, because unless you fuel your body with the proper nutrition, you will never reach your full genetic potential. Granted, we can't all be Mr. Olympia, but we can certainly improve our physiques. I'm not talking about little changes. I'm talking about changing your biochemistry and priming your body to become a muscle-building/fat-burning machine. Your body will efficiently build muscle and burn off body fat twenty-four hours a day, seven days a week, and 365 days a year. Your muscle mass will continue to increase, your body fat will go down to your desired level, and your strength and energy will go through the roof. All of these changes will occur simply by changing the way you eat. Oh,

1

I almost forgot to mention, you won't be doing cardio anymore! (You'll have to keep reading to find out how to get ripped without cardio.)

No doubt you've tried all kinds of diets and none of them worked—that's my point! Macrobolic Nutrition isn't like any other diet. Macrobolic Nutrition was designed for the hardcore, serious bodybuilder/athlete aiming to pack on lean muscle mass, increase strength, and improve performance. The nutritional requirements of bodybuilders and athletes far exceed those of the average person, because the physical demands a bodybuilder places on his or her body greatly increase the need for nutrition to help the body build and repair itself. When you add the goal of building huge amounts of muscle while decreasing body fat into the mix, it's easy to see why most people never reach their full growth potential.

The purpose of this book is to give you an understanding of food's impact on the many biochemical processes in the body that influence muscle growth and fat burning. The science behind Macrobolic Nutrition is very advanced, but I have simplified it to make it easier to understand, and most important, so that you can apply it to achieving your goal to pack on lean mass. You may feel the information is too detailed or scientific at times, but keep reading and it will all come together. Up until now, how to get big and "shredded" has remained a mystery to you. *Macrobolic Nutrition* is like a good mystery novel. You will pick up key pieces of information, "clues," throughout the book on how to get massive and ripped, and by its conclusion, you will have finally figured out the mystery of how to pack on lean mass!

Here are some highlights of what you are about to learn: First and foremost, not all calories are created equal. *Macrobolic Nutrition* teaches you how to choose the right sources of carbohydrates, proteins, and fats. Macrobolic Nutrition's 45/35/20 lean-mass equation shows you how to eat these sources in the proper ratio of macronutrients so they are optimized for your ability to build muscle, burn fat, and increase performance. You'll also learn about the importance of water, vitamins, and minerals.

Macrobolic Nutrition's "Guide to Estimating Calories" will help you calculate the exact amount of carbohydrates, proteins, and fats that you need to achieve your goals. This book even provides a Macrobolic meal menu, so you can eat a variety of delicious foods and make Macrobolic Nutrition an enjoyable and easy-to-follow program. If you want to be at your best and make continual gains in your bodybuilding efforts, Macrobolic Nutrition will get you there.

CHAPTER 1

Understanding Macrobolic Nutrition

EVER WONDER WHY ALL OF THE BIGGEST and most ripped guys in the gym are on the weight room floor moving heavy steel, while all of the overweight or skinny guys are on the cardio machines?

How would you like to be able to pack on muscle and lose body fat without ever having to do cardio again? Yes, you read it right. Pack on muscle and lose body fat without *ever* doing cardio! You are about to learn how the top bodybuilders in the world pack on muscle and stay hard year-round, without cardio and without starving themselves. It all comes down to food, and what professional bodybuilders call Macrobolic Nutrition's lean-mass equation. Macrobolic Nutrition heralds a new era in bodybuilding and performance enhancement. This nutrition program is designed to create the ideal metabolic and hormonal environment for incredible gains in muscle size, strength, and endurance, while burning fat quickly and efficiently. In fact, your body will become so metabolically efficient, you won't have to do cardio to burn body fat. You won't have to starve yourself either. You'll be eating more food than you could imagine every two and a half to three hours. But before I get into the specifics and science of Macrobolic Nutrition's lean-mass equation, let's clear the air right now about the biggest mistake amateur bodybuilders make in their quest for rock-hard mass—low-carb diets. The huge amount of media attention on low-carb diets may have led you to believe that was how to get a lean, muscular physique. Unfortunately, you probably found out the hard way that a low-carb diet isn't giving you the results you want. Rather than becoming big and hard with dense, full muscles, you feel small, flat, and weak! If you don't believe me, keep reading, because science doesn't lie. Not only does science prove it, the impressive mass achieved by the world's top bodybuilders proves it as well.

3

Testimonial

"Early in my bodybuilding career, I made the mistake of going on a low-carb diet the last twelve weeks before a show. I always ended up losing a ton of muscle mass and always showed up looking flat, small, and smooth. Macrobolic Nutrition has made all the difference in the world. Now, instead of losing mass pre-contest, I actually grow right into the show. This allows me to hit the stage looking hard, dense, and full."

—Chris "Big Guns" Bennett,
NPC Top National Bodybuilder

MACROBOLIC NUTRITION'S 45/35/20 LEAN-MASS EQUATION

The 45/35/20 lean-mass equation is the foundation of Macrobolic Nutrition. This will be the equation for your success in achieving your muscle-building and performance goals. 45/35/20 represents the ratio of carbohydrates, proteins, and fats you need to consume in your diet. I didn't pick these numbers randomly. They are based on proven science and my own personal experience of what your body needs to stimulate muscle growth, burn fat, and support recovery. If you are putting your body through rigorous workouts to build muscle and burn body fat, you better be taking in the proper nutrition. Otherwise, all your training efforts are going to be for naught, and you'll never make the gains you're looking for. The reason why most people never reach their full growth potential is not because of their lack of training, but because of their lack of nutrition.

Macrobolic Nutrition heralds a new era in performance enhancement with its design to create the ideal metabolic and hormonal environment for increased muscle size, strength, and endurance, while reducing body fat. Macrobolic's fundamental principle that "all calories are not created equal" is sure to raise controversy. Many other diets are based on the simple premise that caloric intake minus caloric expenditure determines weight gain or weight loss. This is true to an extent, but it is oversimplified when your goal is to improve body composition by adding lean mass and decreasing body fat. I am not disputing that every gram of protein yields four calories, every gram of carbohydrate

Photo by Garry Bartlett.

Testimonial

"When I turned pro in 1999, I competed at a body weight of only 211 pounds. I knew that in order to compete as a pro, I needed to be much bigger. I went to Venice, California, to find out what the secret was on how these guys were getting so huge. Believe it or not, I found out all the top pros were following the same basic principles of Macrobolic Nutrition. Making these simple changes is all it took and now I compete at over 230 pounds. And the only thing I changed was my diet."

—**Mike Morris,** *IFBB Professional Bodybuilder*

yields four calories, and every gram of fat yields nine calories. However, these oversimplified diet programs, written by so-called "diet experts," recommend that you consume less food (calories) than you burn (expend) if you want to lose weight, and more calories than you expend if you want to gain weight. Wow—isn't that brilliant?! How many years of school did they have to go through to come up with such an earth-shattering revelation?

Well, it's not that simple. Whether you are trying to gain weight or lose weight, these primitive diet plans will lead anyone to fail in obtaining his or her goals, especially bodybuilders and athletes. If your goal is to gain weight, you'll gain weight all right, but it will be all fat! I know you're not busting your ass in the gym lifting the heavy iron to put on fat. When a bodybuilder says he wants to get big, he's talking about packing on rock-hard slabs of muscle, not about becoming a "big fatty." Conversely, if you follow this kind of diet plan for weight loss, half of the weight you lose in the first month will be fat, but the other half will be hard-earned lean muscle. After the first month or so, your metabolism will slow down so much and you'll be eating so little that most additional weight loss will be muscle. All that hard work you put in at the gym trying to build muscle will be wasted. Eventually, you'll be left with a thin, soft, mushy body—what I call a "thin fat" body. Worse yet, you'll get so disgusted with these diminished results that you'll start eating poorly again out of frustration, and will blow up into a "big fatty."

I'm not trying to sound obnoxious, but these diets, which so many people follow, set them up for failure. And it annoys me to see people bust their asses in the gym, while they follow these diets, only to be disappointed.

I can't take full credit for many of the key scientific approaches used to develop Macrobolic Nutrition. I must commend both Dr. Robert Atkins and Dr. Barry Sears for paving the way and opening the eyes of the medical community and dieticians, who are often blind to new science. I'm sure most of you are familiar with Dr. Atkins's high-protein/very low-carb "Atkins diet" and Barry Sears's "Zone diet." Both of these diets have considerable scientific merit and have been effectively used for weight reduction by millions of people. But what effect do they have on muscle mass and performance?

The fundamental theory behind the Atkins diet involves ingesting calories primarily from fat and protein. Your body resorts to using stored body fat as an energy source when carbohydrates are restricted from the diet. This process is known as ketosis. However, your body may switch to protein as another source of energy, instead of entering ketosis. When this happens, the liver converts protein into blood sugar via a process called gluconeogenesis. This is where the controversy for athletes begins to arise. How will your body discriminate between the protein in muscle or the body fat stored around it? While there is no doubt that the Atkins diet leads to weight loss in inactive people, it can lead to disaster for bodybuilders and athletes. A no-carbohydrate diet such as the Atkins diet leads to low energy levels and hinders performance. It also will lead to loss of muscle and ineffective recovery from exercise. Studies performed by the U.S. Olympic Committee have shown that an intake of anything less than 42 percent carbohydrates will hinder performance and energy. Carbohydrates are stored in the muscle as glycogen. Glycogen is what muscle uses for energy. In the absence of carbohydrates, precious protein is converted to glycogen instead of being utilized as a building block for muscle growth. This is the last thing a bodybuilder wants to have happen. To make matters even worse, gluconeogenesis, the process for converting protein to glycogen, is not nearly as efficient as the process of converting carbohydrates to glycogen, so less glycogen will be present in the muscle if carbohydrates are not available. Plus, glycogen makes muscles look full and hard, so a low carbohydrate intake is going to result in flat, soft-looking muscles.

The bottom line is that your nutritional requirements are different from your mom's, so get off her diet. A no-carb diet will hinder your ability to pack on muscle, and will leave you feeling weak and looking flat and small. You bust your ass in the gym to look good, so why waste your efforts by eating the wrong foods? Your body needs the right nutrition to get *big* and *ripped*!

Barry Sears's Zone diet is a little closer to the mark. Sears's approach closely examines blood sugar stabilization and insulin levels, much the way that Macrobolic Nutrition does. In the Zone diet, 40 percent of your calories come

About Glycogen

Glycogen is a long chain, or polymer, of glucose molecules that is stored in the brain and liver, but mostly in muscle. Our bodies store carbohydrates as glycogen to be used for energy and to stabilize blood sugar during activity. As a rule of thumb, our bodies will store about 60 grams of carbohydrates in the liver and about 300 grams in the muscle, all of this as glycogen. Of course, the bigger you are and the more muscle you have, the more glycogen you can store. This is another benefit of having more muscle tissue than body fat. This is one of the reasons why a 250-pound athlete requires more carbohydrates and calories than a 160-pound athlete. Muscle glycogen is important to support your energy demands during workouts and to prevent the catabolic process gluconeogenesis.

from carbohydrates, 30 percent from fat, and 30 percent from protein. Sears's ratios are fine for a nonathlete and close to ideal for a regular athlete, but the 30 percent fat proportion tends to compromise the quality of the calories consumed. In order to eat that amount of fat, I feel you will inevitably raise your intake of saturated fat. Macrobolic Nutrition puts more emphasis on the quality of the calories you eat. When it comes to outrageous muscle growth, the Zone just does not pack the punch you need to pack on the mass. It proves effective for endurance athletes, but falls short in protein demands for bodybuilders and strength athletes—for them, too little protein will hinder performance, recovery, and muscle growth. Macrobolic's shift in caloric ratios is just what your body needs to keep it in an anabolic state, the state in which new muscle is built.

Success with Macrobolic Nutrition relies not only on using the 45/35/20 lean-mass equation for your diet, but also in selecting the right sources and combinations of macronutrients (carbohydrates, protein, and fats) to maximize lean mass, strength, and overall performance. Macrobolic Nutrition's key points include optimizing and regulating hormones, meal frequency, the thermogenic effect of food, and its *net effect* on metabolic efficiency. These scientifically advanced concepts will be discussed in easy-to-understand detail so you can apply them to your training program.

Because every athlete is at a different level of conditioning, Macrobolic Nutrition outlines three different formulas for calculating your total Macrobolic caloric needs. (See Chapter 7.) Use these formulas to calculate your own calorie requirements based on your current condition and goal. A Macrobolic caloric requirements table for each goal is included in Appendix A to make following the program even easier. These tables give the amount of carbohydrates, proteins, fats, and total calories athletes should consume depending on their level of conditioning. You will be able to customize a Macrobolic Nutrition diet specifically for you, taking into account your current body weight and body composition, occupation, lifestyle, workout regimen, and most important, your *goal*!

GOALS

- **Gain Lean Muscle/Lose Body Fat**
- **Gain Lean Muscle/Maintain Current Body Fat**
- **Gain Lean Muscle/Gain Body Fat**

The key to any long-term nutrition program is consistency, but don't worry about this being a boring diet. Chapter 10 presents some really tasty Macrobolic meals for you. From quick meals to exotic specialty meals, they are all delicious and they are all Macrobolic! The longer you follow Macrobolic Nutrition, the bigger, leaner, stronger, and healthier you will become. You won't want to stop, once you see the changes and incredible results. That is why Macrobolic Nutrition is called the long-term, permanent solution.

Photo by Frank DeJianne.

Testimonial

"I'm known by Strongman competitors as an overachiever. I am not the most gifted athlete, so I have to rely on a superior training and nutrition regimen to compensate. My training sessions are so intense that I burn through training partners every few months. Macrobolic Nutrition fuels my body with the nutrients I need for muscle growth, strength, and recovery."

—**Steve Kirit,** *USA Strongman Champion in 2002 and 2003*

Testimonial

"I've been involved in power-lifting, Strongman, and strength coaching for over fifteen years. And I have never seen a program that compares to Macrobolic Nutrition for strength training athletes. An athlete's nutrition requirements are far greater than the average person's and to opti-

mize lean mass requires even more precise nutrition. Macrobolic Nutrition really provides the best sources and balance of nutrients for athletes looking to gain size, strength, and improve performance."

—*Mark Philippi,* Former USA Strongman Champion and Collegiate Strength Coach

Photo by Frank DeJianne.

A DIET FOR BODYBUILDERS AND POWER ATHLETES: BUILD MUSCLE, BURN FAT, AND INCREASE STRENGTH AND PERFORMANCE

The primary goal of every bodybuilder and athlete is to reach his or her full genetic potential. This can be achieved only through proper diet and training. Diet is even more critical than training, because diet influences your training capacity. A compromised diet means compromised training, and ultimately compromised "poor" results. If you want to be the best at your sport, you need to eat for your sport. Macrobolic Nutrition is the bodybuilder's and power athlete's diet; it is designed to fuel muscles with the necessary nutrients to supply energy for heavy weight training, increased muscle building, and optimal fat burning. The goals here are simple: build muscle, increase strength, and control body fat.

LEAN-MASS EQUATION

Let's start with a simple example to illustrate Macrobolic Nutrition's fundamental principle, "All calories are *not* created equal," before we even get to the science to prove it. Which breakfast do you think your body will respond to best for the goal of building muscle and controlling body fat?

Dieticians would argue that all four breakfasts yield approximately the

BREAKFAST #1 (MACROBOLIC)
Eggs and Oatmeal with Strawberries

Food Item	Quantity	Energy (kcal)	Carbohydrate (g)	Protein (g)	Fat (g)
Oatmeal	1½ cup cooked	240	45	6	2
Egg whites	8 large eggs	85	—	27	—
Strawberries, whole	1¼ cup	60	15	—	—
Whole eggs	2 large	150	—	14	10
	TOTALS	535	60	47	12
			45%	35%	20%

BREAKFAST #2 (BLUE COLLAR)
Bacon, Egg, and Cheese Sandwich

Food Item	Quantity	Energy (kcal)	Carbohydrate (g)	Protein (g)	Fat (g)
Bagel, plain	1	150	30	6	—
Whole egg	1 large	75	—	7	5
American cheese	1 ounce	100	—	7	8
Bacon	3 slices	100	—	7	8
Orange juice	1 cup	120	30	—	—
	TOTALS	545	60	27	21
			45%	20%	35%

BREAKFAST #3 (LOW CARB)
Bacon, Egg, and Cheese Omelet

Food Item	Quantity	Energy (kcal)	Carbohydrates (g)	Protein (g)	Fat (g)
Butter	1 tsp	45	—	—	5
Whole eggs	4 large	300	2.44	21	15
Cheddar cheese	1 ounce	100	0.36	7	8
Bacon	3 slices	100	—	7	8
	TOTALS	545	2.80	35	36
			2%	30%	68%

BREAKFAST #4 (WALL STREET) Corn Muffin and Orange Juice					
Food Item	Quantity	Energy (kcal)	Carbs (g)	Protein (g)	Fat (g)
Corn muffin	1 medium	335	57.52	6.67	9.49
Butter	2 tsp	90	—	—	10.00
Orange juice	1 cup	120	30.00	—	—
	TOTALS	545	87.52	6.67	19.49
			63%	5%	32%

same amount of calories, so they would all have the same impact. The low-carb community would argue that breakfast #3 is going to facilitate fat burning best. Common sense and knowledge of Macrobolic Nutrition tell you that the balanced breakfast #1 would be best, and this book is going to prove it to you.

The cornerstone of Macrobolic Nutrition is the 45/35/20 lean-mass equation. Breakfast #1 is a good example of a Macrobolic meal. Macrobolic Nutrition derives its calories from select "nutrient-dense" sources, in a ratio of 45 percent carbohydrates, 35 percent proteins, and 20 percent fats. This ratio was determined through extensive research to be the optimal macronutrient profile for creating the most favorable hormonal, metabolic, and thermogenic effects from food.

The ratio and selection of macronutrients (carbohydrates, proteins, and fats) are critical when composing meals. Each macronutrient influences different hormones and chemical processes. Optimal hormonal homeostasis ("balance") can be achieved only with the right ratios and sources of macronutrients in each meal. Macrobolic Nutrition's 45/35/20 lean-mass equation creates the ideal hormonal and metabolic response for building muscle and burning body fat. In the chapters that follow, I will examine how each of the macronutrients influence chemical processes within the body and how they react with one another.

CHAPTER 2

Carbohydrates— Don't Count Them Out

SINCE MANY OF YOU MAY BE STRUGGLING to believe you can get lean with 45 percent of your calories coming from carbohydrates, they will be the first macronutrient discussed. You'll soon find out how it is possible to lose body fat and consume 45 percent of your calories from carbohydrates. But let's first discuss how important carbohydrates are for strength, muscle growth, and performance.

Carbohydrates are the most efficient nutritional source for the body's energy requirements, because carbohydrates are more easily converted to glucose than proteins and fats. Glucose is used by every cell in the body as fuel for energy. Some of the glucose is carried around in your bloodstream to supply your brain and other organs, but most of it is stored as glycogen in the liver and skeletal muscle. When blood sugar levels are low, this glycogen serves as a reserve to replenish blood sugar to meet your body's energy needs. Another very important role of carbohydrates is their "protein-sparing" effect. Carbohydrates protect your protein from being converted to glucose when blood sugar and glycogen are low.

Your body burns more energy when you exercise, so its need for blood glucose increases. Your body taps into the muscles' glycogen reserves to meet these energy demands, so it is critical that bodybuilders consume adequate amounts of carbohydrates to support their energy demands. A 2002 review on diet and anaerobic exercise (weightlifting) in *Strength and Conditioning Journal* concluded that diets containing less than 42 percent carbohydrates do not meet the energy demands or provide adequate glycogen stores for bodybuilders, given their intense workouts. The physical demands bodybuilders place on their bodies creates a greater need for the kind of heavy-duty nutrition that repairs muscle fiber and sustains growth.

Photo by Clark Jackson.

Testimonial

"Most bodybuilders make the mistake of restricting carbs from their diet. Carbs are essential for glycogen replenishment and sparing aminos in muscle tissue. Another common mistake bodybuilders make is avoiding soy as a protein supplement. Soy is one of my favorite protein sources because of its high bioavailability. And unlike meat, milk, and whey proteins, which are acidic, soy is less acidic and easier on your stomach. When you are taking in large amounts of protein, this is very important. Macrobolic Nutrition stresses the importance of low-glycemic carbs and utilizing a variety of protein sources, which are the backbone of my nutrition program."

—*Gary Strydom,* IFBB Professional Bodybuilder

THE LOW-CARB CONUNDRUM: BURNING FAT AT THE EXPENSE OF MUSCLE

The huge amount of media attention on low-carb diets may have led you to believe that the low-carb diet was the route to getting a lean, muscular physique. Unfortunately, you probably found out the hard way that the low-carb diet you tried didn't give you the results you wanted. Rather than becoming big and hard with full dense muscles, you feel flat, small, and weak!

The fundamental theory behind low-carb diets is that when carbohydrates, the body's preferred source of energy are restricted, the body resorts to using stored body fat as an energy source. In the process known as ketosis, the body breaks down triglycerides for use as a source of energy. Ketosis is not nearly as efficient as using carbohydrates for energy or glycogen replenishment. This lack of efficiency in the absence of carbohydrates can result in the body's also using protein (which is made up of amino acids linked together) from food and muscle tissue for energy. Certain amino acids in the protein you eat and in the protein that makes up your muscle tissues can be converted to glucose. As mentioned earlier, this process is called gluconeogenesis. Amino acids are the building blocks of protein and muscle tissue. Two such acids used for gluconeogenesis are glutamine and alanine. Later in the book, you'll learn more about these amino acids and protein's importance. We already know that bodybuilders need adequate protein to support training, muscle growth, and recovery, so having your body cannibalize protein for energy from the foods you eat, or even worse, from your "hard-earned muscle," is a catastrophe for any bodybuilder.

Carbohydrates are too important a nutrient for bodybuilders and athletes to completely restrict from their diets. You will never make the gains in size and strength you are looking for on a low-carb diet. True, low-carb diets can be effective in reducing body fat, but they can also burn off precious muscle. That's not what you want to achieve from your diet. Remember the goals of Macrobolic Nutrition are to build muscle, increase strength, and control body fat.

ALL CALORIES ARE NOT CREATED EQUAL!

Macrobolic Nutrition's fundamental principle "All calories are not created equal" applies to all the macronutrients: carbohydrates, proteins, and fats. Mac-

Testimonial

Photo supplied by Dave Hawk.

Before

"Coming back to professional bodybuilding after a twelve year layoff and competing in the 2002 Masters Mr. Olympia was a dream. Thankfully, I had the opportunity to work with Gerard Dente to help structure my nutrition and some of my supplementation program. In my earlier competition days I followed a high-protein/low-carb diet while preparing for contests. I was usually cut but always lost a lot of size leading up to a show. During my layoff I really let my physique go and put on a lot of body fat. My first instinct was to cut carbs; however, Gerard convinced me that if I wanted to be bigger and better than ever, I had to change my diet. Amazingly, using the Macrobolic Nutrition regimen along with my Return to Dominance supplementation program, I competed bigger, harder, and fuller at the age of 40 than I did in my last pro show at the age of 28."

—**Dave Hawk,** *IFBB Professional Bodybuilder*

Photo by Sumio Yamaguchi.

After

robolic Nutrition places great emphasis on choosing your carbohydrate sources wisely. While all carbohydrates yield four calories per gram, their impact on the body can greatly differ.

Carbohydrates can be broken down into three general categories: monosaccharides, disaccharides, and polysaccharides. Monosaccharides and disaccharides are commonly referred to as sugars or simple carbohydrates, while polysaccharides are called complex carbohydrates.

Monosaccharides are carbohydrates that have one sugar molecule. Common sources include glucose, fructose, sorbitol, galactose, mannitol, and mannose.

Disaccharides are carbohydrates with two sugar molecules. Common sources include sucrose and lactose.

Polysaccharides are carbohydrates with three or more sugar molecules. Sources include dextrin, cellulose, and starches.

Another kind of carbohydrate is fiber, which is composed mainly of undigestible polysaccharides. Fiber plays an important role in the next topic of discussion, the glycemic index (GI). Though the classifications of monosaccharides, disaccharides, polysaccharides, and fiber help differentiate carbohydrates, Macrobolic Nutrition puts great emphasis on the glycemic index when choosing carbohydrate sources.

Table 2.1 on the next page lists the carbohydrate sources I recommend and their caloric, carbohydrate, protein, and fat content.

What Is the Glycemic Index?

The glycemic index (GI) was developed in 1981 as a way to classify carbohydrates. As defined by Jennie Brand-Miller, Associate Professor of Biochemistry at the Human Nutrition Unit of Sydney University, Australia, the glycemic index of a food is a measure of the power of the carbohydrate content in a specific food to raise blood glucose levels after being eaten. The glycemic index is a ranking of carbohydrates based on their immediate effect on blood glucose (blood sugar) levels. It compares carbohydrate foods gram for gram. Carbohydrates that break down quickly during digestion have the highest glycemic indexes and a blood glucose response that is fast and high. Carbohydrates that break down slowly, releasing glucose gradually into the bloodstream, have low glycemic indexes.

The GI of a carbohydrate is determined by measuring blood sugar levels after ingesting 50 grams of the carbohydrate in a fasting individual. Foods that measure a GI of 70 to 160 are considered high GI foods, foods that measure 56 to 69 are considered medium GI, and foods that measure 55 or less are low GI. The GI of a carbohydrate can be influenced by a number of factors: the fiber content, the ripeness, methods of cooking and processing, the types of pre-

TABLE 2.1 CARBOHYDRATE SOURCES RECOMMENDED FOR MACROBOLIC NUTRITION

Source	Portion	Calories	Protein	Fat	Carbohydrates
Grains					
Couscous	1 cup	175	6.0	—	36.0
Oats	½ cup	155	6.0	2.5	27.0
Rice, brown cooked	1 cup	216	5.0	2.0	45.0
Rice, white cooked	1 cup	200	4.0	0.5	43.0
Pasta (semolina)	2 oz	200	7.0	1.0	41.0
Wheat bread	1 slice	70	3.0	1.0	13.0
Vegetables					
Potato, baked with skin	1 med	160	4.0	—	37.0
Sweet potato	1 cup	206	3.0	1.0	49.0
Fruit					
Apple with skin	1 med	80	—	—	21.0
Banana, just ripe	1 med	110	1.0	0.5	28.0
Blueberries, fresh or frozen	1 cup	80	1.0	0.5	20.5
Cantaloupe	1 cup	55	1.0	—	13.0
Grapefruit	½ med	40	0.7	—	10.0
Orange, Florida	1 med	65	1.0	—	16.0
Pear with skin	1 med	100	0.6	0.6	25.0
Raspberries, fresh or frozen	1 cup	60	—	—	15.0
Strawberries, fresh or frozen	1 cup	50	—	—	12.0

servatives used, and the types and amounts of macronutrients (other carbohy-drates, proteins, fats) and micronutrients (vitamins and minerals) ingested with the carbohydrate.

What Is the Significance of the Glycemic Index in Macrobolic Nutrition?

The reason it is so important to measure a carbohydrate's impact on blood sugar is because of its influence on insulin production. Insulin is a hormone released by the pancreas in response to changes in blood sugar levels. The faster carbohydrates are digested and converted to glucose, the more rapidly insulin is produced to stabilize blood sugar levels, using the glycemic index as a measure.

The GI and Insulin

- Low GI means a smaller rise in blood glucose levels after meals.
- Low GI diets can help people lose body fat and increase lean muscle mass.
- Low GI diets can improve the body's sensitivity to insulin.
- Low GI diets can improve the ratio of insulin to glucagon.
- Low GI foods can help replenish carbohydrates stores after exercise.
- Low GI can prolong muscle endurance and energy levels.
- Low GI can improve diabetes control.
- Low GI foods keep you feeling fuller for longer.

Using the glycemic index as a measure, carbohydrates that are digested faster have a higher GI because they cause a greater increase in blood glucose and insulin levels. A bodybuilder wants to avoid high insulin levels, because insulin suppresses fat utilization and promotes fat storage. The rapid increase in blood sugar caused by high GI carbohydrates can also have a negative impact on performance.

High GI carbohydrates also elevate free fatty acids in the blood, further promoting increased body fat. They have also been shown to predispose the development of type 2 diabetes in insulin-resistant individuals. In response to fast-rising blood sugar levels, your pancreas releases large amounts of insulin in an effort to compensate and stabilize the blood sugar. Often, the overproduc-tion of insulin can result in low blood sugar levels or temporary hypoglycemia, a condition in which blood sugar levels drop below normal range. Hypo-glycemia can cause fatigue, anxiety, perspiration, light-headedness ("delirium"), and, in severe cases, coma.

These fluctuations in blood sugar levels from very high to very low can hinder your ability to train and perform at maximum capacity. Nothing will zap your energy, strength, and performance like a bout of hypoglycemia during your workout. Temporary hypoglycemia can usually be corrected by consuming more carbohydrates, but it is a condition you want to avoid. If you ever get to this point of temporary hypoglycemia, you will know it. You'll feel super weak and disoriented, and you will usually break out in a cold sweat. If you experience these symptoms, grab yourself some carbohydrates and scoff them down.

Macrobolic Nutrition places great emphasis on consuming carbohydrates with low to moderate GI for these reasons. Low-to-moderate GI carbohydrates are digested more slowly, providing a gradual, steady supply of blood sugar. This slow, steady supply of blood sugar is critical for peak energy and performance. It also maintains muscle glycogen stores and helps to regulate two very important hormones, insulin and glucagon, for optimum muscle growth and fat loss.

Insulin and glucagon are both influenced by blood sugar levels. High-glycemic carbohydrates such as sugar cause insulin levels to be high and glucagon levels to be low. Since insulin promotes the increase in body fat and glucagon mobilizes and burns body fat, this obviously isn't the metabolism we want. Lower glycemic carbohydrates, especially when they are consumed with protein, shift the levels of these two hormones, lowering insulin and slightly raising glucagon. This is the correct "hormonal profile" for effective fat burning.

Table 2.2 on the next page lists the GI of common carbohydrate sources, broken down into high, moderate, and low GI classes. Try to limit your selections to moderate and low whenever possible. The items included in these tables are primarily foods considered to be "carbohydrate sources," which means most of their caloric content comes from the carbohydrates and they provide proportionately very little protein or fat. These listed carbohydrate sources would need to be consumed with other food sources higher in protein and/or fat to provide the Macrobolic Nutrition 45/35/20 ratio. When these carbohydrates are consumed with these other foods as part of a Macrobolic meal, they will yield lower glycemic values.

Keep this in mind when looking up the glycemic index of specific "junk foods." Their glycemic index may seem suitable for Macrobolic Nutrition from a GI standpoint, but they may fall short in many other areas of Macrobolic Nutrition, with inadequate protein content and high levels of saturated fat.

TABLE 2.2. GLYCEMIC INDEXES OF COMMON CARBOHYDRATE FOODS

HIGH GLYCEMIC

Food Item	GI	Food Item	GI
White bread	70	English muffin™	77
Pop Tarts™	70	Cornflakes™	77
Golden Grahams™	71	Corn Pops™	80
Bagel, white	72	Special K™	84
Wonder Bread™	73	Rice cakes, plain	94
Cheerios™	74	Glucose	100
Total Cereal™	76	Maltodextrin	107

MODERATE GLYCEMIC

Food Item	GI	Food Item	GI
Cranberry juice	56	Banana (just ripe)	62
Baked potato, russet	56	Long grain rice, white	64
White rice, boiled	56	Spaghetti, durum wheat	64
Sourdough rye bread	57	Cantaloupe, raw	65
Pita bread, whole wheat	57	Wholemeal rye bread	66
Blueberry muffin	59	Cream of Wheat™	66
Sweet corn	59	Croissant	67
Bran muffin	60	Grapenuts™	67
Couscous	61	Shredded Wheat™	67
Just Right Just Grains™	62	Cornmeal	68

LOW GLYCEMIC

Food Item	GI	Food Item	GI
Cashew nuts	22	Banana, slightly unripe	42
Cherries, raw	22	Spaghetti, whole meal	42
Grapefruit, raw	25	Spaghetti, white	44
Barley	27	Pumpernickel, whole grain	46
Lentils, boiled	28	Spaghetti, semolina	46
Peach, raw	28	Sweet potato	48
Milk (skim)	32	Orange	48
Pear, raw	33	Brown rice, steamed	50

LOW GLYCEMIC *(continued)*			
Milk (whole)	36	Durum wheat	50
Yogurt	36	Oat bran, raw	50
Pinto beans, boiled	39	100% whole-grain bread	51
Apple, raw	40	Kidney beans, canned	52
Strawberries, fresh	40	Spelt wheat-flour multigrain bread	54
Chickpeas	41	Oatmeal	54

GI Table Explanation

When looking up GI values, you may run into what seems to be conflict between this GI table and that of other established GI tables. For example, you may type in "GI value for white rice" on the Internet and you may find multiple values for the same food. This may seem very confusing, but there is an accepted and reasonable explanation for this.

Different methods of processing used by particular manufacturers can lead to significant differences in the rate of carbohydrate digestion by the human body. (The degree of starch gelatinization used in the process may differ, for example.) Also, there may be botanical differences in the type of food being tested. Rice can be from anywhere in the world, and one "white rice" may contain more amylose than another. Amylose is digested more slowly than amylopectin, which is another starch found in other "white rice." Another difference may even be related to the methods that the research team used to test the GI of a food. GI values can vary greatly due to the amount of time the researchers used to conduct the test or different portion sizes of the test foods, or even due to the source of the drawn blood (venous versus capillary).

So use your better judgment, but don't be fanatical. Macrobolic Nutrition has devoted valuable time and resources to creating what I believe is the most accurate and relevant GI table available. This GI table lists the foods that you will most commonly eat on your Macrobolic Nutrition program. So, you can use this guide with a great degree of certainty.

INSULIN'S POWERFUL EFFECTS ON BODY COMPOSITION

Insulin has both anabolic (muscle-building) and hyperlipidemic (fat-storage) properties. The key to building lean mass is to control insulin to promote muscle growth and burn body fat. Is insulin needed for muscle growth or does it just store fat? How does insulin affect performance? What are some of the other negative effects of insulin? What is insulin resistance? These questions are addressed in the following sections.

Fiber–The Forgotten Carbohydrate

Fiber plays a critical role in Macrobolic Nutrition. Fiber is the most recognized of all carbohydrates in terms of being important for disease prevention and general health. Fiber is classified into two different types: soluble and insoluble. Insoluble fiber aids in intestinal cleansing and slows down digestion through the gastrointestinal tract, an important concern for a bodybuilder, since it allows for more thorough nutrient absorption.

Soluble fiber, on the other hand, is an invaluable factor in Macrobolic Nutrition's theory that a calorie is not just a calorie. According to a study published by M. Chandalia, et al., in *The New England Journal of Medicine* (2000), a diet containing 50 grams of fiber (25 soluble, 25 insoluble) can:

■ lower cholesterol

■ improve glycemic control

■ decrease hyperinsulinemia (the overproduction
of insulin by the pancreas)

These findings are very interesting to a bodybuilder wishing to control the glycemic index of meals. By ingesting soluble fiber at mealtime, we can prevent spikes in blood sugar levels and reduce the overall secretion of insulin.

Natural oat fiber reduced blood glucose and insulin levels in a study by J.T. Braatan, et al., discussed in the *American Journal of Clinical Nutrition* (1991). The soluble fiber used in this study was beta-glucan. Oats and barley are good natural sources of beta-glucan. In a 1994 study published in *Diabetic Medicine* by Braatan, et al., patients who were fed wheat farina with oat bran showed a marked decrease in postprandial (after a meal) blood glucose levels and lower overall insulin secretion.

These studies support the great importance of fiber in Macrobolic Nutrition. Its impacts on maintaining lower blood glucose and lower insulin levels are conducive to increased fat burning as well as to decreased cortisol and increased growth hormone (GH) levels. Cortisol and GH are two important hormones for bodybuilders, and are described in detail later in this chapter. These are all the things your body needs to pack on the lean mass you want.

Insulin: Is it Anabolic or Hyperlipidemic?

One of the primary concerns that Macrobolic Nutrition's ratio of calories and low-glycemic carbohydrates addresses is the effect blood sugar levels have on insulin. Insulin is a very powerful hormone, and it needs to be regulated through proper nutrition. Not everything about insulin is bad. In fact, insulin is very anabolic! Insulin increases the transport of glucose, amino acids, and other nutrients into muscle, so it has a very anabolic effect. The increased transport of glucose to muscle serves to increase glycogen stores, which are important for muscle performance. The increased shuttling of amino acids results in increased protein synthesis and nitrogen retention, both essential for muscle growth. So far, it sounds like we should want to load up on insulin, doesn't it? But that's not the case. Elevated insulin can be very hyperlipidemic, which means it can increase body fat. One way insulin increases body fat is by assisting in the formation of glycerol and fatty acids into triglycerides, which are stored as body fat. Elevated insulin not only promotes the storage of triglycerides, it also inhibits the body from breaking them down into burnable fatty acids. So, elevated insulin promotes the storage of body fat, and also inhibits the body from breaking down body fat into usable energy. It's easy to see that elevated insulin levels will make you fat if they are not managed properly by controlling blood sugar.

Controlling Insulin for Optimum Performance

Insulin release must be managed carefully to take advantage of insulin's powerful anabolic effects and to avoid its fat-storing effects. Macrobolic Nutrition will elicit the ideal controlled blood sugar level to keep insulin in the desirable "anabolic zone." The slow, steady release of blood sugar from a Macrobolic meal causes the pancreas to gradually release insulin into the bloodstream to manage blood sugar. This is what you want, to get the anabolic effects of insulin while avoiding the storage of body fat.

Figure 2.1 illustrates the effects on blood sugar of a low-glycemic meal versus a high-glycemic meal. Blood sugar levels were tested at 15, 30, 45, 60, 90, and 120 minutes after the meals. As you can see, the Macrobolic meal provides a much more gradual and steady blood sugar level, while the high-glycemic meal causes a rapid increase in blood sugar and then a quick drop off (even below baseline).

The steady blood sugar levels resulting from the Macrobolic meal causes a gradual release of insulin from the pancreas. This insulin shuttles the glucose (sugar) provided by the carbohydrates to your muscles to be stored as glycogen. The insulin also shuttles the amino acids into the muscle, a process that stimulates muscle growth by keeping you in the positive nitrogen balance needed for

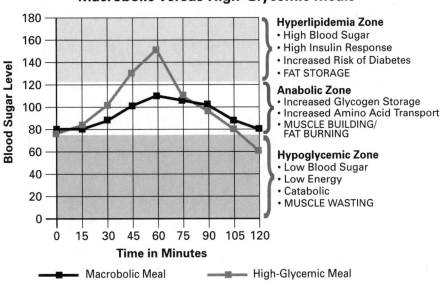

Figure 2.1. Blood Sugar Values of Macrobolic versus High-Glycemic Meals

muscle development. These are the effects we want from a meal, and the reason why I call it the "anabolic zone."

On the other hand, the rapid increase in blood sugar caused by the high-glycemic meal causes your pancreas to produce a lot of insulin to try to quickly lower the blood sugar. These highly elevated insulin levels put you in the "hyperlipidemia zone" and promote the storage of body fat. But that isn't the only problem such insulin levels create.

The Negative Effects of Insulin

Hypoglycemia

The rapid release of insulin to compensate for high blood sugar actually results in low blood sugar, or hypoglycemia, as mentioned earlier. Some of the symptoms of hypoglycemia include low energy levels, dizziness, moodiness, light-headedness ("delirium"), shakiness, and sweating followed by extreme hunger. Bodybuilders refer to this state as crashing, and this is obviously a condition we want to avoid. I don't know if you have ever experienced this, but it is definitely not a good feeling. Depending on how low your blood sugar drops, you can feel like you are going to pass out. In the most severe cases you can pass out and wind up in a coma. The remedy for this condition is to slam a bunch of carbo-hydrates in the hope of bringing your blood sugar back up. This is only a Band-

Aid on the problem, however, because your body will now release more insulin to compensate for all the carbohydrates you just ate, and in a little while, you will be right back where you started.

Your body will never get rid of stored body fat if your meals continually do this to you. Regular bouts with hypoglycemia resulting from large consumption of simple, high-glycemic carbohydrates can eventually lead to insulin-resistance syndrome, or to type 2 diabetes, which comes with a long list of permanent health issues. Dr. Joseph Mercola's paper on this topic, "Reduce Grains and Sugar to Lose Weight and Improve Health," recommends consuming 40 to 45 percent of your calories from carbohydrates to prevent this "crash." This is exactly the level of carbohydrate intake used as the basis for Macrobolic Nutrition. Using low-glycemic carbohydrates in conjunction with protein and fat in meals prevents the spikes in insulin and rapid drops in blood sugar.

Insulin Resistance

If there ever was a valid medical argument to support Macrobolic Nutrition, insulin-resistance syndrome (IRS) is it—the reason you should take advantage of the caloric ratios we advocate. (Syndrome X is a common name for insulin resistance.) I choose to speak about it here as it is a primary concern of a high-carbohydrate diet.

With IRS, muscle cells and tissues in the body develop a reduced sensitivity to insulin's actions of delivering blood glucose to them to use as an energy source. As a result, the body senses a high blood sugar level, which signals the

Photo supplied by Mike Miller.

Testimonial

"As a record holding powerlifter and coach to many aspiring and professional powerlifters, I know the importance of nutrition to fuel big lifts. Macrobolic Nutrition is all about eating big to increase brute strength and power. Since following Gerard Dente's results-oriented Macrobolic Nutrition program, I've personally added 285 pounds to my competition total (squat + bench press + deadlift), going from 2,225 to 2,510 pounds. The amazing part is, I lost 60 pounds of body fat while getting stronger. I didn't think it was possible, but it is!"

—*Mike Miller*, 2nd Highest Subtotal of All-Time: 1,855 lbs.

pancreas to secrete more insulin to lower it. Eventually a person may develop type 2, or noninsulin-dependent diabetes, because the pancreas just can't make enough insulin to handle the high blood sugar levels. Along with the diabetes come high blood pressure, high triglycerides, and high cholesterol.

Sounds like some scary stuff, doesn't it? I think so. If you think about it, this is all due to your blood sugar's being too high all the time, and your body's secreting too much insulin in an attempt to control it. This is exactly what happens when you eat too much sugar and high-glycemic carbohydrates. Macrobolic Nutrition takes advantage of a diet that is moderate in carbohydrates (only 45 percent, not like the typical 80 percent most Americans eat) and generous in the muscle-building protein and fat your highly trained body will crave. As far as restoring insulin sensitivity and getting your body back on track, Macrobolic Nutrition has the prescription for success: frequent meals (every two and a half to three hours) with each meal containing 45 percent low-glycemic carbohydrates, 35 percent protein, and 20 percent fat; a diet high in fiber; and regular exercise. Not only does Macrobolic Nutrition address the demands your body experiences through athletics, it also gives you the plan you need to be healthy and fit for your lifetime.

MACROBOLIC NUTRITION'S EFFECT ON KEY HORMONES: INSULIN, GLUCAGON, GROWTH HORMONE (GH), AND CORTISOL

I've already established the importance of managing insulin due to its very anabolic (muscle-building) and hyperlipidemic (fat-storing) properties, as well as its influence on health. However, insulin has an even bigger impact on your ability to build muscle and burn fat through its influence on other key hormones: glucagon, growth hormone (GH), and cortisol. All of these hormones can be manipulated through Macrobolic Nutrition to achieve the ideal hormonal profile to build a "rock-hard" physique.

Here is how it works. Macrobolic Nutrition keeps blood sugar steady while supplying amino acids and glycogen to muscle tissue. Keeping blood sugar under control also keeps insulin levels low. When insulin is low and amino acid levels are high, the pancreas releases a hormone called glucagon. Glucagon is responsible for mobilizing stored body fat and utilizing this fat as an energy source. Figure 2.2 on the next page shows the intimate relationship between insulin, glucagon, and blood sugar levels.

Low insulin levels also increase GH levels. Every bodybuilder is familiar with GH. If you aren't so sure about what GH is or does, let's just say its name says it all—or I should say almost all. You see, not only will GH make you big like its name implies, it will also burn fat and get you shredded. GH stimulates

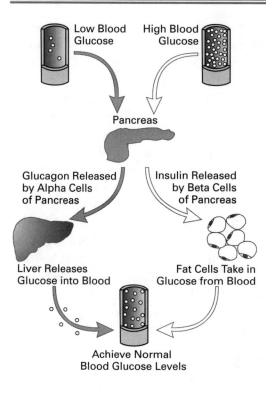

Low Blood Glucose

High Blood Glucose

Pancreas

Glucagon Released by Alpha Cells of Pancreas

Insulin Released by Beta Cells of Pancreas

Liver Releases Glucose into Blood

Fat Cells Take in Glucose from Blood

Achieve Normal Blood Glucose Levels

Figure 2.2. Normalization of Blood Glucose in the Body

muscle growth by increasing protein synthesis and nitrogen retention, so you'll get even better utilization of your quality protein sources and create an even more anabolic environment. What most people don't know is that GH also has lipolytic (fat-burning) properties. Elevated GH levels have been shown to increase fat oxidation and mobilization, resulting in a reduction in body fat stores. You will optimize glucagon and GH levels and further enhance muscle building and fat burning by keeping your insulin under control.

In addition to its importance to glucagon and GH, insulin also has a direct effect on another hormone, cortisol. Cortisol is extremely catabolic and will actually break down and eat away your muscle tissue. High levels can send your training and growth into a declining tailspin. As a bodybuilder, the last thing you want is elevated cortisol. Keeping cortisol levels under control is no easy task, however, because the two things that shoot cortisol levels through the roof are intense training and insulin. If you want to get big you have no choice but to train hard, so pussyfooting around the gym and training like a wimp isn't the solution to keeping cortisol down. The good news is that Macrobolic Nutrition will take care of it for you. The first way Macrobolic Nutrition helps keep cortisol under control is by keeping insulin levels down. Coritsol and insulin have a direct effect on each other, and elevations in insulin induce elevations in cortisol. You can see that avoiding cortisol's catabolic effect on your muscle tissue is another good reason to keep insulin levels low and under control.

The other way Macrobolic Nutrition helps keep cortisol in check is by supplying large amounts of glutamine and amino acids from its sources of protein. Your body produces cortisol in response to physical and emotional stress, so you are vulnerable to its catabolic effects after an intense workout. That is why it is supercritical to supply your body with a Macrobolic meal that supplies high concentrations of amino acids, especially glutamine, after your workout. Glutamine has been shown to neutralize the catabolic effects of cortisol. Supplementation with additional L-glutamine and phosphatidylserine postworkout is also a good idea to help suppress cortisol.

Macrobolic Nutrition primes your hormonal environment for serious muscle building and fat burning. The 45/35/20 ratio of nutrients provides the optimal hormone profile:

- Low and controlled insulin release

- Slightly elevated glucagon levels

- Increased growth hormone

- Low cortisol levels

TABLE 2.3 MACROBOLIC NUTRITION'S HORMONAL EFFECTS ON BODY COMPOSITION		
⇨ Insulin	Body Fat ⇩	Muscle Mass ⇧
⇧ Glucagon	Body Fat ⇩	Muscle Mass ⇨
⇧ HGH (IGF-1)	Body Fat ⇩	Muscle Mass ⇧
⇩ Cortisol	Body Fat ⇩	Muscle Mass ⇧
⇧ INCREASE ⇨ STABLE ⇩ DECREASE		

Table 2.3, although it might be new to you, is no secret to professional bodybuilders. They've been optimizing and manipulating the levels of key hormones for years to get in critical contest shape.

Insulin's impact on glucagon, growth hormone, and cortisol makes a very strong case for Macrobolic Nutrition's emphasis on controlling blood sugar. Optimizing the levels of these hormones is the only way you're ever going to be able to pack on the mass and keep your body fat in check. If you're wondering about testosterone, don't worry. I didn't forget about it. It will be covered in the discussion on fats in Chapter 4.

CHAPTER 3

Protein—
Choosing the Right
Building Blocks

PROTEIN IS ONE OF THE KEY NUTRIENTS your body needs to support muscle growth and repair, to form neurotransmitters in the brain, and to create hormones. Protein serves as the source for the amino acids your body craves after you train. Since growth occurs after you lift, it only makes sense that you give your body a constant supply of protein to make sure there is a constant supply of amino acids. The trick for a bodybuilder is making sure to consume different types of protein. Different proteins are made up of different concentrations of amino acids, but some protein sources lack certain amino acids. With regard to muscle growth, the value of a particular protein depends on the proportion or number of essential amino acids (the ones your body cannot synthesize) it contains. Most animal-based proteins are high in these particular amino acids, while vegetable source proteins tend to lack at least one of the essential amino acids.

As a rule, athletes and individuals who work out have higher demands for protein than do sedentary individuals. After a workout, muscle growth is stimulated by insulin's increased transport of amino acids into the muscle tissue. Increased amino acid transport increases the amount of nitrogen present, a critical factor for muscle growth. Additionally, certain amino acids actually help increase the release of anabolic hormones, like growth hormone. This is the metabolic environment your body needs for you to pack on the mass. Current research on strength athletes shows that you need to ingest about 1 to 1.5 grams of protein per pound of body weight daily.

Using this research as a guide for protein requirements, a 200-pound strength athlete or bodybuilder would need between 200 and 300 grams of protein per day. Macrobolic Nutrition provides even more precise requirements, because it takes into account other important criteria such as your goal, your lifestyle (activity level), and the length of your workout sessions. As you will see from the Macrobolic Nutrition caloric calculator in Chapter 7, the same 200-pound athlete would have the protein requirements set forth in Table 3.1.

TABLE 3.1. 200-POUND ATHLETE CALORIC/PROTEIN REQUIREMENTS			
Activity Level	Workout Time	Total Calories	Protein Requirements (35% of Total Calories)
GOAL: GAIN MUSCLE/LOSE BODY FAT			
Sedentary	60 minutes	2,600	228
Moderate	60 minutes	3,000	263
Active	60 minutes	4,000	350
Sedentary	90 minutes	2,900	254
Moderate	90 minutes	3,300	289
Active	90 minutes	4,300	376
GOAL: GAIN MUSCLE/MAINTAIN BODY FAT			
Sedentary	60 minutes	3,200	280
Moderate	60 minutes	3,600	315
Active	60 minutes	4,600	403
Sedentary	90 minutes	3,500	306
Moderate	90 minutes	3,900	341
Active	90 minutes	4,900	429
GOAL: GAIN MUSCLE/GAIN BODY FAT			
Sedentary	60 minutes	3,800	333
Moderate	60 minutes	4,200	368
Active	60 minutes	5,200	455
Sedentary	90 minutes	4,100	359
Moderate	90 minutes	4,500	394
Active	90 minutes	5,500	481

Training intensity is a key component in determining the amount of new muscle growth you can achieve. Workout intensity needs to be high enough to challenge the body's growth, but it can't be so intense that it causes an overload and shuts down the body's metabolic response for new tissue growth. No amount of protein or nutrition can compensate for overtraining. Most people, myself included, are guilty of overtraining. Your determination to get big can work against you if you are not careful. Once you understand Macrobolic Nutrition and realize how these nutritional changes are going to unlock your growth potential, your enthusiasm to get to the gym and train your ass off is going to be at an all-time high. Be careful not to let your determination and enthusiasm lead to overtraining.

Research has shown that high-intensity anaerobic (weight-training) sessions lasting sixty minutes are the most effective for stimulating muscle growth. Of course, not all athletes train for the same purpose. While bodybuilders are mainly concerned with building as much muscle mass as possible and keeping body fat low, other athletes may be just as concerned with muscle strength and endurance. So, you need to train for your sport. The good thing is, Macrobolic Nutrition will support the training regimen of every athlete.

Let's look at how protein in Macrobolic Nutrition supports training and muscle growth. Intense training has a huge impact on your body's metabolic processes. The hour immediately after an intense workout is called the "anabolic window." During the anabolic window period, the hormonal landscape is primed for muscle building; testosterone is high, growth hormone is high, and insulin is low. To take advantage of this "hormone heaven," it is important to consume a meal high in quality protein and moderate to low glycemic carbohydrates—yes, a Macrobolic meal. I will expand further on this later. For now, let's stay focused on protein.

The body's synthesis (utilization) of protein increases for about forty-eight hours after an intense training session. By making sure you take in protein immediately after your workout and continuing to do so every few hours, you will make sure your body stays in an anabolic environment. Protein donates amino acids to the body, and amino acids donate nitrogen. When the body has

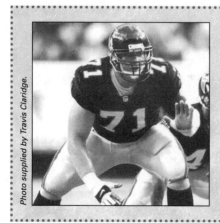

Photo supplied by Travis Claridge.

Testimonial

"I have seen a tremendous improvement in all areas of my performance since using the Macrobolic principles. I am bigger, stronger, and have much better muscle endurance and energy."

—**Travis Claridge,** Offensive Guard, Atlanta Falcons

an excess of nitrogen, it is in an anabolic state and builds muscle tissue. Your body's demand for amino acids can be met by one of two sources: the dietary protein found in the foods or supplements you eat, or by the catabolic process of breaking down your own muscle tissue. The last thing you want is for your body to break down muscle to meet your protein demands. This is exactly the opposite of the anabolic state we want to maintain to maximize muscle growth. To avoid catabolism, adequate protein from quality sources must be eaten every two to three and a half hours throughout the day. What are quality protein sources, you ask? The rest of this chapter will answer this question.

MAKING THE GRADE FOR ATHLETES

The bodybuilding industry has many different ways to grade protein sources. Biological value (BV), protein efficiency ratio (PER), net protein utilization (NPU), chemical score, and protein digestibility corrected amino acid score (PDCAAS) are the most common terms you may come across in various articles and ads while reading through a muscle magazine.

BV is one of the most commonly used and is arguably the best measure of a protein's quality. BV is based on how much of the protein consumed is actually absorbed and utilized in the body. The higher the amount of protein (nitrogen) that is actually retained, the greater the BV. If a protein has a BV of 100, it means that all of the protein absorbed has been utilized, and none has been lost. Whole eggs score the highest of all foods with a BV of 100, while beans have a BV of only 49.

Many advertisements for whey list their products as being between 105 and 107 on the BV scale when it really has a BV of near 100. Since BV is defined as "the amount of N [nitrogen] retained for growth and/or maintenance that is expressed as a percentage of N absorbed."

When a protein has a BV of 100+, the company intentionally manipulates the numbers for marketing purposes. They do this by making references to studies in which chemical scores of the whey protein is compared to the amino acid patterns of an "ideal reference protein" to test protein. In this instance, it is possible for the score to exceed 100.

Surprisingly, researchers and the industry seem to consider PER and PDCAAS as the gold standards in protein grading. PER is determined by evaluating how much weight a rat gains while being fed a particular protein compared with a standard such as egg white. The higher the PER, the greater the quality of the protein. The problem is, we are talking about rats! What good is that for humans? Well, the researchers realized that as well, and as a result came up with the PDCAAS. This method uses human amino acid requirements to calculate the amino acid score of proteins. PDCAAS compares the amino acid profile of a particular protein to the exact amino acid requirements for humans as set forth by the Food and Agriculture Organization. The World Health Organization (WHO) and the U.S. Food and Drug Administration (FDA) use PDCAAS. When a protein fulfills the requirements for humans, it receives the highest score of 1.0.

Since proteins that have a PDCAAS of 1.0 may have a lower PER, and more important, a lower BV, I felt that I needed to establish an even better criteria for grading protein. As mentioned, BV is a measure of how much of the protein will actually be assimilated by the body, but it pays no attention to the amino acids critical for actual muscle growth. Based on my research, I determined that, along with BV, the most important factors relevant to bodybuilders is the concentration of what I will call the "critical five" amino acids and their absorption rate. The five amino acids most important to bodybuilders are glutamine, arginine, leucine, isoleucine, and valine. These critical five amino acids are those most often and most rapidly depleted by athletes due to their training, and the most crucial to muscle recovery and overall growth. Macrobolic Nutrition emphasizes the importance of these five amino acids when choosing protein sources. The release rate or absorption rate is the rate at which the protein source is broken down to raise blood levels of these amino acids. A protein that provides fast-, medium-, and slow-release rates is optimal. This is covered in greater detail later in the discussion on absorption rates.

Why Nitrogen Balance Is Important

In addition to carbon and hydrogen, amino acids also contain nitrogen as part of their molecular structure. This is a unique characteristic of protein. Specifically, nitrogen balance refers to the condition in which the amount of nitrogen ingested from protein is equal to the amount of nitrogen eliminated as ammonia. A positive nitrogen balance occurs when the body has a surplus of nitrogen. This surplus allows for increased protein synthesis and an anabolic environment to support muscle growth. A negative nitrogen balance, which results from inadequate protein intake, can result in the body's cannibalizing muscle tissue to get nitrogen from the amino acids in your muscles (a catabolic environment). So, the goal is to maintain a positive nitrogen balance and prevent a negative nitrogen balance. Macrobolic Nutrition allows you to stay in a positive nitrogen balance and be anabolic—all of the time.

Amino Acids

Amino acids are the building blocks of all proteins. Different proteins are made up of different combinations and concentrations of amino acids. When we ingest protein, whether it is from food or supplements, it is digested in the stomach and broken down into its amino acid constituents. These amino acids enter what is known as the amino acid pool. This is the body's storage mechanism for excess amino acids, which will be used at a later time for either:

1. Muscle growth

2. Conversion into glucose for energy

3. Synthesis of fatty acids and ketone bodies

4. Maintenance of nitrogen balance

Amino acids can be classified as either essential or nonessential. By essential, I mean those particular amino acids that can't be synthesized by the body but must be derived from the foods we eat. The nine essential amino acids are isoleucine, lysine, methionine, phenylalanine, threonine, tryptophan, valine, leucine, and histidine.

As mentioned earlier, the value of a protein for new tissue growth is determined by the presence and concentration of these amino acids. Since some amino acids are found in smaller amounts in some foods, the supply of these amino acids will be used up faster in the growth of new muscle if these foods are your primary protein sources. In foods, these amino acids are considered "limiting." The way to avoid limiting amino acids and therefore inhibiting muscle growth is to vary protein sources taken in throughout the day. Consequently, Macrobolic Nutrition recommends utilizing various protein sources. This gives the body a better spectrum of amino acids, since different proteins contain different amounts of certain amino acids. Animal source proteins have a better overall concentration of essential amino acids, which becomes a problem for vegetarian bodybuilders. Vegetarians need to complement (combine) certain protein sources in order to make up for the gaps created by limiting amino acids. The problem this creates with Macrobolic Nutrition is that most vegetable source proteins are much too high in carbohydrate content. This makes it nearly impossible for a vegan (one who eats no animal products) to adhere to the Macrobolic principles, unless they compensate for these deficiencies through supplementation. Even then, it would be very difficult to get adequate amounts of the crucial amino acids.

For an athlete, the most crucial amino acids are the critical five of Macrobolic Nutrition: glutamine, arginine, leucine, isoleucine, and valine. As I stated earlier, these amino acids are utilized by working muscle tissue for a variety of functions and are rapidly depleted in the body. In gluconeogenesis, a catabolic process, the body breaks down protein into amino acids and converts them to glucose when blood sugar levels get too low. This commonly occurs in low-carb diets; that is why Macrobolic Nutrition places such emphasis on eating carbohydrates to be utilized for glucose, so that the body will not draw on protein or muscle tissue for this purpose.

The Critical Five Amino Acids

Glutamine. This member of the critical five amino acids is quite possibly the most important amino acid for athletes to replenish through food and supplementation. Although glutamine is considered a nonessential amino acid because it can be synthesized (manufactured) by the body from glutamic acid, I consider it essential to athletes because of their increased need and demand for this multifunctional amino acid.

Glutamine is the most abundant amino acid in skeletal muscle. Your body is constantly tapping into your muscles' glutamine reserves to perform various functions. Heavy weight training has been shown to deplete glutamine from muscle tissue, in response to the physical stress involved. Long, strenuous workouts trigger the release of cortisol. Cortisol is a catabolic hormone, which your body releases in response to physical and emotional stress. Supplementing glutamine after workouts has been shown to offset the catabolic effects of cortisol. This is extremely important, because the last thing you want is to be in a catabolic state after a workout. You want the exact opposite, an anabolic state, to occur. Taking glutamine immediately following your workout will help shift you into an anabolic state.

Glutamine can also help buffer lactic acid. You know that feeling you get when you're training hard, and your muscles feel so burnt and exhausted that you can't squeeze out another rep? That feeling is caused by lactic acid buildup in your muscles. Glutamine helps buffer the lactic acid and delay muscle exhaustion. Lactic acid can be even further buffered by taking glutamine in a bicarbonate (effervescent) form, because minerals like sodium bicarbonate and potassium bicarbonate have a buffering effect on lactic acid.

Glutamine also plays an important role in strengthening your immune system by acting as an antioxidant enhancer. Intense training increases the production of free radicals, invaders that attack your cells. Glutamine helps raise levels of the powerful antioxidant glutathione to combat the damage caused by free radicals. In addition, glutamine protects the body from high levels of the toxic compound ammonia, which can increase as a result of exercise.

Glutamine allows more vitamins, minerals, water, carbohydrates (such as glycogen), and protein (such as amino acids) to enter the muscle, thus performing as a cell "volumizer." The improved nutrient absorption provided by glutamine increases muscle size not only by increasing intercellular capacity, but also by feeding your muscles to stimulate muscle growth and improve recovery.

Another benefit to increased cell volumization is the heightened sensitivity the now "swelled up" cell will have to anabolic hormones (like insulin and testosterone). Researchers measured the response of anabolic hormones in cells that were volumized and cells that were shrunk. First, the cells were increased in volume by changing the osmolarity, or salt content, of the fluid around the cell. When these cells were exposed to the anabolic hormones, they swelled up with water, just like a sponge. Now, we want that water inside the cell. This is what helps to push carbohydrates into the cell and to promote glycogen storage. When researchers ran the same test without the use of the anabolic hormones (that is, increased the volumization of the cells), the cellular response was the same. The cells grew. However, cells that were shrunk down or dehydrated became catabolic and did not respond to the stimulus. So, it is pretty simple: increasing the cell volume is anabolic; decreasing cell volume is catabolic. When you supplement with glutamine, the amino acid transporters on the cells will carry the glutamine into the cell, resulting in swelling. The research tells us that this swelling will put the cell in an anabolic environment, leading to progressive muscle gains.

Wait! There is even more to say about this dynamic amino acid. Glutamine is also one of the most researched and effective natural growth hormone (GH) boosters. Many studies have been performed validating glutamine's effects in raising GH levels. And we all know that elevated GH means increased muscle and decreased body fat. In most of the early studies, fairly large doses of glutamine were required to show significant raises in GH. This is due to the fact that stomach acids destroy a lot of the glutamine and a considerable amount is used up by the small intestine. However, in a more recent study by Thomas Welbourne reported in the *American Journal of Clinical Nutrition,* only 2.5 grams of glutamine in a bicarbonate (effervescent) drink was found to increase GH levels by 30 percent. What that 30 percent increase means to you is more lean body mass. If I were you, I'd take advantage of this and slam down 2–4 grams of Effervescent Glutamine right after every workout.

So, as you can see, glutamine is invaluable to an athlete. Aside from these many benefits, glutamine is a major contributor to some key principles of Macrobolic Nutrition such as maintaining lower blood sugar levels, higher glycogen levels, and nitrogen balance. Exercise increases your body's demand for both carbohydrates and protein, and a sound Macrobolic Nutrition diet provides the carbohydrates and protein you need to meet these demands. However, glutamine supplementation is even more important if you're not meeting these demands, because in that case you are not calculating your nutrition requirements accurately, you are not following the program correctly, or you are severely overtraining. As you may recall from Chapter 2, your body converts glutamine to glucose through gluconeogenesis in the absence of carbohydrates and glycogen. The glucose is then used as an energy source. If glutamine is not replenished quickly, this can rapidly deplete your body's glutamine stores and result in a negative nitrogen balance and in catabolism.

My recommendation is to choose protein sources high in glutamine (see "Glutamic Acid" in Table 3.10 later in this chapter) to ensure that you get enough of this critical amino acid. Supplementing with additional glutamine postworkout is also a good idea.

Arginine. Arginine is one of our acclaimed critical five amino acids, and it is crucial for muscle growth. For an athlete, arginine is actually a conditionally essential amino acid. Exercise, like intense training in the gym, increases your body's demand for this amino acid. Arginine has been shown to decrease somatostatin in the body. Somatostatin is the hormone that inhibits GH release. GH has tremendous muscle-building and fat-burning properties. If we want to pack on lean mass, we definitely do not want to limit the amount of GH being released from the pituitary. Arginine's somatostatin-inhibiting effects will elevate GH levels.

As far as strength is concerned, arginine is used as a metabolic intermediate in the formation of creatine phosphate. Creatine phosphate has been shown to increase cell ATP (adenosine triphosphate), which is your muscle cells' first source of energy for any action. By increasing your ATP, you will help increase your muscle strength and performance.

The cardiovascular benefits of arginine are well documented. Arginine works as a potent vasodilator via nitric oxide, as shown in a study by A. Calver, et al., reported in *Clinical Science* in 1991. Arginine is a precursor for the production of nitric oxide, which has been show to increase dilation in the peripheral vasculature (veins), a great asset for bodybuilders. By increasing blood flow, you will maximize and maintain pumps during and after your workout. You will also increase the blood flow into your working muscle cells. This serves two purposes: First, it allows for an increase flow of nutrients, like amino acids, into your muscles. Second, it allows for better removal of free radicals and ammonia from the breakdown of muscle tissue. By ingesting about 4 grams of L-arginine daily in one dose, athletes can increase the production of nitric oxide. This is a pretty large dose, but it is the amount needed to significantly increase nitric oxide production. Some companies are making supplements utilizing AAKG (Arginine Alpha Ketoglutamate), but no research has been done on AAKG, so stick with pure arginine if you want to be sure of the true benefits and mega pumps.

Another function of arginine for athletes is its role in ammonia detoxification. High levels of ammonia in cells can be toxic. Arginine converts ammonia to urea, which is then excreted by the body. Since exercise can increase the production of ammonia, arginine would be beneficial for highly trained athletes.

Furthermore, arginine had been found to improve wound healing and to play a role in the immune system. For all of the reasons discussed, arginine is one of the critical five amino acids.

BCAAs: Leucine, Isoleucine, and Valine. The branched-chain amino acids (BCAAs) are made up of valine, leucine, and isoleucine. These three amino acids are considered essential because our bodies do not create them, and we need to get them from our diet. We store these amino acids in our liver and in skeletal muscle. For bodybuilders, these three aminos are a very important part of the critical five. Our bodies need them for the maintenance of muscle tissue, preservation of muscle glycogen, and prevention of the breakdown of muscle protein.

Ingestion of BCAAs has been shown to preserve muscle glycogen levels. This occurs because the BCAAs are a primary amino acid energy source for your body. To produce energy, your body burns the carbon skeletons from these amino acids and then converts the nitrogen residues into alanine. The additional alanine formed from this process is shuttled to the liver to produce glucose via gluconeogenesis. The glucose is transported to working muscles to be used as fuel. In the case of bodybuilders and strength athletes, BCAAs preserve muscle glycogen levels and prevent muscle breakdown by giving the body the starting materials it needs for this energy-producing process, so your body does not need to derive the BCAAs from skeletal muscle. Sparing the muscle glycogen also preserves muscle volume and prevents muscle breakdown. Since an athlete's training creates a great demand for BCAAs to replenish glycogen and provide energy, it is important to consume foods or protein supplements high in BCAAs.

Supplementing the Critical Five

A Macrobolic diet should provide good quantities of the critical five amino acids from whole-food proteins and protein supplements. In addition to what you will get from these sources, I would also recommend taking a 4-gram dose

RESEARCH UPDATE
BCAAs Aid in Increasing Strength and Lean Body Mass

A 1997 study reported in *Medicina Dello Sport* looked at the effect of taking supplemental BCAAs on bodybuilding progress. The study involved thirty-one male bodybuilders between the ages of eighteen and thirty-four, all of whom were natural, drug-free bodybuilders and had at least two years of training experience. The subjects were divided into two groups—one group of sixteen took a placebo and the other group of fifteen took 0.2 gram of a BCAA supplement per kilogram (2.2 pounds) of body weight thirty minutes before training and thirty minutes after training. The results showed that while both groups experienced increases in body weight, the BCAA group had greater weight gains. An analysis of the weight gain in the BCAA group showed increases in the lean body mass in that group whereas the group taking the placebo showed no lean-mass gains. Strength gains and improvements in exercise intensity were also seen in the BCAA group in both the squat and bench-press exercises. The placebo group gained strength only in the squat exercise.

of arginine preworkout and 2–4 grams of glutamine (preferably Effervescent Glutamine) postworkout. I don't feel taking supplemental BCAAs is necessary, because your Macrobolic meals and protein supplements should provide enough. However, if you eat a lot of vegetable proteins, taking some extra BCAAs may be a good idea.

CHOOSING QUALITY PROTEIN SOURCES

Now that you can clearly see the importance of protein for muscle growth and now that you are aware of the important components to look for in your protein sources, let's look at which protein sources will provide high concentrations of critical amino acids and high biological values, along with low levels of saturated fat.

Whole Foods versus Supplements

Which is a better source of protein: whole foods or quality-protein supplements? Ten years ago this book may have recommended whole-food protein sources over protein supplements. But today, thanks to recent developments and advancements in protein supplement manufacturing technologies, I feel that both whole-food sources and the right protein supplement sources should be part of your Macrobolic Nutrition program.

Whole-food protein sources are an extremely important part of Macrobolic Nutrition. The recommended food sources for protein include lean red meat, chicken, turkey, fish, whole eggs and egg whites, and some low-fat dairy sources. Each of these sources not only provides protein and all of the essential amino acids, but they also provide other important nutrients to support muscle growth, performance, and overall health. Animal proteins are better sources than plant proteins because they have the proper proportions of essential amino acids. They are called complete proteins because they contain all the essential amino acids in amounts that are sufficient for the maintenance of growth. Vegetable sources are considered incomplete proteins and are usually deficient in one or more of the essential amino acids.

Because whole foods require digestion, they provide a slow, steady release of amino acids into the bloodstream. This slow release helps you to maintain a positive nitrogen balance from meal to meal. Good digestion is another important reason to be sure to eat a few whole-food meals and a few protein supplement meals. The human body is designed to digest whole foods. Our digestive systems cannot handle being fed predigested protein powders all day long. You must feed your body whole foods to take full advantage of the di- and tripeptides available after foods are digested. Ingesting whole food is also important to keep your body producing the enzymes needed to break down and digest food and to help elimination processes.

Digestion of Protein and Amino Acids

The mechanical digestion of protein begins in the mouth during chewing. In the stomach, the enzyme pepsin joins in, breaking down the protein into shorter peptides. The partially digested protein then passes into the intestines, where the free-form dipeptide and tripeptide amino acids immediately begin to be absorbed. Enzymes continue to digest any polypeptides as they travel down the intestines.

Once the free-form dipeptide and tripeptide amino acids enter the bloodstream, they are transported to the liver, where a few things may happen to them. They may be converted into other amino acids, they may be used to make other proteins, they may be further broken down and either used for energy or excreted, or they may be placed into circulation and continue on to the rest of the body. Proteins empty from the stomach in two to three hours, depending on how much fat is present.

The other natural benefit of whole foods is the thermic effect of food (see the inset "The Thermic Effect of Food" in Chapter 6). This refers to the amount of calories your body needs to digest and use the nutrients found in the food. For some protein foods, such as chicken, the thermic effect may be as high as 30 percent of the calories contained in the food. So, to digest and use a 200-calorie chicken breast, your body may need about 60 calories. In actuality, then, the chicken is only providing 140 net calories for energy or fat storage. On the other hand, something like orange juice, which does not require as many calories to break down, will yield more net calories per 200 calories consumed. If you are aware of this factor, you can avoid packing on the fat.

While whole food must be a main source of protein, I feel protein supplements also need to be taken, especially at critical times. Aside from being a quick and convenient way to make sure you're getting enough protein, protein supplements are now superior to what they once were due to the recent advancement of technologies used to develop them. I remember when I started training in the 1980s how nasty some of the stuff tasted, but an even bigger problem was that the processing techniques compromised the quality of the protein. Today, processing techniques keep the integrity of the protein while removing the components in the food source you don't want, like the lactose and fat in whey.

Protein supplements can also be designed to combine several protein sources like whey, soy, and milk to get high concentrations of essential amino acids. Protein manufacturers are also adding other ingredients to their protein supplements to increase its effectiveness and provide additional benefits. For example, the addition of fiber slows the absorption of the protein supplement to help maintain nitrogen balance. Some products are adding free-form amino acids to improve the amino acid profile.

Now that technologies allow manufacturers to really custom design supplements, they can be better than whole food at certain times. Look for a supplement that combines whey, soy, and casein. This trio of proteins provides sustained release of high quantities of the critical five amino acids. This is exactly what you need to stay in a positive nitrogen balance and feed your muscles what they need to grow. I feel that the properly designed protein supplement should be taken three times a day: first thing in the morning, postworkout, and before bedtime.

My overall recommendation is to consume three to four whole-food meals and two to three supplement meals each day, as this will provide you the best balance of Macrobolic Nutrition. Remember, different protein sources have different concentrations of amino acids. By rotating food and supplement meals and eating every two to three and a half hours, you will minimize any limiting of amino acids, maximize the supply of critical amino acids, and keep your muscles primed for growth!

TABLE 3.2. WHOLE FOOD NUTRIENT CONTENT					
Source	Portion	Calories (kcal)	Protein (g)	Fat (g)	Carbohydrates (g)
Chicken breast, boneless	4 oz	130	27.0	1.5	—
skinless	6 oz	187	39.0	2.0	—
Pork, tenderloin	4 oz	162	21.0	8.0	1.0
Turkey, ground	4 oz	170	20.0	9.0	—
Beef, tenderloin	3 oz	200	23.0	11.0	—
Venison	3 oz	127	25.0	2.0	—
Beef, ground, 95% lean	3.5 oz	137	22.0	5.0	—
Turkey breast	3.5 oz	110	22.0	2.0	—
Tuna	6 oz	220	41.0	5.0	—
Salmon, filet	7 oz	281	40.0	12.0	—
Whitefish	7 oz	265	38.0	12.0	—
Tofu, raw regular	4 oz	94	10.0	6.0	2.0
Cottage cheese 1%	8 oz	163	28.0	2.0	6.0
Skim milk	8 oz	80	8.0	—	12.0
Yogurt, low-fat	8 oz	140	14.0	0.5	19.0
Chicken leg, meat and skin	1	190	18.0	12.0	—
Eggs, whole, large	1	75	6.0	5.0	0.6
Egg white, large	1	17	3.5	—	0.3
Egg substitute, liquid	3 oz	80	11.0	3.0	1.0

WHOLE-PROTEIN SOURCES

Beef: The Big Mass Protein

Any bodybuilder knows that beef is a staple in the diet when packing on the mass. Beef definitely has its place in the Macrobolic cookbook. Beef's popularity can be linked to the fact that it is an excellent natural source of both creatine and L-carnitine. Both of these nutrients have been shown to enhance cardiovascular health as well as aid in muscle growth. No wonder athletes love it! Beef is also an excellent source of zinc, vitamin B_{12}, and phosphorus. Beef has a good amount of the essential amino acids, especially the BCAAs, making it great as far as muscle growth is concerned. And in my opinion, it is the best tasting of all the protein sources. On the flip side, not all is good. Some sources of beef are very high in saturated fat and cholesterol, two things that will definitely sabotage your cardiovascular health. You must choose lean beef cuts such as top round, flank steak. These sources will provide a good protein along with beef's other attributes.

TABLE 3.3. PROTEIN/NUTRITIONAL VALUE OF SELECT CUTS OF BEEF

6 ounces (raw weight)	Tenderloin	Tip round	Top round	Top blade	Flank
Calories	454	303	277	231	306
Protein (g)	30.65	33.58	37.13	32.71	33.51
Fat (g)	31.11	15.24	11.14	8.78	15.85
Saturated Fat (g)	14.53	6.97	5.10	3.39	7.69
Total BCAAs (g)	5.23	6.20	6.41	6.21	5.79
Total Critical Five Amino Acids (g)	11.69	13.86	14.33	13.50	12.94
BV (g)	76	76	76	76	76

Chicken Breast: The Bodybuilder's Easy Choice!

Chicken breast's popularity can be completely linked to the fact that it has an extremely high protein to fat ratio. This food protein is low in fat and saturated fat is almost nonexistent, making it a heart-healthy choice. This makes it safe as a frequent protein source in your diet. It is also a great source of potassium. The natural low-fat content makes it a great protein source in a Macrobolic meal and leaves room for the addition of good fat sources such as olive oil to your salad or vegetables.

TABLE 3.4. PROTEIN/NUTRITIONAL VALUE OF CHICKEN BREAST

Serving Size	6 ounces
Calories	195
Protein (g)	40.75
Fat (g)	2.25
Saturated Fat (g)	0.60
Total BCAAs (g)	7.24
Total Critical Five Amino Acids (g)	15.84
BV (g)	76

Whole Eggs: Don't Throw Out All the Yolks

As far as food protein is concerned, eggs are the king! A whole egg has a BV of 100, equal to many protein powders, and also is a great source of the omega-3 fatty acids your body craves to decrease cholesterol levels, aid in joint inflammation, and increase hormone production. Whole eggs also serve as a great source of sulfur. Your body utilizes sulfur in the formation of many anabolic hormones in the body. Eggs are high in the BCAAs, which make them ideal for muscle growth, and they score a 1 on the PDCAA scale. This is due to the fact that they have an amino acid pattern very similar to mother's milk, the protein most fully assimilated by our bodies. With such a high level of essential amino acids and BCAAs, egg is the Macrobolic Nutrition's first choice of food proteins.

Since the egg yolk is the source of fat and some of the essential amino acids, it is necessary to include some yolk in a whole egg/egg white mix to achieve the optimal ratio of nutrition. A whole egg has about 7 grams of protein with 3.5 grams from the yolk and 3.5 grams from the white. The yolk

TABLE 3.5. PROTEIN/NUTRITIONAL VALUE OF WHOLE EGGS AND EGG WHITES	
Whole Eggs	
Serving Size	1 whole egg
Calories	75
Protein (g)	6.25
Fat (g)	5.00
Saturated Fat (g)	1.55
Total BCAAs (g)	1.25
Total Critical Five Amino Acids (g)	2.45
BV (g)	100
Egg Whites	
Serving Size	3 egg whites
Calories	50
Protein (g)	10.40
Fat (g)	—
Saturated Fat (g)	—
Total BCAAs (g)	2.13
Total Critical Five Amino Acids (g)	4.08
BV (g)	100

has about 3.5 grams of protein and about 5 grams of fat. I have found that including one yolk with every four whites (one whole egg and three extra whites) delivers 17.5 grams of protein and about 4 to 5 grams of fat. So, if a dozen eggs are used, you will have three whole eggs and nine additional whites. This will deliver approximately 52.5 grams of protein and 15 grams of fat.

Fish: A Great Catch

Tuna is a favorite among bodybuilders. Its most redeeming quality is its almost nonexistent fat content. Tuna has about the best protein to fat ratio of all whole food proteins. It has a pretty good concentration of BCAAs, so it ranks fairly well for a whole-food protein source. Like red meat, tuna also has a high amount of creatine in it, which is a nice bonus from a protein source.

Tuna is not the only fish acceptable in the Macrobolic plan. Salmon is exceptionally high in omega-3 fatty acids (good fats) and is a solid source of complete protein high in essential amino acids. Macrobolic Nutrition is also an

TABLE 3.6. PROTEIN/NUTRITIONAL VALUE OF FRESH TUNA AND SALMON	
Tuna	
Serving Size	6 ounces
Calories	197
Protein (g)	43.40
Fat (g)	1.40
Saturated Fat (g)	0.40
Total BCAAs (g)	7.76
Total Critical Five Amino Acids (g)	16.83
BV (g)	76
Salmon	
Serving Size	6 ounces
Calories	306
Protein (g)	34.10
Fat (g)	17.75
Saturated Fat (g)	4.26
Total BCAAs (g)	6.09
Total Critical Five Amino Acids (g)	13.23
BV (g)	76

advocate of any white fish such as haddock, flounder, shark, swordfish, and mahi-mahi. All of these are lean choices with a high protein to fat ratio.

Fish, like any other food protein, must undergo digestion in order to release amino acids into the bloodstream. This makes it a slow-release protein source, but it is faster than the harder-to-digest food sources like red meat.

New Research Bulletin

Fatty fish may offer an added fat-loss perk. Incorporating a daily meal of fatty fish may decrease fat cells and enhance fat loss by raising the amount of leptin in the body. Leptin is a hormone that decreases hunger and shrinks the site of fat cells—good stuff!

Pork Tenderloin

Yes, pork is the other white meat. Certain cuts of pork are a very lean source of dietary protein that can add a little variety to your diet. Pork is high in zinc, iron, and B vitamins and has an excellent protein to fat ratio. Most of the fat in pork is on the outside of the actual meat fibers, rather than intertwined within them. This means that when the fat is trimmed off the meat, very little fat remains. Pork has about 3 grams of fat for every 30 grams of protein, which is an exceptional ratio. About two-thirds of the fat in pork is unsaturated. Unsaturated fat cannot be converted into cholesterol, so lean pork will have no impact on your blood cholesterol levels. Pork actually contains less cholesterol than chicken. I recommend using the tenderloin cuts as part of your Macrobolic diet. Sorry, bacon, pork sausage, and spareribs aren't on the Macrobolic menu—only lean cuts will do.

TABLE 3.7. PROTEIN/NUTRITIONAL VALUE OF PORK TENDERLOIN	
Serving Size	6 ounces
Calories	204.00
Protein (g)	35.70
Fat (g)	5.80
Saturated Fat (g)	2.00
Total BCAAs (g)	6.47
Total Critical Five Amino Acids (g)	14.28
BV (g)	76.00

PROTEIN SUPPLEMENT SOURCES

As I mentioned earlier, various protein supplements are now available, which can be very beneficial in helping athletes meet their protein requirements. In some instances supplements are better than whole foods, thanks to major advancements in manufacturing technologies. Let's take a look at some of the best protein supplement sources out there.

Whey

Whey protein is a very popular protein source used in sports nutrition supplements. Some of this popularity is due to whey's many benefits, while some is also the result of advertising hype by companies looking to sell product. As you thumb through the muscle mags, you see ad after ad from supplement companies touting their whey to be the "superior protein." All hype aside, whey protein ranks high in Macrobolic Nutrition, but it's not the answer to all your protein supplement needs. Let's take a look at what whey protein really has to offer.

Believe it or not, whey was once looked upon as a waste product of the cheese manufacturing process. Whey makes up 20 percent of milk protein (casein makes up the other 80 percent) and is a byproduct from the separation of the liquid whey from the more solid curd in cheese manufacturing. Cheese manufacturers used to throw away the liquid whey until someone finally realized they were disposing of the most nutritious part of the milk. Depending on the processing techniques used, whey can contain anywhere from 34 to 90 percent protein. The whey with lower concentrations of protein are typically used in food products, while the whey with higher concentrations are used in nutritional supplements.

Whey Grades: Concentrate and Isolate

The whey proteins used in sports nutrition usually contain protein in a range of 70 to 90 percent or more. Those that range from 70 to 89 percent are classified as whey protein concentrate (WPC). A concentration of 80 percent is usually the standard used in most WPC supplement products. Whey with a protein content of 90 percent or higher is classified as whey protein isolate (WPI). The higher the concentration of protein, the lower the fat and lactose content, so WPI obviously has a higher protein content with less fat and lactose than WPC. In fact, WPI is virtually lactose and fat free, containing less than 1 percent of each. (See Table 3.8.) The higher protein content in WPI also yields a higher concentration of amino acids. However, both WPC and WPI contain high levels of BCAAs and glutamine (in the form of glutamic acid) and a fair amount of arginine. So, it ranks pretty well on our Macrobolic critical five score.

Whey ranks very high with a PDCAA of 1.14 (actually over the top 1.0 ranking set by the USDA) and also gets the highest BV score available at 100. Whey's high BV of 100 reflects how efficiently the body will utilize its amino acids to maintain nitrogen balance.

Aside from whey's high protein, high amino acid content, and high BV, it also contains protein fractions. The protein fractions lactalbumin, lacto globulin, immunoglobulin, lactoferrin, and lactoperoxidase offer important benefits. Studies have shown that these fractions have effective antioxidant and immune support benefits, which can improve a bodybuilder's recovery from a stressful workout. These whey protein fractions also work to remove ammonia, lactic acid, and cortisol, three catabolic byproducts of exercise that hinder muscle growth and performance. The removal of these catabolic substances is critical for achieving maximum muscle growth, performance, and recovery.

TABLE 3.8. TYPICAL PRODUCT ANALYSIS OF WHEY PROTEIN

Whey Protein Concentrate (WPC)	Value
Protein (N x 6.38) as is	81.00%
Moisture	4.10%
Ash	2.50%
Carbohydrates as Lactose	2.60%
Fat	7.90%
Whey Protein Isolate (WPI)	**Value**
Protein (N x 6.38) dry basis	92.00%
Moisture	4.00%
Ash	3.00%
Carbohydrates as Lactose	<1.00%
Fat	<1.00%

The process in which whey is manufactured is critical for obtaining these fractions. Some processing techniques denature whey and destroy these fractions. WPC is typically higher in protein fractions than WPI. Ion-exchanged WPI processing retains lactoglobulins and lactalbumin but is lacking in the other fractions. One type of WPI processing called "membrane processing" passes the whey through a variety of different membrane type filters, which separates out of the fat and lactose while retaining the protein and immuno-globin. As you can see, processing also makes a difference in the quality and functionality of whey supplements. The good news is that most reputable supplement companies are using the proper manufacturing processes to produce quality whey products.

The Final Analysis

Whey makes a great source of protein with its BV score of 100, high amino acid content, and protein fractions. The fact that it is a fast (rapidly absorbed) protein needs to be considered. As a fast-release protein, it will quickly supply amino acids to your muscles to stimulate muscle growth and prevent catabolism. This makes whey a great postworkout protein source, as it will quickly replenish depleted amino acid levels. However, whey protein's fast-release property means it will not maintain amino acid levels. Therefore, I recommend using it in conjunction with the other slower-release proteins.

All in all, WPC and WPI definitely make great protein sources for athletes. Whey should definitely be one of your protein sources, but don't believe all the advertising hype and disregard other great protein supplement sources like casein, soy, and milk protein isolate.

Caseinate

Caseinate, or casein, has made a sudden surge into the sports nutrition arena. Once thought of as an inferior protein because of its low BV of 77, casein has recently gained praise from sports nutritionists. For years, the whey industry pounded the comparison of whey's BV of 100 to casein's measly 77. But a study conducted by Dr. Yves Boire reported in the *Proceedings of the National Academy of Sciences* in 1997 gave casein some firepower to fight back. In this study, cows were fed radioactively labeled leucine. The milk from these cows was separated into labeled whey and labeled casein, and both were fed to humans. The study showed that whole-body muscle breakdown was inhibited by 34 percent after ingestion of the casein, while these effects were not seen in the whey group. The whey produced a short-lived elevation in blood amino acid, while casein provided a more level plateau of increased blood amino acids. This resulted in better nitrogen retention and an overall increase in anabolism with a decrease in muscle catabolism. I'd say casein just leveled the playing field on whey's higher BV!

Additional benefits of casein supplements include its high protein content. Most casein yields between 85 and 90 percent protein and is extremely low in fat, carbohydrates, and lactose. Casein is also fairly high in BCAAs and glutamine.

TABLE 3.9. TYPICAL PRODUCT ANALYSIS OF CALCIUM CASEINATE	
Calcium Caseinate	Value
Proteins	88.00%
Moisture	6.00%
Total Fat	1.80%
Ash	5.00%
Lactose	0.20%

Casein's slower release rate and its ability to maintain blood amino acid levels for a longer period of time will keep you in a positive nitrogen balance between meals and during the night while sleeping. Combining casein with whey ensures both fast amino acid saturation and sustained nitrogen retention.

Egg Protein Powder

Egg protein is generally sourced from either egg whites or whole egg. Ovalbumin or egg white is generally used as the reference protein for PER (protein efficiency ratio) comparisons when grading protein quality. Egg protein has slowly lost favor, due to its higher price tag in the supplement industry. An article published in *Functional Foods and Neutraceuticals,* by R. Kreider, discusses research by V. Gattas which illustrates that egg protein promotes anabolism by promoting nitrogen retention. The results show that egg is as good as whey, casein, and colostrums for making these anabolic changes happen.

Since egg protein powder may not be high on the list for taste, I must recommend the use of eggs in your diet on a daily basis. Egg whites have classically been a favorite of bodybuilders, but for every four whites, you must have a yolk. The egg yolks strengthen the amino acid profile and add omega-3 fatty acids (the importance of which is covered in the discussion on fats). Twelve egg whites and three yolks are an easy, and relatively cheap, way to get about 50 grams of high-quality food protein for one of your Macrobolic meals.

Soy

What I'm talking about here is soy protein powder, more specifically, Supro® soy protein, which is the only vegetable protein that is a complete protein. The Solae Company has changed the rules as far as soy protein powder is concerned with the introduction of their Supro® powder. Unlike other foods (like bread), which are processed to extend shelf life and to improve flavor, proteins are processed to increase BV and actually improve their functionality. Manufacturers can sometimes turn a crappy protein into a muscle-building giant.

This is the definitely the case with (Supro®) soy protein isolate. By using advanced manufacturing techniques, Solae, the makers of Supro, have been able to use an inferior source like soy beans to create a superior muscle-building protein. With a BV of 100 and large amounts of glutamine, arginine, and BCAAs, Supro rates high in Macrobolic Nutrition!

The health benefits of soy protein have been well documented and researched by the Solae Company. For athletes, these benefits are even more important because they serve both general health and physical performance-enhancement functions. A compilation of thirty-eight studies (by J. W. Anderson, et al., published in the *New England Journal of Medicine* in 1995) reported that soy protein consumption resulted in a significant reduction in both total cholesterol and LDL cholesterol as well as in serum triglycerides. The FDA approved a claim linking soy protein consumption to decreased cardiovascular risk in October 1999. The claim states that a diet low in saturated fat and cholesterol in combination with daily consumption of 25 grams of soy protein reduces the risk of coronary heart disease.

Increased physical activity leads to an increase in oxidative stress and damage to the body and an elevation in serum (blood) free radicals. Skeletal muscle is especially susceptible to oxidative stress and damage. In 1995 Anderson, et al., noted that supplementation with Supro® soy protein (with high levels of isoflavones) appeared to provide potent antioxidants that delivered protective antioxidant properties. In a whey/soy study conducted by Rossi and colleagues at the Ohio State University in 1998, two groups of subjects were given either 40 grams of Supro® soy or 40 grams of whey. After three weeks, the soy group had significant increases in their total antioxidant status, while the whey group had significant reductions.

The view that soy will increase estrogen levels in men is very inaccurate. In fact, it is my belief and the belief of many scientists that soy actually lowers estrogen activity in men. The key word here is "activity." Let me explain why this is so.

The view that soy functions as an estrogen stems from the isoflavones found in soy. These compounds have chemical structures similar to estrogen, and because of this similar chemical structure, they bind to and block estrogen receptor cells. By blocking the estrogen cell receptors, the estrogen circulating in the blood will not have any estrogenic effects and is inactive. These isoflavones work similarly to the popular antiestrogen drug Nolvaldex™ (Tomoxifin Citrate) used by bodybuilders. Lowering estrogen activity is always a goal for bodybuilders, because estrogen increases body fat, water retention, and gynecomastia (excessive development of the breast in the male), which are all highly undesirable characteristics for men and particularly for body-builders.

Furthermore, the isoflavones in soy are considered the key compounds responsible for many of the health benefits associated with soy consumption. In a recent study (see "Research Update" below), young men consumed soy protein daily over a two-month period. Over the course of the study, soy consumption decreased DHT (the testosterone derivative that is associated with benign prostastic hyperplasia—prostate enlargement) and baldness, but *did not affect* other types of testosterone.

So, let's set the record straight about soy protein. High-quality soy-based protein supplements have many advantages for bodybuilders and athletes, and should definitely be an important part of their nutrition program.

RESEARCH UPDATE
Effects of Soy Isoflavone Consumption on Reproductive Hormones in Healthy Young Men

Thirty-five healthy men (average age range of 22 to 33 years old) consumed milk protein isolate (MPI), low isoflavone soy protein isolate (low-iso SPI); 1.6 +/– 0.19 milligrams isoflavones/day) and high isolflavone SPI (high-iso SPI; 61.7 +/– 7.4 milligrams isoflavones/day) for fifty-seven days, each separated by four-week washout periods, in a randomized crossover design. Conclusions: Soy protein, regardless of isoflavone content, decreased serum DHT and DHT/testosterone with minimal effects on other androgens, estrogens, gonadotropins, or SHBG [sex-hormone-binding globulin] in healthy young men.

B. L. Dillingham, B. L. McVeigh, J. W. Lampe, and A. M Duncan,
"Effects of Soy Isoflavone Consumption on Reproductive
Hormones in Healthy Young Men," Department of Human Biology
and Nutritional Sciences, University of Guelph, Ontario, Canada.
Fred Hutchinson Cancer Research Center, Seattle, Washington, USA

AMINO ACID CONTENT OF PROTEIN SOURCES

Table 3.10 on the following pages provides the amino acid content of various protein sources, along with its total critical five amino acid content based on 100 grams of protein. Note: Probolic™ protein, which will be discussed shortly, has the highest total value of critical amino acids to support muscle growth.

TABLE 3.10. AMINO ACID PROFILES OF COMMON PROTEIN SOURCES

Ingredient	Probolic™	Soy Protein Isolate	Egg Protein (Dried)	Milk Protein Isolate	Calcium Caseinate
Alanine	4.23	4.30	5.77	3.50	3.00
Arginine	7.04	7.60	5.43	3.50	3.70
Aspartic Acid	11.13	11.60	10.18	8.00	6.90
Cysteine/Cystine	1.25	1.30	2.59	0.60	0.40
Glutamic Acid	21.71	19.10	13.29	20.80	20.90
Glycine	3.83	4.20	3.49	1.90	1.80
Histidine	2.60	2.60	2.26	2.70	2.90
Isoleucine	5.95	4.90	5.66	4.40	4.60
Leucine	7.65	8.20	8.41	10.30	9.10
Lysine	6.50	6.30	6.80	8.10	7.70
Methionine	1.38	1.30	3.44	3.30	2.90
Phenylalanine	5.10	5.20	5.82	5.00	5.10
Proline	5.43	5.10	3.91	9.50	10.40
Serine	5.18	5.20	6.88	6.20	5.80
Threonine	3.89	3.80	4.55	4.50	4.30
Tryptophan	1.28	1.30	1.23	1.40	1.20
Tyrosine	3.86	3.80	3.91	5.20	5.50
Valine	6.01	5.00	6.37	5.70	5.70
Critical Five Amino Acids	48.36	44.80	39.16	44.70	44.00

STAY ANABOLIC: WHAT PROTEINS AND WHEN?

One of the major aspects of Macrobolic Nutrition is meal timing. The 45/35/20 lean-mass equation is designed to keep your body in an anabolic state throughout the day by optimizing key hormones and maintaining positive nitrogen retention. This is covered in greater detail in the discussion on meal frequency. For now, let's look at protein's role in the equation.

Protein must be ingested frequently throughout the day to deliver a steady supply of amino acids into the blood to be delivered to muscle tissue. This steady supply provides a positive nitrogen balance and an anabolic (muscle-

Ingredient	Whey Protein Isolate	Whey Protein Concentrate	Beef	Chicken	Fish (Tuna)
Alanine	5.77	4.82	6.02	5.44	6.05
Arginine	2.09	2.70	6.83	6.02	5.96
Aspartic Acid	11.80	12.26	10.00	8.89	10.24
Cysteine/Cystine	2.55	2.28	1.06	1.29	1.07
Glutamic Acid	19.00	17.20	16.04	14.98	14.93
Glycine	0.81	2.00	4.74	4.90	4.78
Histidine	1.88	1.90	3.22	3.10	2.96
Isoleucine	6.28	6.60	5.17	5.28	4.65
Leucine	9.90	10.70	8.85	7.50	8.12
Lysine	8.11	9.83	9.40	8.50	9.18
Methionine	2.61	2.20	2.83	2.77	2.96
Phenylalanine	3.26	3.10	4.35	3.96	3.89
Proline	5.21	6.28	4.21	4.12	3.53
Serine	4.79	6.24	4.00	3.45	4.08
Threonine	5.53	4.90	4.64	4.22	4.38
Tryptophan	1.45	1.40	1.06	1.17	1.12
Tyrosine	3.06	3.50	3.68	3.38	3.38
Valine	5.90	4.60	5.42	4.96	5.16
Critical Five Amino Acids	43.17	41.80	42.30	38.74	38.82

building) environment. If blood amino acid levels drop, your body pulls these amino acids from muscle tissue. This puts you in a negative nitrogen balance and catabolic state. Your body actually "eats away" your hard-earned muscle in order to maintain blood amino acid requirements.

This can easily occur if a highly trained athlete is not careful. Intense training depletes amino acid stores. To make matters worse, building more muscle requires more amino acids. Therefore, it is extremely important that you take in adequate amounts of protein from sources with high concentrations of essential amino acids, especially the critical five amino acids.

The whole idea behind Macrobolic Nutrition is to give your body the tools it needs to grow muscle. Your protein intake must be staggered throughout the day to deliver a steady supply of amino acids to the blood and to provide ample nitrogen (donated by the amino acids) to shift the body into an anabolic, or muscle-building, state. Whether you derive the protein from food or supplements depends on convenience and availability. The only thing we know for sure is that at bedtime a protein drink, lower in carbohydrates and fat, is superior for several reasons. One reason is that food protein increases stomach acidity, which is not good at bedtime and may result in a feeling of heartburn. Conversely, a shake containing Probolic-engineered protein is lower in acidic proteins and higher in critical-cluster amino acids than any other protein on the market. This provides exactly what we need at bedtime, which includes:

1. Lower insulin levels

2. Increased glucagon levels to stimulate the conversion of stored triglycerides into usable fatty acids, thereby facilitating body-fat reduction

3. Suppressed somatostatin (due to the increased glucagon) for a more efficient GH release

4. Amino acids, supplied by the delayed-release protein blend, as building blocks needed in the newly created anabolic environment

The most critical times of the day are the one-hour periods prior to and after your workout. If you want to grow, two basic aspects of these time periods must be evaluated: energy levels and recovery nutrients. A Macrobolically-balanced meal eaten about ninety minutes prior to your workout will provide you with the blood sugar level your body depends on when trying to grind through a grueling workout. A blended-protein source with varying release rates will ensure that a steady supply of the critical five amino acids are available for energy and muscle growth.

Postworkout is also best addressed with a Macrobolic meal or Macrobolic meal replacement drink. Again, the low-glycemic carbohydrates contained in the meal will supply the muscle glycogen in a steady manner, while a steady source of amino acids aids in muscle recovery and an elevation in protein synthesis to stimulate muscle growth.

ABSORPTION RATES OF PROTEINS

Absorption rates are another important factor to consider to avoid falling into a negative nitrogen balance. The absorption rates of protein have become a hot topic in the supplement industry, spurred by the whey and milk protein industries in their fight for market share in protein supplements. Different proteins raise blood amino acid levels at different rates. This is termed "release rate." Proteins can be categorized into three groups: fast release, medium release, and slow release. Which category is the most effective for athletes has been a heated debate in recent years. Each category has its own characteristics:

■ **Fast release**—increases blood amino acid levels rapidly, but amino acid levels also fall rapidly. Sources: whey protein isolate, whey protein concentrate.

■ **Medium release**—takes a little longer to raise blood amino acid levels and drops slower. Sources: milk protein isolate, soy isolate, soy concentrate.

■ **Slow release**—provides a gradual increase and maintains blood amino acid levels for a longer duration of time. Sources: casein, whole foods.

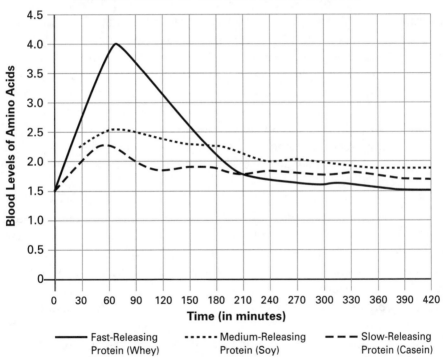

Figure 3.1. This graph illustrates the release rates of whey, soy, and casein. As you can see, each protein source has a different release rate. Whey protein provides a quick release while soy protein provides a medium release and the casein provides a slow release of amino acids. Therefore, combining all three protein sources will provide a constant supply of amino acids to muscle tissue for optimum nitrogen retention.

Combining Fast, Medium, and Slow Proves Best

The truth is, all of these protein sources have their benefits, and ideally are best used together. Remember, if you are following Macrobolic Nutrition properly, you will be eating 35 percent of your total calories from protein spaced throughout the day into five to seven meals every two and a half to three hours. Out of these meals, three to four should be whole-food meals and two to three should be supplements. Whole-food protein sources such as chicken provide a slow release of amino acids, due to the body's need to break down and digest the proteins. When proteins are eaten with carbohydrates and fats, the amino acids are released even more gradually. Macrobolic whole-food meals in the 45/35/20 ratio provide a favorable release of amino acids and an anabolic hormonal environment. Protein supplements and meal replacements, on the other hand, have to be chosen carefully, but if formulated properly, supplements can actually be more beneficial than whole foods at certain times of the day.

Morning, postworkout, and before bed are all times in which the properly formulated supplement can offer a tremendous advantage. The first thing in the morning and postworkout are both times when blood amino acid levels are low, either from being in a rested state (during sleep) or from being depleted by exercise. You're in jeopardy of being in a catabolic state at these times, so you want to quickly replenish amino acids to get back to a positive nitrogen balance and shift from being catabolic to anabolic. A supplement containing fast-, medium-, and slow-release proteins such as whey, soy, and casein will provide a quick infusion of amino acids to get you back to positive nitrogen balance and will let you maintain high blood amino acid levels for many hours until your next meal.

Many of us have busy schedules and don't always have the time to sit down and eat a Macrobollically-balanced meal, let alone cook and prepare one, so supplements can offer a quick and convenient alternative. Who has the time to prepare, cook, and eat seven meals a day? Good thing there have been advancements in supplement technology. When I was competing back in the late 1990s, these types of quality supplements didn't exist. The development of high-quality supplements allows you to get your five to seven Macrobolic Meals in—no excuses!

Consuming a slow-release protein before going to bed helps prevent catabolism during the many hours of fasting while you sleep. Whole food provides a slow release of amino acids, which is what you want to maintain blood amino-acid levels during the night, but they can wreak havoc on your stomach. Food proteins, especially meat and dairy, are acidic and can cause stomach discomfort and heartburn during the night. A protein shake containing the whey, soy, and casein combination I mentioned earlier will have the preferred sustained-release

---

RESEARCH UPDATE
Combining Fast- and Slow-Release Protein
Improves Nitrogen Retention

In 1997, French researcher Yves Boirie and colleagues introduced the terms "fast" and "slow" dietary proteins to describe the differences in whey and casein digestion. The higher concentrations of plasma amino acids in the three-hour period following a whey meal results in higher rates of protein synthesis. After this period, it is casein and not whey that results in higher rates of protein synthesis, a condition that is maintained for several hours.

Combining whey with casein provides both fast, high concentrations of amino acids and long-term high concentrations of amino acids to maintain muscle nitrogen retention and improve protein synthesis. *This supports Macrobolic Nutrition's recommendation to combine protein sources such as whey, casein, and soy for optimal protein synthesis to support muscle growth and prevent catabolism.*

Yves Boire, et al., "Slow and Fast Dietary Proteins Differentially
Modulate Postprandial Protein Accretion,"
Proceedings of the National Academy of Science 94 (1997) 14930–5.

---

profile, and is also less acidic and easier to digest. This precisely formulated combination is what I refer to as a Probolic protein. A Probolic protein is one that yields a sustained-release profile of the critical five amino acids, to optimize the blood amino acid levels conducive to an anabolic environment.

It is also important to note that a supplement taken at night before going to bed should be high in protein, very low in carbohydrates, and high in fiber, which is not the typical Macrobolic ratio. The Macrobolic 45/35/20 creates the ideal hormonal environment during the day, but you want a different hormonal landscape while you sleep. A Probolic protein taken before bed will do the following:

1. Decrease insulin

2. Increase glucagon

3. Suppress somatostatin and increase growth hormone (GH)

4. Supply high levels of amino acids and maintain positive nitrogen balance for many hours

Engineering the Perfect Anabolic Protein: MHP's Probolic Protein Blend

For an athlete, a variety of protein sources may not only be a good idea, but also a necessity. Different proteins are composed of varying concentrations of different amino acids, so a blend of protein sources, if chosen wisely, provides an even distribution and concentration of the amino acids necessary for optimal growth. For an athlete, protein demands exceed the RDA (recommended daily allowance set up by the federal government) due to the increase in muscle breakdown caused by extensive training and limited recovery. The even distribution of amino acids and their duration in the bloodstream are both of concern. Different proteins have different release rates and different rates of absorption, factors that affect how long the blood amino acid levels remain elevated.

The blend utilized in Probolic is, in essence, a delayed-release protein. The whey in the formula possesses a fast release rate and rapidly elevates blood amino acid levels. The soy, on the other hand, is classified as a medium-release protein, and will extend the amino acid release into the bloodstream past that of the whey concentrate. The addition of calcium caseinate helps maintain an elevated blood amino acid level beyond that provided by the soy, and provides the slowest release rate of the three proteins. This protein blend provides amino acids that effectively donate nitrogen for up to three hours after the ingestion, preventing the body from slipping into a catabolic environment.

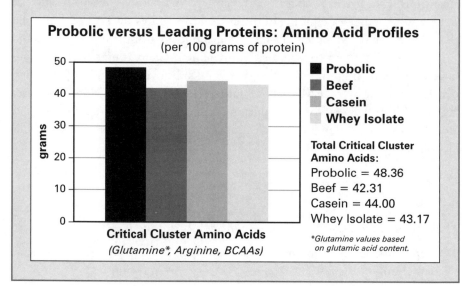

Probolic versus Leading Proteins: Amino Acid Profiles
(per 100 grams of protein)

- Probolic
- Beef
- Casein
- Whey Isolate

Total Critical Cluster Amino Acids:
Probolic = 48.36
Beef = 42.31
Casein = 44.00
Whey Isolate = 43.17

Critical Cluster Amino Acids
(Glutamine*, Arginine, BCAAs)

*Glutamine values based on glutamic acid content.

WHAT DOES ALL OF THIS MEAN TO YOUR TRAINING?

The impact your diet (in this case, the protein you consume) has on the results of your training is the key element in determining the outcome of all your efforts. Everyone knows that you need protein to build muscle, but I have given you the "master key" as far as protein consumption is concerned. The information outlined in this chapter tells you why, how much, and when to eat the right proteins, and most of all, what they will do for you. We all know that athletes have a higher demand for protein than the average individual, but how that extra protein is consumed is what will actually make or break you. The rules for success with protein intake are:

1. Consume 35 percent of your total calories from protein sources high in essential and critical five amino acids.

2. Consume different sources of protein. For example, one meal of eggs and egg whites, one meal with tuna, one meal with chicken, some red meat at one meal, and a couple of supplement meals will provide a wide variety of absorption rates and amino acid profiles. This variety will ensure that you receive a steady source of high levels of all the amino acids necessary for muscle growth. Remember, different proteins score differently in different categories, such as in the biological value (BV) category, so a variety of the highest-scoring protein sources is the best.

3. Eat five to seven meals per day, two and a half to three hours apart. Three to four of these meals should be from whole foods and two or three meals per day should be from protein supplements. Research shows that meal frequency is important to maintain nitrogen retention and improve protein synthesis.

4. Choose protein supplements wisely and take them at critical times of the day. A supplement combining whey, soy, and casein provides a quick, medium, and slow release of the essential and critical five amino acids. Optimum times for Probolic protein supplements are:

   a) First thing in the morning as part of a 45/35/20 Macrobolic meal

   b) Postworkout as part of a 45/35/20 Macrobolic meal

   c) Before bedtime: One-quarter gram (0.25 g) of protein per pound of body weight (body weight × 0.25), high in fiber to further prolong amino acid release

Therefore, a 200-pound athlete would consume a 50-gram serving of Probolic protein supplement high in fiber and low in carbohydrates before bedtime (200 lbs × 0.25 g = 50 g).

If you follow these protein guidelines, you will remain in an anabolic (muscle-building) state twenty-four/seven. When my protein intake is frequent and I am taking my bedtime shake, my muscles feel fuller and harder. I don't know if it is due to the glycogen-sparing effects, or the anabolic effects, or a combination of both, but I definitely see and feel a difference. Remember, your best twenty-three hours of growth potential each day are the twenty-three hours after you train, but you need to supply your body with the amino acid building blocks if you want to grow!

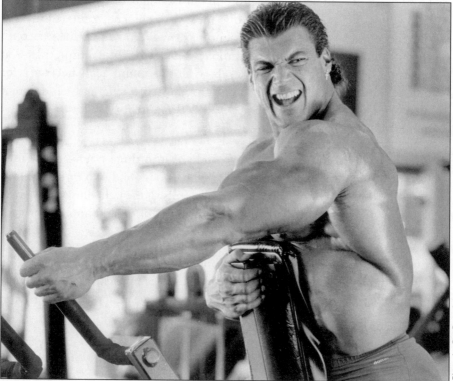

Photo by Per Bernal.

CHAPTER 4

Fat—It Is Essential!

FATS ARE AS ESSENTIAL AS ANY OTHER NUTRIENT in the human body. They are the richest source of energy, donating nine calories per gram as compared with only four calories per gram provided by both carbohydrates and protein. Dietary fat also helps you absorb the fat-soluble vitamins A, E, D, and K. Fat consumption needs to be monitored, though, because while certain sources offer health benefits, others can present serious health risks including cardiovascular disease, cancer, and obesity. Dietary fats vary in their activity and function in the body. You have probably heard the terms or concepts of "good fats" and "bad fats." The fats you choose should come from the naturally occurring fat found in lean animal protein sources like chicken, beef, tuna, salmon, and whole eggs, along with other select sources high in essential fatty acids such as seeds, nuts, olive oil, and flaxseed oil. Even though certain animal-based protein sources contain saturated fat, selecting the leanest cuts will ensure that you keep saturated fat at a safe level. In Macrobolic Nutrition, 20 percent of your calories are recommended to be derived from fat. The body needs some fat, primarily in the form of fatty acids, in order to perform optimally and maximize muscle growth. When a fatty acid cannot be manufactured by the body and has to be derived from the diet, it is called an essential fatty acid, or EFA. EFAs are responsible for the formation of prostaglandins and other hormonelike substances that regulate blood pressure, fight infection, regulate growth in children, and have an anti-inflammatory effect. They are also responsible for skin and hair growth. Fatty acids are long chains of carbon, hydrogen, and oxygen all joined together. How the carbon, hydrogen, and oxygen atoms are joined together determines whether it is a saturated, monounsaturated, or polyunsaturated fat. The structure also affects their stability, shape, and how they work in the body.

Unsaturated fatty acids have carbon chains linked together by double bonds. Saturated fats like butter and fatty acids with trans double bonds (the carbon chains are on opposite sides of the bond) like margarine tend to be solids at room temperature, while cis fatty acids (both carbon chains are on the same side of the bond) tend to be liquids at room temperature. Vegetable oil is an example of a cis fatty acid.

When the food industry artificially hydrogenates oils, they reduce the double bonds by adding hydrogen atoms. The result of this process is the creation of trans fatty acids. Trans fatty acids are what keep the oil in processed peanut butter from separating out as it does in natural peanut butter. The problem with trans fatty acids is that they reduce the fluidity of your cell membranes and actually make it harder for cells to function. Trans fatty acids are minimized in the Macrobolic cookbook, and serve no purpose for a bodybuilder trying to maximize hormone production and muscle growth.

Essential fatty acids are very important for health and performance. The two fatty acids that are considered essential are alpha linolenic and linoleic. These two fats make up two distinct families of fatty acids; the omega-3 family, from alpha linolenic and the omega-6 from linoleic. Seeds and grains are the primary source of omega-6 fatty acids in the diet. Sunflower, safflower, and corn oils are excellent choices to increase your omega-6 intake. The American diet usually provides sufficient omega-6, but is often proportionately low in omega-3. Therefore, omega-3 fatty acids are more commonly

---

RESEARCH UPDATE
Trans Fats Hinder Muscle Growth

A new study describes yet another insidious effect of trans fats: muscle loss. Focusing on the effects of trans-fat ingestion in seventeen women and fifteen men, age thirty-eight to eighty-three, the study found that it interferes with the metabolism of essential fatty acids by inhibiting their conversion into eicosanoids. It turns out that some of these vital eicosanoids control protein metabolism and synthesis in the body. When the trans fats lowered eicosanoid production, protein synthesis declined, leading to amino acid loss and subsequent muscle-tissue loss.

Hubbard, R., et al., "Apparent Skeletal Muscle Loss Related to Dietary Trans Fatty Acids in a Mixed Group of Omnivores and Vegetarians." *Nutrition Research* 23(2003): 651–658.

supplemented, and can be derived from dark green leafy vegetables. Even though fish oil is not high in the primary omega-3 fatty acid, alpha-linolenic acid, it is exceptionally high in the omega-3 derivatives EPA (eicosapentaenoic acid) and DHA (docosahexaenoic acid). These two fats are essential for neurological development and brain function. In one study performed on rats, it was proven that a diet high in saturated fats impaired learning, while a diet high in the omega-3 fatty-acid derivatives DHA and EPA heightened mood and improved cognitive function. As we age, levels of DHA decrease in the brain. So it is imperative to pay additional attention to this fat if you want to stay sharp.

Another function of the omega-3 family of essential fatty acids involves insulin secretion and insulin sensitivity. This is extremely important to Macrobolic nutrition, since our emphasis is on low-glycemic carbohydrate sources and on optimizing insulin levels throughout the day. In Chapter 2, I explained in detail how insulin affects our bodies. Studies show that omega-3 fatty acids actually increase membrane permeability of the beta cells in the pancreas (where insulin is made), thus allowing for insulin to be released easier. This helps prevent the oversecretion of insulin (hyperinsulinemia or Syndrome X). Since the muscle cells also have a phospholipid or fat layer with insulin receptors on it, the omega-3 fatty acids increase the cells' insulin-binding affinity and sensitivity, enhancing glucose transport across the cell membrane. This change results in increased glycogen storage and leads to fuller, harder muscle and increased energy storage.

Joint pain and inflammation are major concerns for many people, especially athletes. Joint pain and inflammation can sideline your ability to train and perform optimally and hinder your progress. In a study by M. J. James, et al., published in the *Journal of Biological Chemistry* in 2000, omega-3 fatty acids were shown to decrease COX-2 (cyclooxygenase), decrease the enzymes associated with joint degradation, and decrease the cytokines (messenger chemicals) associated with inflammation. The COX-2 enzyme is induced by inflammation, and is involved in most diseases associated with chronic inflammation. Joint pain and inflammation as well as joint deterioration will be highest when this enzyme is turned on. The omega-3 derivatives EPA and DHA have exhibited strong anti-inflammatory activity and help shut down the COX-2 enzyme. The studies actually substantiate the anticatabolic effects that the omega-3 family has on joint tissue. Since joint pain and degradation can plague bodybuilders, it's critical to make smart choices (like the omega-3s) for your fat intake.

In all of the studies I have examined, the anti-inflammatory effect of the

NEW SCIENCE UPDATE
Study Proves Eating Unsaturated Fats Instead of Saturated Fats Helps Reduce Body Fat

Piers and coworkers conducted a randomized crossover study of eight overweight or obese men (aged 24 to 49 years with BMI 25.5–31.3 kg/m[2]). These subjects followed two diets for four weeks each to determine whether substitution of saturated fat with monounsaturated fat affects body weight and composition. The male subjects were provided with all food and beverages during the study period. The percentage total energy from fat for each test diet was as follows: On the saturated fatty acid-rich diet, 24 percent saturated fat, 13 percent monounsaturated fat, and 3 percent polyunsaturated fat; on the monounsaturated-rich diet, 11 percent saturated fat, 22 percent monounsaturated fat, and 7 percent polyunsaturated fat.

During the study period, the researchers kept track of body composition, blood pressure, energy expenditure (resting and postprandial metabolic rates, substrate oxidation rate, physical activity), serum lipids, the fatty acid profile of serum cholesteryl esters, and plasma glucose and insulin concentrations. The researchers used some of these measurements to determine if the subjects followed the diets, for example by keeping track of cholesterol levels and the fatty acid composition of serum cholesteryl esters in their blood.

The study revealed that the men had a lower body weight (–2.1 kilograms) and lower body-fat mass (–2.6 kilograms) at the end of the monounsaturated fat-rich diet as compared with values at the end of the saturated fat-rich diet. No significant differences were detected in energy or fat intake, energy expenditure, substrate oxidation rates, or self-reported physical activity. The researchers concluded that substituting dietary saturated fat with unsaturated fat (predominantly monounsaturated fats) can cause a small but significant reduction of body weight and body-fat mass without a significant change in total energy or fat intake. This study provides more evidence that "all calories are not created equal"!

Piers L.S., Walker K.Z., Stoney R.M., Soares M.J., O'Dea K. "Substitution of Saturated with Monounsaturated Fat in a 4-week Diet Affects Body Weight and Composition of Overweight and Obese Men." *British Journal of Nutrition* 90, No. 3 (Sept 2003): 717–727.

omega-3 family is best achieved when the omega-3 fatty acids are derived from fish oils. Incorporating salmon into your Macrobolic plan provides an excellent source of these fatty acids. In the case of the omega-3 fatty acids, supplementing with some MaxEPA (fish oil) would benefit the bodybuilder, ensuring ample intake of this EFA. Fatty acids in the cell membrane also gives the body the ability to produce hormonelike substances called eicosanoids that produce localized effects in any tissue or organ in the body. These short-acting "hormones" have a direct effect on preventing inflammation and on the blood flow into and out of tissue, which is important to maximize nutrient delivery to growing muscle cells.

Cholesterol is another hormone precursor manufactured from dietary fat in the body. I know that cholesterol has gotten a bad rap in the last few years, but the truth is you need some of it to serve as the starting material for all steroid hormones (like testosterone) in your body. Cholesterol also makes up a great deal of the brain matter and is used in vitamin D production and in the formation of bile, which is used to emulsify fats. Dietary intake of cholesterol is not necessary because your liver can manufacture it from the low levels of saturated fats you receive from your lean animal-protein sources. Cholesterol forms the basic ring structure molecule that your adrenal gland will take to manufacture corticosteroids, testosterone precursors, estrogens, and progesterone.

As you know, the formation of hormones is extremely important for muscle growth. Testosterone is an androgenic hormone responsible for male characteristics such as facial hair, body hair, deepened voice, male sexual functions, and muscle growth. All guys, especially bodybuilders, want to have as much testosterone floating around in their bodies as possible. Studies show that you must take in a minimum of 20 percent of your total calories from fat (yes, the same amount recommended by Macrobolic Nutrition) to maintain normal testosterone synthesis. Saturated fat is the preferred form of fat for the biosynthesis of cholesterol to testosterone. This important need for saturated fat is another reason why I believe in consuming protein sources like red meat and whole eggs. Maybe this is why most hardcore bodybuilders and power lifters say red meat makes them strong.

Since intense training can actually weaken your immune system, it is worthwhile mentioning the effect that fat intake has on immune function. T cells, B cells, and macrophages all have a strong presence of fatty acids in their cell membranes, so the EFAs are essential for the proper development of these immune cells. Omega-3 fatty acids also produce eicosanoids, compounds that have been shown to elicit a strong inflammatory response to injury and infection. Eicosanoids increase fever and swelling along with immune globulin E (IGE), all-important defenses of the immune system. Higher body temperature kills bacteria, while increased sensitivity to pain inhibits you from moving an area that is injured (which may lead to further damage), and IGE increases the production of allergic antibodies. These all serve as first-line defenses of your body's immune system, and help ensure efficient recovery from intense training.

This makes a great argument for Macrobolic Nutrition's requirement to derive 20 percent of your total daily calories from fat. Fat actually helps slow digestion of a meal, delaying the release and absorption of nutrients into the blood. This delayed release helps lower overall glycemic response to a meal and keeps blood sugar from spiking and insulin release stable. Slowing down digestion of a meal also prolongs the release of amino acids from protein into your bloodstream, improving nitrogen retention and keeping you in an anabolic state. Fat also increases the release of CCK (cholecystokinin), a hormonelike cytokine that sends a message to the brain that the body is no longer hungry. Couple the anti-inflammatory, hormone-producing, and insulin-modulating effects with the digestive benefits of fat, and it is a no-brainer why fat is essential in your diet. Just be sure to keep track of how much fat you consume, because at nine calories per gram, the calories can add up pretty quickly. Sorry, this isn't the Atkin's diet, so forget about the crisp bacon sizzled in butter!

FACTS ON FAT

Trans fats: Damaged fats formed when oil is hydrogenated or foods are fried. They may raise your risk of cancer and heart disease.

Hydrogenated oil: Oil that has had extra hydrogen added to keep foods like margarine firmer and longer lasting at room temperature. Hydrogenated oils are found in most supermarket margarines, cookies, doughnuts, cakes, and many other processed foods. This type of fat has been linked to an increased risk of cancer and heart disease.

Saturated fat: Type of fat found in abundance in butter, lard, red meat, and whole milk. Saturated fat has been blamed for increasing the risk of obesity, heart disease, and cancer. These fats get their name from the fact that they are saturated with hydrogen atoms.

Unsaturated fat: Type of fat found in plant oils and considered less harmful than saturated fats. However, experts now feel that unsaturated fats rich in omega-6 fatty acids can increase your risk of chronic disease if you don't consume enough omega-3 fatty acids. They are called unsaturated because chemically, their molecules have room for the addition of more hydrogen. Oils high in unsaturated fats that some experts recommend include olive oil, hemp oil, peanut oil, and macadamia oil.

Omega-3 fatty acids: Type of fat found in fish, hemp seed, pumpkin seed, and flax oil. Experts believe we should consume more of these fats, since they reduce inflammation and produce a wealth of health benefits.

Omega-6 fatty acids: Group of fatty acids abundant in the American diet. While these fats are not necessarily harmful, they may foster heart disease and other chronic illnesses when consumed in large quantities without sufficient omega-3 fats. Corn oil, safflower oil, and soybean oil are rich in omega-6 fats.

Monosaturated fatty acids: The type of fatty acids found in olive oil and nuts like peanuts, macadamias, almonds, and walnuts. These fats are believed to lower the risk of heart disease and cancer.

Photo by Per Bernal.

CHAPTER 5

Water— The Nutritional Paradox

YOU'VE SEEN PICTURES OF PROFESSIONAL BODYBUILDERS working out. Expressions of intense determination convey the pinnacle of athleticism, only to be overshadowed by the sheer size of the muscles being bombed. This level of intensity is magnified by the beads of sweat forming on their bodies from the amount of effort they are putting into every rep to pack on muscle mass.

Have you ever considered what single nutrient makes all of this possible? What nutrient enables energy metabolism, protein synthesis, and virtually all other chemical reactions used by the body for performance? Most average bodybuilders overlook this cardinal nutrient because of its simplicity. But you are not the average bodybuilder. You are on the path to becoming the best and achieving your maximum human performance. With that in mind, let us consider this supreme compound, known simply as water.

Many overlook water as a nutritional staple. It is a nutritional paradox; this simple compound has no caloric value from carbohydrates, proteins, or fats; nor does it contain any vitamins or minerals. It is almost ironic; pure water is a nutrient that clearly has no nutritional value as far as macro- or micronutrients are concerned. Yet, despite this fact, it is so essential to the performance of the human body that if even 2 percent of your body weight in water was lost, you would begin to lose the edge in the gym. In light of this, water cannot be overlooked in Macrobolic Nutrition.

Certain minerals, such as the electrolytes, need the presence of water to function properly. Potassium (K^+) and sodium (Na^+) are both cations (positively charged ions). Because of their charge, they can interact with the partially negative oxygen part of H_2O. Thus, both potassium and sodium are dissolved in the presence of H_2O. Without proper levels of hydration, the functions of these two electrolytes will falter. The importance of these two electrolytes with reference to performance is covered in Chapter 8.

68

All body functions that include enzymatic activity need water to function properly, including glucose utilization, nutrient delivery, and waste transport. Due to its chemical composition, water really is the universal solvent; it allows all body functions to proceed smoothly. I could go into great detail about how water is crucial to each of these avenues of performance, but to be practical, I won't do so. Instead, let's briefly view the additional benefits to the body that water provides, aside from the direct biochemical aspects of this nutrient.

Water contained within the cell is called intracellular fluid. This fluid accounts for 30 to 40 percent of a person's body weight, and is typically high in the macrominerals potassium and phosphate. The water between the cells, which is high in the concentrations of sodium and chloride, is called interstitial fluid. Interstitial fluid is a main component of extracellular fluid, which in total accounts for 20 percent of the total body weight of a person. The body will adjust its water intake and excretion to maintain the proper balance of these fluids.

WATER'S IMPACT ON PERFORMANCE

To illustrate the sheer magnitude of water and its "weight" in the body, let's look at muscle tissue. Muscle tissue is made up of roughly 70 percent water. With a decrease of only 2 percent total water weight, nerves that direct the function of the muscle tissue will be compromised, with noticeable decreases in muscle control and strength. Your strength training will decrease by about 21 percent and your aerobic capacity will drop by 48 percent with a water weight loss of about 2 percent. Protein synthesis and anticatabolism are in effect when muscle cells are properly hydrated. So, water is absolutely necessary for your performance in the gym and your growth outside the gym.

To further illustrate the importance of water, consider the following functions. Water flushes lactic acid from muscle cells, serves as the key component of lubricating fluids for the joints, and serves as a shock protector in the joints and vertebral disks. In addition, water stabilizes body temperature through perspiration. Clearly, proper hydration is the fundamental cornerstone for upping the muscle mass in anyone.

MAINTAINING HYDRATION LEVELS IN THE BODY

Dehydration is avoided when one responds to the thirst sensation. Yet in some instances, dehydration has a rapid onset due to various factors. This could include a willful deprivation of water such as when wrestlers stop drinking to make their weight class or bodybuilders stop drinking to lose subcutaneous water to appear more cut. Excessive water loss also occurs due to vomiting, dehydration, diarrhea, and in the case of the athlete, sweating. The symptoms of dehydration vary with the loss of body water weight (BWW). The thirst sensation, weakness, loss of appetite, and slight discomfort are associated with a 1 to 2 percent loss of water. If the athlete avoids drinking water and loses 3 to 4 percent of BWW, the performance of the athlete will suffer, as described earlier. When the loss of BWW rises to 5 to 6 percent, the body will have trouble regulating its temperature and it will increase its respiratory rate. When it reaches the point of 7 to 10 percent loss of BWW, muscle spasms, exhaustion, decreased ability to maintain balance, and collapse will result. Normally, the athlete who follows a proper diet program can avoid these conditions. Yet endurance athletes should be aware of the conditions that develop when water levels drop in the body.

The best source of water is obviously water, but it is also found in all foods. Foods such as watermelon, strawberries, nonfat milk, spinach, broccoli, and lettuce all contain 90 to 99 percent water. In addition to the water found in foods, the body actually generates water as a byproduct of energy metabolism. When carbohydrates, proteins, and fats are broken down, their carbon and hydrogen components combine with oxygen to form carbon dioxide and water.

Water is lost through many avenues, so it must be replaced constantly. The most influential variable for water loss is sweating, so Macrobolic Nutrition suggests drinking at least 4 ounces of water per 100 kcals (kilogram calories) burned during exercise. This may seem too little to support proper body function, but this is the bare minimum that must be consumed when compensating for lost fluids caused by excessive perspiration. Excessive perspiration will result from an intense workout and the temperature of the gym. To ensure peak performance, I always recommend sipping on cool (not ice-cold) bottled water throughout the duration of your workout. I recommend cool, as opposed to cold, because cool water is absorbed more quickly than cold water. This is pivotal for keeping energy production at its maximum and lactic acid saturation to a minimum, which means better workouts and better results. You will also want to drink often throughout the day, since the athletes who follow Macrobolic Nutrition will want to keep their bodies at the optimum level of hydration so they can train at their maximum capacity. Remember, even with Macrobolic Nutrition, you'll have to hit the weights "heavy and hard"!

Water is essential to life, and it is also essential to maximum human performance, so let's not overlook its importance. You train hard to be your best, so it would be shameful to screw it up by not doing something as simple as drinking enough water!

CHAPTER 6

Macrobolic Meals to Muscle Mass

NOW THAT YOU KNOW HOW THE RIGHT SELECTIONS of carbohydrates, proteins, and fats react in the body, we need to look at what happens when you eat these food sources in a 45/35/20 Macrobolic meal. I want you to understand how this method of eating is going to make you bigger and leaner starting with digestion and ending with the nutrients going into your muscle cells. To begin this chapter, I will show how food is mechanically digested in the mouth and chemically broken down in the gastrointestinal tract, and how different hormones shuttle the nutrients released in the digestive process right to your growing muscle cells—all of this while making sure not to overload these processes and promote any storage of body fat.

THE PROCESS OF DIGESTION

When we eat whole foods, the nutrients (carbohydrates, protein, and fat) we need to get from them are not readily available until the food undergoes the process of digestion. Digestion starts in the mouth with chewing, the mechanical breakdown and mixing of foods. Larger particles are broken down into smaller ones. Smaller particles increase the surface area of the food particles so the digestive enzymes can break down the food more thoroughly. After you chew, digestion begins with the release of salivary amylase, an enzyme that is part of the saliva in your mouth. This enzyme is the first step in the breakdown of carbohydrates. After you chew your Macrobolic meal, swallowing is achieved by a wave of muscular contractions called peristalsis. The muscles of the esophagus propel food down into your stomach like an ocean wave moving through water. As the food approaches the stomach, muscles relax and the food passes through a ringlike structure of muscle called the esophageal sphincter. This muscular ring prevents food from being regurgitated into the esophagus.

The chewed-up food is now in the stomach. The stomach is an organ that performs three main mechanical functions related to digestion. In the first function, the upper part of the stomach must relax to be able to accept large portions of food and liquids. The second function involves mixing the food and liquid with the digestive enzymes (like hydrochloric acid) produced by the lining of the stomach. This lining produces both the enzymes that break down the food and the hormones that control hunger and digestion. This is the stage of digestion where protein foods begin to be broken down into peptides and amino acids, to be absorbed and used by your muscles. At this point, all nutrients have begun to be broken down, getting closer to the point where your body can actually utilize them. The third function of the stomach is to empty the partially digested contents into the small intestine to undergo further digestion. The rate at which the stomach empties is controlled by several factors. The protein and fat content of the meal, and the overall physical state of the meal (whether it is solid or liquid) determine the speed at which the stomach empties. A fatty meal may take up to three and a half hours to empty out of the stomach, whereas a liquid shake low in fat will empty in about a half hour. The other contributing factor that will slow gastric emptying is the fiber content of the meal. Fiber also slows down transit of the food through the intestine, allowing for more thorough absorption of the nutrients. This is important and will help keep blood sugar and blood amino acid levels where they need to be. Ideally, a Macrobolic meal's protein, fat, and fiber content allows for optimal absorption and a gradual release of nutrients.

Inside the small intestine, digestive enzymes from the pancreas, the liver, and the intestine break down the carbohydrates further, to result in glucose molecules that the body can readily absorb into the blood. Absorption of these glucose molecules increases the blood sugar. Remember, Macrobolic Nutrition's low/moderate-glycemic carbohydrates take longer to break down to glucose, and fat and fiber slow down gastric emptying, so the glucose from the carbohydrates are not released in one big load into the intestine. This prevents any spikes in your blood sugar and prevents insulin from shooting up to high. In a sense, by adding protein, fat, and fiber, you are lowering the glycemic index of the carbohydrates in the meal.

Let's take a look at what happens to the other nutrients in the small intestine. Fats are emulsified by some of the pancreatic enzymes and the bile, which is produced by the liver and stored in the gallbladder. The emulsified fats are easily converted into the fatty acids the body needs for efficient absorption. The pancreas also produces some proteolytic enzymes that finish off protein digestion. The protein foods you ate are now amino acids, dipeptides, and tripeptides, all of which can be absorbed in the small intestine and actively transported into the blood, where they circulate to the muscle cells that crave them. As the amino acids are absorbed into the blood from the intestine, the blood amino acid level goes up, stimulating muscle growth and signaling an increase in glucagon levels. Glucagon mobilizes stored body fat for energy utilization.

Insulin and glucagon are essential for transport of the nutrients to the cells, but there are three other hormones that play a key role in the digestion of your Macrobolic meal. They are cholecystokinin (CCK), gastrin, and secretin. Gastrin is the hormone that signals the stomach to produce the acid that breaks down the protein you eat into peptides. It is also necessary for the growth of the stomach lining, the intestinal lining, and the lining of the colon. Secretin is the hormone that signals the pancreas to start sending out the digestive enzymes such as pepsin to break the protein peptides into amino acids. Secretin also triggers the release of bicarbonate into the intestinal tract so the amino acids are absorbed efficiently without being denatured (broken down) by the acid from the stomach. In the presence of fat, secretin signals the liver to produce bile. This is its major role in the digestion of fats. CCK causes the pancreas to produce the enzymes that make up the pancreatic juice released into the small intestine. CCK also signals the gallbladder to release bile for the breakdown of the fatty part of the meal. Additionally, CCK is a messenger hormone that tells the brain that we are no longer hungry.

UTILIZATION OF MACROBOLIC NUTRITION

Now that you know how a Macrobolic meal is broken down into the nutrients we need to support muscle growth and optimize hormonal levels, let's take an in-depth look at how Macrobolic Nutrition creates the ideal anabolic and metabolic environment to stimulate gains in lean mass.

The 45/35/20 ratio of select nutrition is designed to have all the macronutrients work in synchronization. This is why it is referred to as the 45/35/20 lean-mass equation. This ratio of nutrients will feed your muscles throughout the day and keep muscle-building and fat-burning hormones in check.

Low-glycemic carbohydrates, protein, and fat in a 45/35/20 ratio will provide a gradual and controlled release of insulin. As you recall, you want to avoid high spikes of insulin, but you want a meal to elicit some insulin because it helps shuttle glucose, amino acids, and other nutrients into your muscles. This steady, controlled release of insulin pushes the high concentrations of critical amino acids provided by the protein sources in the meal to the muscles. This constant supply of amino acids will keep you in positive nitrogen balance, and continually supply muscle-building amino acids. Aside from helping slow digestion and the release of glucose and amino acids into your bloodstream, fats improve insulin sensitivity and are used for the production and formation of hormones.

Macrobolic meals are designed to keep your body running optimally for approximately three hours. Here's a list of what a Macrobolic meal provides:

1. Sufficient supply of carbohydrates to meet energy demands

2. Controlled insulin release to shuttle amino acids and glucose to muscle tissue

3. Controlled insulin release to prevent the transformation of triglycerides into body fat

4. Steady supply of amino acids from quality protein sources to maintain positive nitrogen balance

5. Raised glucagon to increase fat burning

6. The necessary supply of fat (especially EFAs) to support hormone production, prevent inflammation, and slow digestion to control blood sugar and amino acid release

7. A thermogenic effect

After a Macrobolic meal, all these great things are going on at once. Your body is running optimally and you are in anabolic state. However, this is where meal frequency becomes important. A Macrobolic meal only fuels your body for so long. As I said, you'll be running optimally for about three hours. If you want to keep your body running like a finely tuned muscle machine, you're going to have to refuel with another Macrobolic meal.

Okay, so now your body is running on all cylinders. You're eating every three hours, fueling your body with the right stuff. All systems are in check, you're as anabolic as a bottle of testosterone. Amino acids are being shuttled to your muscles, stimulating new muscle growth, and fat is being emulsified and burned throughout the day.

Nighttime is a different story. You need to keep insulin low and keep nitrogen high during the nighttime fasting hours. At night, you slam down a Probolic sustained-release protein shake before going to bed, again creating the ideal anabolic environment for muscle growth and fat burning. Let's look at our nighttime checklist:

1. Steady supply of critical five amino acids from sustained-release protein to maintain nitrogen balance during sleep

2. Low insulin levels due to very low-carbohydrate content of shake

3. Elevated human growth hormone (HGH) due to low insulin levels during sleep

The Thermic Effect of Food

By now, you are probably tired of hearing that a calorie is not just a calorie. I cannot emphasize this enough. I've already covered the difference in impact of carbohydrate, protein, and fat sources on hormones and metabolism even though they contain the same amount of calories. And I think that you now understand the importance of choosing the right macronutrient source. But there is yet another factor to consider when estimating calories, and that is food's thermic effect. It may sound strange to hear that food is thermogenic. When we speak of thermogenics, the first thing that usually comes to mind are fat burners like ephedrine, synephrine, and caffeine. You probably wonder why I would be talking about any kind of thermogenic effect in a book devoted to packing on mass. Well, understanding the effect that the food you eat has on energy is essential to figuring out how many calories you need, so you will pack on lean muscle and not become fat. What we now refer to as the thermic effect of food (TEF) was previously called the specific dynamic action. It is the increase in heat, or oxygen consumption, in your body after you eat a meal. Calories are a measure of heat, so an increase in heat production actually means an increase in calories burned.

Each nutrient (fats, proteins, and carbohydrates) has a different effect on the TEF. Additionally, different types of fats, carbohydrates, and protein will have either a greater or lesser effect on TEF. Basically, the harder nutrients are to digest, the higher the TEF. First, let's talk about carbohydrates and the effect different types have on thermogenesis. A meal that contains an elevated percentage of high-glycemic carbohydrates, like white bread, increases blood glucose and insulin levels more rapidly and has a lower TEF than a meal that contains low-glycemic carbohydrates, like oatmeal. Low-glycemic carbohydrates (especially high-fiber foods) increase thermogenesis and the oxidation of the carbohydrates is more efficient. This would explain why people tend to lose body fat while restricting their carbohydrate intake to mainly low-glycemic foods. A study conducted by Schwartz, et al., illustrated the differences in the TEFs of low and high-glycemic carbohydrates.

In a study performed in 1974, subjects consumed protein, glucose (a high-glycemic carbohydrate), or a combination of the two. The results illustrated a 17 percent increase in basal metabolic rate (BMR) in the protein group, a 14 percent increase in BMR in the carbohydrate group, and a 17 percent increase in the group fed protein and carbohydrate. This study illustrates that the right combination of carbohydrates and protein will have the same thermogenic effect on your body that plain protein will have, which is why Macrobolic Nutrition emphasizes the types of food you eat and the proportions and times you eat them. You need to take advantage of this easy way for your body to utilize excess calories. To top it off, the more muscle you put on, the higher this number gets. That's right, you read that correctly—the more muscle you pack on, the more metabolically efficient your body will get.

Table 6.1 illustrates the results of a Swiss study by J. M. Schwartz, et al., reported in the *American Journal of Clinical Nutrition* in 1989, which found that lean men experienced a higher TEF than obese men. This proves my point. The leaner you are, the more calories you need to sustain your body weight and prevent losing muscle.

TABLE 6.1. TEF IN LEAN VERSUS OBESE MEN		
Parameter	Lean	Obese
Body weight (kg)	57	84
BMR (cal/hr)	69	74
TEF	+13%	+5.2%

This point was further proven in a study published by Segal in *Endocrinology and Metabolism* where subjects with a higher lean body mass were found to have a higher TEF from meals eaten pre- and postworkout. One thing is for sure, an athlete needs to do two things to maximize the TEF: (1) increase his or her lean body mass, and (2) eat frequently, approximately every two and a half to three hours, so you do not slow down your metabolism.

It's an interesting point, and one that is familiar to dieters: Eat fewer calories, and you will slow down your metabolism, causing fat loss to cease. This is not the case with Macrobolic Nutrition. Our "muscle-friendly" ratio of calories will prevent slowing your metabolism, while simultaneously packing on lean, hard muscle. Dramatically reducing calories has been shown to decrease muscle mass, which is undesirable. We have already hypothesized that a higher lean body mass (more muscle) actually increases the thermic effect of food and BMR (the amount of energy expended in a resting state).

In a study conducted by Westerterp and published in the *European Journal of Clinical Nutrition,* diets containing different proportions of carbohydrates and fat were evaluated for their effect on thermogenesis. The researchers found that meals containing carbohydrates, protein, and fat produced the greatest thermogenic effect, while meals high in fat produced a very low TEF. This study further supports the ratios prescribed in Macrobolic Nutrition.

While all of this is very interesting, protein is still the best source for increasing TEF. In a 1984 study performed by Jequier, fat was found to have a 2 to 3 percent TEF, and carbohydrates a 6 to 8 percent TEF, while protein elicited a 30 to 40 percent TEF. While the protein numbers may appear high, in all of my research, the lowest TEF for protein I found was 25 percent. This means that if you eat 200 grams of protein (which is 800 calories), your body actually requires anywhere from 200 to 320 calories to utilize it. This is unbelievable! The increased TEF of protein is linked to the increase in nitrogen turnover, caused by an increase in protein metabolism. Basically, we want to utilize protein's higher TEF to maximize caloric expenditure at certain times of the day when we are less active. At night, meals higher in protein will generate a higher TEF, allowing your body to expend more calories while at rest. Couple the protein with a little fat and we delay the gastric emptying of the protein, thus stretching this TEF out over a longer period of time. You see, you want your body to have a demand for calories, even while you sleep. Without carbohydrate floating around as glucose in your blood, your body switches to the triglycerides stored in your fat cells. The protein further increases this caloric demand, while increasing glucagon, which signals the release of the stored fat (as discussed in Chapter 2).

So, the Macrobolic ratio also maximizes the thermogenic effect of food. The prescribed 35 percent of total calories from protein in combination with 45 percent low-glycemic carbohydrates and 20 percent unsaturated fats eaten in frequent meals throughout the day will require a good amount of calories to digest and metabolize. The meal frequency of every two and a half to three hours not only provides a continual thermogenic effect, but it also boosts your metabolism. By increasing thermogenesis and boosting your metabolism, you optimize your BMR significantly.

Additionally, Macrobolic Nutrition's recommendation to supplement with a Probolic protein high in fiber and low in carbohydrates allows you to create the ideal hormonal and metabolic environment to build muscle and burn body fat while you are sleeping. How awesome is that?!

4. Increased fat burning due to raised glucagon, energy requirements of basal metabolic rate (BMR), and thermic effect of last meal

Yes, everything is in check and you're primed for growth—even while you're sleeping. When you wake up, it starts all over again. You see what's happening? You're a muscle-building, fat-burning machine. Your body is running optimally twenty-four/seven and it's in the highest possible anabolic state.

RESEARCH UPDATE
Carbohydrates and Essential Amino Acids Are Anabolic

Strength training builds muscle tissue by triggering tension receptors in the muscle and by creating small injuries to the fibers. In response, the body creates special repair units called satellite cells that are incorporated with the contractile fibers of the muscle cells and makes those cells larger. Also, tension triggers the movement of amino acid into the cells, which makes new protein (muscle). Muscle growth or atrophy (cell shrinkage) is a balance between protein synthesis and protein breakdown. After a heavy workout, protein breakdown usually exceeds protein synthesis—at first. Gradually, protein synthesis exceeds breakdown if the right fuels and hormones are available. University of Texas scientists found that feeding a carbohydrate/essential amino acid supplement after weight training slowed protein breakdown and accelerated protein synthesis. This is more evidence of the importance of taking a protein supplement after your workout.

Rassmusen, B.B., K.D. Tipton. "An Oral Essential Amino Acid-Carbohydrate Supplement Enhances Muscle Protein Anabolism After Exercise." *Journal of Applied Physiology* 88, No. 2 (Feb 2000): 386–392.

IT DOESN'T GET ANY BETTER THAN THIS!

On Macrobolic Nutrition, you can't help but get big and lean. You see, being in an anabolic state throughout the day, day after day, is going to allow you to continually pack on muscle mass. And if you monitor your calories correctly, you *will* continually burn body fat. In fact, as your muscle mass increases, your caloric requirements will increase. It takes additional calories to maintain muscle mass. So, as your muscle mass increases, your BMR and caloric intake also increase.

What Is BMR?

Basal metabolic rate (BMR), also referred to as resting metabolic rate (RMR), is the amount of calories your body needs to support normal body functions to maintain "life" at total rest. Lifestyle would cover the calories needed to support the energy required for your occupation and other "nonexercise" voluntary activities. Exercise energy (calorie) requirements are those needed or expended specifically during your workout. Your BMR, lifestyle, and exercise routine are the three biggest determinants used in calculating daily caloric needs.

SAY NO TO CARDIO—FOR MAXIMUM GROWTH AND STILL GET RIPPED!

Early in this book, I said that Macrobolic Nutrition could get you big and ripped without cardio. I'm not a big fan of cardio. Besides the fact that I think running on a treadmill or stepper like a gerbil on an exercise wheel is boring, I feel it is counterproductive to building mass. If you train hard and follow Macrobolic Nutrition, there is no need for cardio! I know that is a bold statement, but let me explain how this is possible.

First, let's look at the reasons why people do cardio in the first place. They want to:

1. Burn calories

2. Increase metabolism

3. Improve cardiovascular health

4. Increase cardiovascular endurance

True, these all look like great reasons to do cardio, but isn't building rock-hard freaky muscle what really matters to you? Unless you are an endurance athlete, I see absolutely no need for you to be doing cardio. You can get the same or even better results from intense weight-training sessions. An hour of intense weight training will burn more calories and boost your metabolism better than an hour of jogging on the treadmill, with equal benefits to your cardiovascular health.

Cardio does absolutely nothing to stimulate muscle growth. In fact, it will hinder muscle growth. Aerobic activities like jogging, cycling, and the stepper deplete your body of glycogen, amino acids, and other precious muscle-building nutrients. Depleting glycogen and amino acids from your muscles can cause your body to spiral into a catabolic state, eating away hard-earned muscle with every pointless step. Long aerobic sessions have also been shown to raise levels of the catabolic hormone cortisol.

I probably still haven't convinced you not to do cardio. And, if so, you forgot to consider one important new factor—Macrobolic Nutrition. Remember, if you're following Macrobolic Nutrition, your body is running optimally. Through your diet, you have optimized your metabolism and hormones to efficiently build muscle and burn body fat. You have calculated your caloric needs and each calorie is being utilized to perform its proper function—*every calorie counts!* If you are following Macrobolic Nutrition properly and training intensely, you will not have to rely on cardio to burn body fat.

Exceptions to the No-Cardio Rule

(Okay, I'll make two exceptions.)

1. If you participate in a sport that also requires endurance conditioning. As I've said before, you have to train for your sport. Cardiovascular training is essential for some sports, like boxing, wrestling, and basketball, because they require high levels of endurance. These athletes usually need to train at a 70 to 80 percent target heart rate. The good news for you is that Macrobolic Nutrition is the best program to support your endurance needs and still optimize muscle mass, even with high levels of aerobic exercise. Just remember to increase your calories to compensate for the extra calories burned during your exercise sessions.

2. If you're starting the Macrobolic Nutrition program with more than 15 percent body fat, you may include cardio in an effort to get body fat down more quickly. But don't overdo it. Remember, you should be using the appropriate caloric requirements chart with the reduced calorie adjustments for people with more than 15 percent body fat.

   My recommendation for you is forty-five minutes at a moderate pace (60 to 70 percent of target beats per minute) first thing in the morning on an empty stomach, three to five days per week. To figure your target heart rate, see Figure 6.1 and Table 6.1.

   Following the diet, accurately counting the calories you consume, and weight training intensely and consistently are ultimately what's going to help you lose body fat and achieve a lean, muscular physique.

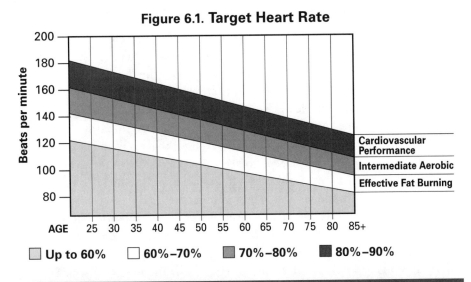

Figure 6.1. Target Heart Rate

Up to 60%   60%–70%   70%–80%   80%–90%

TABLE 6.1. TARGET HEART RATE					
	Low Impact for Fat Burning 60%–70%		**Intermediate 70%–80%**		**Advanced 80%–90%**	
AGE	Beats/ min	Beats/ 10 sec*	Beats/ min	Beats/ 10 sec*	Beats/ min	Beats/ 10 sec*
to 19	121–141	20–24	141–161	24–27	161–181	27–30
20–24	119–139	20–23	139–158	23–26	158–178	26–30
25–29	116–135	19–23	135–154	23–26	154–174	26–29
30–34	113–132	19–22	132–150	22–25	150–169	25–28
35–39	110–128	18–21	128–146	21–24	146–165	24–28
40–44	107–125	18–21	125–142	21–24	142–160	24–27
45–49	104–121	17–20	121–138	20–23	138–156	23–26
50–54	101–118	17–20	118–134	20–22	134–151	22–25
55–59	98–114	16–19	114–130	19–22	130–147	22–25
60–64	95–111	16–19	111–126	19–21	126–142	21–24
65–69	92–107	15–18	107–122	18–20	122–138	20–23
70–74	89–104	15–17	104–118	17–20	118–133	20–22
75–79	86–100	14–17	100–114	17–19	114–129	19–22
80–84	83–97	14–16	97–110	16–18	110–124	18–21
85+	81–95	14–16	95–108	16–18	108–122	18–20

*To use six-second counts, multiply by 10 to get beats per minute.

MACROBOLIC MOMENTUM: GETTING BETTER WITH TIME

The longer you are on Macrobolic Nutrition, the more efficient your body will become. It takes more calories to maintain muscle than fat. As lean body mass increases, your caloric requirements throughout the day will increase. This means that as Macrobolic Nutrition shifts your body composition to a higher percentage of muscle and a lower percentage of body fat, you will need to feed it more carbohydrates, protein, and fat. I like to call this phenomenon "Macrobolic Momentum." Basically what's happening is that your ability to pack on lean muscle accelerates over time if you stay on Macrobolic Nutrition, because your body becomes so metabolically efficient. So, in essence, the bigger and leaner you get . . . the bigger and leaner you get.

You've probably seen this Macrobolic Momentum phenomenon happen firsthand and just never realized it. If you look at the progression of some professional bodybuilders, you will see that there was a stage early in their careers where they made some good, steady progress. But then, all of a sudden, they went through a period of explosive growth. This stage of explosive growth occurs because of the accumulation of muscle mass supported by Macrobolic Nutrition. There is no reason why you can't experience this same explosive growth yourself.

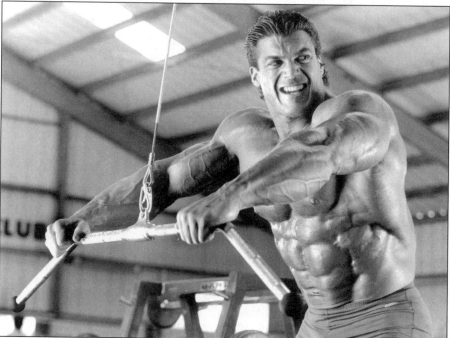

Photo by Per Bernal.

CHAPTER 7

Guide to Estimating Caloric Requirements

MACROBOLIC NUTRITION HAS TAUGHT YOU about the powerful effects of food. You've learned that all calories are not created equal and the importance of choosing the right ratio and sources of macronutrients. You've also learned that the 45/35/20 lean-mass equation will optimize hormones and metabolic efficiency.

Now that you know how to optimize metabolic efficiency, you must learn the next critical step in achieving lean mass. Like everything in bodybuilding, it comes down to amounts: how many sets, how many reps; how much creatine, how much glutamine? And most important, how much food or how many calories should you be consuming? As I explained earlier, the simple premise that caloric intake minus caloric expenditure will determine weight loss or weight gain does hold merit. Macrobolic Nutrition differs because its influence on metabolic efficiency increases your BMR, allowing you to consume more food "calories" to support muscle growth while burning fat. However, it is still crucial to adjust your caloric intake correctly to achieve your goal of changing body composition. If you eat more calories than you expend (burn), your body fat will increase even if your metabolic efficiency improves. Usually, but not always, the goal for bodybuilders is to decrease body fat while increasing muscle. Bodybuilders who are relatively lean often want to maintain body-fat levels while increasing muscle mass, and strength athletes often want to increase both body fat and muscle mass.

While Macrobolic Nutrition's caloric distribution of 45/35/20 is the ideal ratio for muscle growth, power, and performance, the total caloric intake must be adjusted for each individual and their goals. Also, keep in mind that as Macrobolic Nutrition increases muscle mass and your metabolic efficiency, your caloric needs will continually increase, as more calories will be needed to support this new mass.

So, the question remains, how many calories should you consume to reach your goal? Pinpointing any individual's exact daily caloric needs is very difficult, and many factors must be considered. Not only do these factors vary from person to person, but some factors can vary in the same person from day to day.

As explained earlier, your BMR, lifestyle, and exercise routine are the three biggest determinants used in calculating daily caloric needs. However, Macrobolic Nutrition also takes into account your personal goal, which is, after all, what Macrobolic Nutrition is all about. This unique feature is referred to as the metabolic goal variable (MGV). So, in figuring out your caloric needs, we use your MGV in place of your BMR.

MACROBOLIC CALORIC EQUATION

Macrobolic Nutrition has devised a simple, yet extremely accurate formula for you to use to determine your caloric needs to achieve your goal. We refer to this formula as the Macrobolic caloric equation.

> (Bodyweight x MGV) + (Bodyweight × Lifestyle)
> + (Exercise Expenditure) = Total Caloric Requirements

Let's walk through this equation, so you can see how easy it will be for you to calculate the Macrobolic Nutrition calories you need to achieve your specific goal. The Macrobolic calorie equation uses MGV, lifestyle, and exercise to figure out your caloric needs, so let's define each of them.

Macrobolic Goal Variables (MGV)

The metabolic goal variable (MGV) is broken down into three possible goals: gain, maintain, or lose. Of course, each of these goals has gaining muscle mass as a constant, but adjusts for your desired body fat.

> ### MGV: Gain, Maintain, Lose
> - **Gain Body Fat/Increase Muscle**
> - **Maintain Body Fat/Increase Muscle**
> - **Lose Body Fat/Increase Muscle**

Gain: The goal is to increase muscle mass and increase body fat. This is usually the goal of strength athletes or "hard gainers." Strength athletes sometimes like to have a slightly higher percentage of body fat covering their muscle mass. "Hard gainers" are those of you who have a genetic predisposition to being lean with low body fat and have a hard time putting on weight. For the gain variable, we use a multiplier of 13. So, in the calculation: MGV = 13.

Maintain: The goal is to increase muscle mass and maintain the current percentage of body fat. Over the long haul, this should be your status. As a bodybuilder, you should strive to get your body fat fairly low. I recommend staying between 6 and 10 percent body fat year-round, and then dropping a few percentage points in your last ten to twelve weeks of contest preparation. This will allow you to make gains and look big, hard, and full year-round. It will also allow you to coast into your contest looking massive and diced, rather than flat and emaciated. For the maintain variable, we use a multiplier of 10. So, in the calculation, MGV = 10.

Lose: The goal is to increase muscle and decrease body fat. This is probably the most common goal since most people want to be bigger and leaner. Now, you can! So, in the calculation, MGV = 7. If you are currently carrying a large amount of body fat (over 15 percent), use 6 as your multiplier—MGV = 6.

MGV Multipliers	
Gain:	13
Maintain:	10
Lose:	7
High percentage of body fat to lose:	6

Lifestyle

Lifestyle includes all forms of daily voluntary activities except exercise. Your occupation, hobbies, recreational activities, and daily chores all come into play, as they all require calories to accomplish. Lifestyle has been broken down into three categories: Sedentary, Moderate/Active, and Very Active.

Sedentary: Believe it or not, many professional and top amateur bodybuilders fall into this category. Remember, lifestyle does not include exercise. You fall into this category if you don't have a full-time occupation or you do very little voluntary or physical activities outside of the gym. I once fell into this category, where all day was spent eating, sleeping, training, or thinking about training. Man, I miss those days.

Moderate/Active: You fall into this class if you are a student or have an occupation that requires little physical activity. You also don't regularly participate in hobbies or sports that require a lot of activity. This is probably the category for most people. This category requires more calories than the sedentary group for your lifestyle outside of the gym.

Very Active: You fall into this group if your job is very labor-intensive, like landscaping, construction, or any manually physical occupation, or if you participate in sports or hobbies that are physical and active.

Lifestyle Multipliers	
Sedentary:	3
Moderate:	5
Very Active:	10

Exercise Expenditure

I have always believed that weight training at a fairly high intensity level is the best way to stimulate muscle growth, elevate testosterone and growth hormone, and boost metabolism. I feel that doing cardio to burn fat is counterproductive to mass building. Intense weight training with Macrobolic Nutrition takes care of the body fat. Your training time and energy should be applied to stimulating growth with an intense weight-training program.

Under this recommended training regimen, I calculate your caloric expenditure during exercise by taking the length of workout (number of minutes) and multiplying it by 10. So, if you train for one hour (60 minutes), your calculated exercise expenditure would be 600 calories (60 × 10 = 600).

Exercise expenditure = Length of workout (minutes) × 10

- If you do low-impact cardio (heart rate of more than 65 percent to less than 80 percent of maximum) such as slow jogging, walking, or stepper, add those minutes to the length of your workout time in the calculation.

For example:
   60 minutes of weight training
   30 minutes of low-impact cardio
   (60 + 30) × 10
      90   × 10 = 900 exercise expenditure

- If you do high-impact cardio (heart rate of more than 80 percent of maximum) like running, take the number of minutes of high impact cardio and multiply it by 12, and add that amount to the exercise expenditure total.

For example:
   45 minutes of weight training
   45 minutes of intense cardio
   (45 × 10) + (45 × 12) =
      450   +   540   = 990 total exercise expenditure

Macrobolic Calorie Equation in Action

Let's say an athlete weighs *180 pounds,* has a *moderate lifestyle,* and trains four days a week. His training sessions are *sixty minutes* of intense weightlifting. His **goal** is to gain muscle while losing his existing body fat. To properly determine his calorie requirements, he will use Macrobolic Nutrition's caloric equation.

Training Days

(BW [180] × MGV [lose]) + (BW [180] × lifestyle [moderate])
   + (60 min × 10) = calories

(180 × 7) + (180 × 5) + (60 × 10)

   1,260   +   900   +   600   =   **2,760**

Nontraining Days

(BW [180] × MGV [lose]) + (BW [180] × lifestyle [moderate]) = calories

   (180   ×   7)   +   (180   ×   5)

         1,260   +   900   =   **2,160**

So, as you can see, this athlete should consume 2,760 calories on his workout days and 2,160 calories on his nonworkout days.

Breaking Down Total Calories for Macrobolic Nutrition's 45/35/20 Ratio

Figuring out the breakdown of carbohydrate, protein, and fat calories to meet Macrobolic Nutrition's 45/35/20 ideal ratio for muscle growth, power, and performance is simple, once we know the required total calories. Let's use our example of the 180-pound athlete with a moderate lifestyle, and figure out his daily requirement for each macronutrient. These calculations are all based on the 45/35/20 lean-mass equation. Remember, 45 percent of the total calories are from carbohydrates, 35 percent are from protein, and 20 percent are from fat.

Let's figure out our 180-pound athlete's daily carbohydrate, protein, and fat requirements on his training days. This athlete's total daily calorie requirements are 2,760 calories. So, to figure out the total calories of each macronutrient, use these formulas.

Carbohydrates: Total calories × 45% = calories from carbohydrates

         2,760   × 0.45 = **1,242**

      1,242 calories from carbohydrates

Protein: Total calories × 35% = calories from protein
                  2,760   × 0.35 = **966**
                      966 calories from protein

Fats: Total calories × 20% = calories from fat
                  2,760   × 0.20 = **552**
                      552 calories from fat

So, this athlete's daily caloric requirements on training days would be:

Carbohydrates + Protein + Fat
    1,242   +   966   + 552 = **2,760** total calories

As you can see, these totals agree with our previous calculation for total calorie intake.

Meal Frequency and Caloric Distribution

All of the resulting numbers from the calculations below can be found in Appendix A of this book. You can also get them by going to www.macrobolicnutrition.com, clicking on calculator, entering your information, and a FREE online calculator will calculate these numbers for you. We've included the following section so that you may understand how we arrived at those numbers.

As you learned from the previous chapter, eating every two and a half to three hours is important for staying in an anabolic state and optimizing your metabolism. So, once you've figured out your total daily caloric intake, you need to break that total down into meal values throughout the day. The 180–pound athlete with less than 15% body fat, and living a moderate lifestyle in our example would divide total calories among four or five Macrobolic meals during the *day,* and 1 meal high in protein, moderate in fat and lower in carbs *before bed,* on both training and nontraining days.

While the Total Daytime calories should be consumed in a 45/35/20 ratio, Total Nighttime calories are derived by multiplying .25 grams of protein per pound of bodyweight, and adding 4 to 8 grams of fat per every 20 grams of protein with very little carbohydrates. This will create the ideal nighttime nutrition. You'll need to look at the relevant chart in Appendix A to figure out your Total Nighttime caloric needs. To arrive at your Daytime breakdown (both calories and grams of macronutrients), you'll have to subtract your total nighttime calories from your Total Calories for the Day.

Training days = 2,760 (total calories) − 315 (total nighttime calories)*
= 2,445 (total daytime calories)

Nontraining days = 2,160 (total calories) − 315 (total nighttime calories)*
= 1,845 (total daytime calories)
*Nighttime calories and caloric ratio taken from Appendix A in back of book

Let's assume this athlete eats 5 daily meals and 1 nighttime meal.

Training days (duration = 60 minutes)
2,445 (calories) ÷ 5 (Macrobolic daytime meals) = 489 calories per meal
1 High Protein Nighttime meal = 315 calories*

Nontraining days
1,845 (calories) ÷ 5 (Macrobolic daytime meals) = 369 calories per meal
1 High Protein Nighttime meal = 315 calories*

*Nighttime calories and caloric ratio taken from Appendix A in back of book

Converting Calories into Grams

To convert calories into grams, you must remember that 1 gram of carbohydrate contains 4 calories and 1 gram of protein contains 4 calories, while fat, being the most calorie dense, contains 9 calories per gram. To figure out the grams of carbohydrates and protein, you must divide the total calories of each by 4, and to calculate the grams of fat you need, you must divide the total fat calories by 9.

Remember, due to rounding and other factors that might cause slight variances in precision, numbers might be slightly skewed for certain calculation procedures. This is normal and should not cause alarm.

Sample 60-Minute Training Day	
DAYTIME = 2,445 calories	
45% Carbohydrates:	Total carbohydrate calories ÷ 4 = grams of carbohydrates
	1,100 calories ÷ 4 = 275 grams of carbohydrates
35% Protein:	Total protein calories ÷ 4 = grams of protein
	856 calories ÷ 4 = 214 grams of protein
20% Fat:	Total fat calories ÷ 9 = grams of fat
	486 calories ÷ 9 = 54 grams of fat
NIGHTTIME = 315 calories	
Carbohydrates:	Total carbohydrate calories ÷ 4 = grams of carbohydrates
	44 calories ÷ 4 = 11 grams of carbohydrates
Protein:	Total protein calories ÷ 4 = grams of protein
	180 calories ÷ 4 = 45 grams of protein
Fat:	Total fat calories ÷ 9 = grams of fat
	81 calories ÷ 9 = 9 grams of fat

*Nighttime calories and caloric ratio taken from Appendix A in back of book

So, our 180-pound athlete would have the following daily nutritional requirements on his workout days:

DAYTIME	**NIGHTTIME**
Total calories: 2,445	Total calories: 315
Total calories from carbohydrates (total grams): 1,100 (275 g)	Total calories from carbohydrates (total grams): 44 (11 g)
Total calories from protein (total grams): 856 (214 g)	Total calories from protein (total grams): 180 (45 g)
Total calories from fat (total grams): 486 (54 g)	Total calories from fat (total grams): 81 (9 g)

To convert the Daytime totals into requirements per meal, you would divide each number by the number of meals you eat each day. Since we decided this athlete eats five times per day, we would divide these daily totals by five. The nighttime meal doesn't apply for the following calculation, being that you only consume one meal at bedtime.

Total daytime calories ÷ 5	=	calories per meal
2,445 ÷ 5	=	**489** calories per meal
Total daily carbs ÷ 5	=	carbohydrates per meal
1,100 calories ÷ 5 *or* 275 g ÷ 5	=	carbohydrates per meal
220 calories *or* 55 g	=	carbohydrates per meal
Total daily protein ÷ 5	=	protein per meal
856 calories ÷ 5 *or* 214 g ÷ 5	=	protein per meal
171.2 calories *or* 42.8 g	=	protein per meal
Total daily fat ÷ 5	=	fat per meal
486 calories ÷ 5 *or* 54 g ÷ 5	=	fat per meal
97.2 calories *or* 10.8 g	=	fat per meal

Calculations Made Simple

If all of this confuses you, don't worry about it! I have included Macrobolic Caloric Requirements Tables that will do the calculations for you, based on your current body weight, goal, lifestyle, and workout schedule, so you will know the exact amount of calories, carbohydrates, protein, and fat you need to maximize muscle mass and target your goals. (You'll find these tables in Appendix A.)

Critique Your Physique

If you want to be as accurate as possible when figuring out your caloric requirements, you need to take a serious assessment of your current condition.

Remember, muscle mass requires a lot more calories to maintain than body fat. For example, a 200-pound person with 5 percent body fat (190 pounds lean body mass) requires more calories than a 200-pound person with 20 percent body fat (160 pounds lean body mass). Critique your physique honestly, because it will help you reach your goal faster.

As explained earlier, there are two different caloric multipliers for the goal of losing body fat: A multiplier of 7 is used for people with less than 15 percent body fat, and a multiplier of 6 is used for people with more than 15 percent body fat. This allows you to calculate your caloric intake more accurately if your goal is to lose body fat.

The goal to maintain body fat is usually for people with 6 to 10 percent body fat, who want to stay at their current body-fat level but increase muscle mass. This group uses a multiplier of 10.

Macrobolic's caloric calculator is as accurate a system as you can find, but it is not an exact science. Your percentage of body fat and your overall metabolism may require you to slightly adjust the recommended calories. Don't make quick changes in your caloric intake, however. Use the recommendations for at least three weeks, and monitor your progress. At first you may gain or lose a few pounds of body fat. You may want to increase your calories if you feel you are losing body fat too fast. Don't panic if you feel you are gaining body fat; you may have underestimated the amount of body fat you are carrying and be consuming too many calories. You can do one of two things at this point (after the first three weeks):

1. Keep your calories the same, because the frequent Macrobolic meals will start to boost your metabolism. Keep in mind that even if you put on a few pounds of body fat, you most certainly are also gaining muscle mass. The increase in muscle mass will demand these calories by increasing your BMR, and the body fat will start to melt away.

2. Adjust the calories slightly in the Macrobolic caloric equation by cutting back to the calorie requirements of a body weight of 10 pounds less than your current body weight. So, if your body weight is 190 pounds, go by 180 pounds when calculating your figures. This will give you a lower daily caloric intake.

Honestly critiquing your body and assessing your progress are critical aspects of any program. The only way you are going to benefit is to make proper assessments and target your goals. The longer you follow the Macrobolic Nutrition program, the more in tune you will become with your body. You know what your goals are, you know what foods to eat, now make every calorie count!

CHAPTER 8

The Important Role of Micronutrients

AS MACROBOLIC NUTRITION'S NAME SUGGESTS, its primary focus is on the macronutrients: carbohydrates, protein, and fat. However, micronutrients also play a vital role in metabolic functions and performance. Therefore, it is important that you gain a general understanding of how vitamins and minerals influence important functions of the body.

This chapter covers the two classes of vitamins (water soluble and fat soluble) and the two classes of minerals (macrominerals and microminerals) and their roles in the body with regard to performance and health. Proper intake levels of the individual vitamins and minerals are discussed, and foods containing high amounts of the particular micronutrients are identified.

VITAMINS

For the elite athlete's performance, vitamins are essential. In fact, an athlete's performance will drop considerably if certain vitamins are deficient in his or her diet. Read on to learn what you need to know about these important micronutrients.

Water-Soluble Vitamins

Water-soluble vitamins are unique in that they are absorbed directly into the blood. Because of this factor, they are able to move freely throughout the body, and once they reach the cell, they can circulate inside its water-filled compartments. Since water-soluble vitamins are extremely mobile, they are also easily excreted from the body. The kidney, whose function is to monitor the blood that flows through it, detects excess amounts of water-soluble vitamins and properly disposes of them. In cases of extreme excess, which is usually due to improper supplementation, there will be certain side effects that may become severe.

The B vitamins are the most crucial water-soluble vitamins that aid in the overall performance of the athlete. While vitamins in general do not yield energy like the macronutrients, the B vitamins actually assist in the utilization of that energy. The B vitamins thiamine, riboflavin, niacin, pantothenic acid, and biotin are all units of compounds called coenzymes. Coenzymes are small organic molecules that are closely associated with certain enzymes, and that aid in their function. Coenzymes are so important that the enzymes cannot function at all without their presence. The other B vitamins are B_6, folate, and B_{12}. B_6 assists enzymes that metabolize amino acids, while folate and B_{12} help in the multiplication of cells.

Energy-Releasing Vitamins

Each of these B vitamins assists, in one way or another, with the production of energy. As you will see, their roles are so critical that even a small deficiency will be detrimental to your performance.

Thiamine (Vitamin B_1). This B vitamin is the vitamin component of the enzyme thiamine pyrophosphate (TTP). TTP's function in the body is the conversion of pyruvate to acetyl CoA, which is essential to the metabolism of energy. Acetyl CoA enters the tricarboxylic acid (TCA) cycle, which is a series of reactions for the production of energy, responsible for the eventual formation of ATP (the energy molecule). In addition to its direct assistance in the production of energy, thiamine also resides on specific sites on nerve-cell membranes, directly affecting the activities of the nerves, and subsequently, the adjacent tissues (muscles).

If you eat enough food to adequately meet your energy requirements, you are probably meeting your thiamine requirements, too. The average intake of thiamine in both the United States and Canada meets the recommended amounts.

Natural sources of this vitamin can be found in all of the food categories, including breads, vegetables, fruits, milk, legumes, and meats. Of these foods, pork products, such as lean ham and lean pork chops, contain the most thiamine. One can also get adequate amounts of thiamine from enriched, fortified, or whole-grain products. However, muscle weakness can result if B_1 requirements are not met, because of its role in the conversion of pyruvate to acetyl CoA and the production of ATP.

Riboflavin (Vitamin B_2). The role of riboflavin is similar to that of thiamine. Riboflavin becomes the coenzymes flavin mononucleotide (FMN) and flavin adenine dinucleotide (FAD) in the body, both of which release energy from the macronutrients. FAD picks up two hydrogen ions from the TCA cycle during the metabolism of the macronutrients and its subsequent release of energy. These two hydrogen ions are then delivered by FAD, which is now FADH$_2$, to the electron transport chain. These two hydrogen ions are "pumped" through the electron transport chain and eventually help produce ATP. In fact, for every FADH$_2$ that passes through the electron transport chain, two ATPs are generated.

Most people in the United States and in Canada get enough of this nutrient from their food and either meet or exceed the established riboflavin recommendations. Some of the better food sources of riboflavin include milk, yogurt, eggs, and liver. Liver is the best source of riboflavin, with a 4-ounce portion of fried liver containing (245 kcals) in about 4.68 milligrams.

Niacin (Vitamin B$_3$). The name niacin actually is shared by two distinct chemical structures; nicotinic acid and nicotinamide (niacinamide). The body has the ability to easily convert nicotinic acid to nicotinamide, which is the most prevalent form of niacin found in the blood.

There are two coenzyme forms of niacin: nicotinamide adenine dinucleotide (NAD$^+$) and nicotinamide adenine dinucleotide phosphate (NADP$^+$). These two coenzymes are essential in the energy production reactions of the macronutrients, fat and carbohydrates. The other compound that releases its energy with the aid of these two coenzymes is alcohol. NAD$^+$ follows the same basic function as FAD. It picks up a hydrogen ion, as NADH, and delivers it to the electron transport chain, thus producing ATP.

Niacin is found in a variety of food sources, including enriched breads, cereals, and nuts. An interesting fact about niacin is that it can be synthesized by the body from the amino acid tryptophan. Since tryptophan is an amino acid, any diet that contains adequate amounts of protein, from both a variety of plant sources and animal sources, will not be deficient in this energy-releasing vitamin/coenzyme. Typically, most people in the United States and Canada have dietary protein intakes that are enough to avoid a niacin deficiency.

Biotin. This B vitamin is the last in the line of B vitamins whose function is solely the release of energy. The coenzyme form of biotin is required to carry a carbon to the 3-carbon pyruvate making it the 4-carbon compound oxaloacetate. Oxaloacetate is then combined with acetyl CoA, enabling the TCA cycle to continue producing products needed to manufacture ATP. The other essential role of the coenzyme form of biotin is gluconeogenesis. As mentioned in Chapter 2, gluconeogenesis occurs when the body does not have enough glucose to carry out metabolic functions. When the body is in this state, it starts metabolizing certain amino acids, and then fat, for the production of ATP.

Gluconeogenesis can have a negative impact on muscle building and perform-ance. Macrobolic Nutrition's 45/35/20 lean-mass equation can prevent this condition. However, gluconeogenesis is critical not only for performance, but also for brain function and other organ functions in the absence of glucose.

Biotin can be synthesized in the gastrointestinal tract by certain bacteria, but the amount of the synthesized biotin that is actually absorbed is not fully known. An elite athlete should rely instead on a variety of foods as established by Macrobolic Nutrition and on supplementation to achieve an adequate amount of biotin.

Pantothenic Acid. This is the only B vitamin that serves many purposes, which range from the production of energy to the formation of steroid hor-mones in the body. In the formation of energy, pantothenic acid actually func-tions as a part of coenzyme A. This compound forms the acetyl CoA in the "bridge" between the end stage of glycolysis (the breakdown of glucose into two pyruvate molecules) and the beginning stage of the TCA cycle. It is essen-tial in the formation of neurotransmitters, which are chemicals produced by neurons used to carry signals to other neurons and to nonneuron cells like skeletal muscle.

Due to its prevalence in food, pantothenic acid deficiencies rarely occur in a person who has a reasonable diet, but they will result in lethargy among other conditions. A diet following the principles of the Macrobolic Food Guide Pyramid (see Appendix B) has a good foundation in whole grains, which are rich in pantothenic acid. In addition to whole grains, beef and poultry provide good amounts of pantothenic acid.

The Anabolic B Vitamins

Vitamins B_6, B_{12}, and folic acid directly affect your body's growth potential. They cover mostly protein synthesis, but they can serve in other functions such as steroid hormone activity. As you read, you will continue to learn the importance of Macrobolic Nutrition and how it relates to maximizing your performance.

Pyridoxine, Pyridoxal, and Pyridoxamine (Vitamin B_6). This B vitamin is like niacin in that it has three chemical forms: pyridoxine, pyridoxal, and pyridoxamine. Any one of these three forms of B_6 can be converted into pyri-doxal-5-phosphate (P5P). P5P plays a significant role in muscle growth, because P5P is the coenzyme that transfers amino groups. This is absolutely essential in amino acid metabolism. When the cells need to manufacture pro-teins, P5P takes freely available amino groups (which are provided by a positive nitrogen balance due to an abundance of protein intake) and synthesizes all eleven nonessential amino acids. For example, as mentioned earlier, the conversion of tryptophan to niacin requires P5P. Vitamin B_6 is unique among the water-soluble vitamins in that it is stored, to an extent, in muscle tissue.

In support of this role, recent studies have shown that B_6 has a positive influence on steroid-hormone activity. Studies have also shown that a large dosage of B_6 does not improve muscular strength or physical endurance, but I must point out that this is in supplemental form. The role of this vitamin is protein synthesis, and an athlete can easily consume his or her RDA of B_6 from a well-balanced diet. Meats such as chicken breast, turkey, and beef are excellent sources of B_6 since it is stored in muscle tissue. So, if you are eating meat sources such as these, you should be getting enough B_6 to carry out these functions

The Dynamic Duo (Folic Acid and Vitamin B_{12})

These two anabolic B vitamins are considered the dynamic duo because the role of each in supporting DNA synthesis and tissue growth is rendered inactive without the presence of the other.

Folic Acid. This B vitamin also goes by the names folate, folacin, and pteroylglutamic acid (PGA). The coenzyme form of folic acid, tetrahydrofolate (THF), is required to transfer the one-carbon compounds that are produced during metabolism. This process aids in the conversion of vitamin B_{12} into one of its coenzyme forms, which plays a role in the synthesis of DNA that occurs in all rapidly growing healthy cells. In food, folic acid is bound with a chain of amino acids called polyglutamate. The body hydrolyzes the polyglutamate to monoglutamate and other glutamates with the aid of enzymes on the surface of the intestinal tract. The monoglutamate is then attached to a methyl group for absorption. At this point, the folate is in the body, but in its inactive state. The coenzyme form of B_{12} removes the methyl group from the monoglutamate, making the folic acid active. If B_{12} was not available to remove the methyl group, the folic acid would be inactive in the cell and unable to support DNA synthesis and cellular growth.

Folic acid directly affects the formation of new cells and protein synthesis, so a deficiency would lead to impaired tissue growth. It is, therefore, a crucial vitamin for everyone, especially the elite athlete. One can achieve an adequate amount of this key vitamin by including a good selection of leafy green vegetables, legumes (kidney beans, black beans), and folic acid–rich fruits (such as oranges) in the diet.

Vitamin B_{12} (cyanocobalamin). As mentioned before, vitamin B_{12} is central for the activation of folic acid, and it also removes the methyl group from the monoglutamate. The methyl group released by folic acid bonds to B_{12}, thus forming the coenzyme form of B_{12}. Methylcobalamin and B_{12}'s other coenzyme, adenosylcobalamin, are key participants in the synthesis of new cells, because both folic acid and B_{12} are used in the synthesis of DNA and RNA.

Vitamin B_{12} can also be classified in its own category because it is the only vitamin that is almost exclusively found in products derived from animals. B_{12} deficiencies rarely occur in people with a well-balanced diet, because a person should be able to meet her or his B_{12} needs with a reasonable consumption of animal products.

Vitamin C/Ascorbic Acid, the Secondary Antioxidant

Vitamin C has a unique role in the body. It serves two main purposes: as an antioxidant and as a cofactor. Vitamin C is also known as ascorbic acid, and for good reason. Ascorbic acid prevents the condition known as scurvy. It does this through its acidic properties. The two hydrogen (H^+) ions from the hydroxyl groups on ascorbic acid have the ability to be donated to (taken up by) free radicals in the body. Free radicals are molecules that have unpaired electrons, and because of this characteristic, they can cause oxidative damage to body tissue. Since ascorbic acid has two H^+ ions, it can help minimize oxidative damage due to free radicals. Thus vitamin C plays a key role in the body, protecting body tissue from oxidative stress by balancing the production of free radicals with the body's ability to manage them.

Unlike the B vitamins, which are coenzymes, vitamin C is a cofactor. A coenzyme is a compound that is made up of several different substances, but a cofactor can help an enzyme in a chemical reaction alone. When vitamin C is present with iron, it helps with the formation of collagen, the fibrous protein structure that is found virtually everywhere in the body. The iron works as a cofactor in the hydroxylation (the addition of OH groups) of two key amino acids, proline and lysine, which become both hydroxyproline and hydroxylysine and facilitate in the bringing together of the collagen fibers. The matrix of the bone upon which minerals are deposited is made up of collagen, and it is present in the walls of our arteries as well as in scars, which are the result of the buildup of collagen. Vitamin C has other crucial functions that influence health, performance, and body composition. It is a cofactor in the formation of carnitine, a compound that transports long-chain fatty acids into the cells' mitochondria for the production of energy during metabolism, and it is important in the production of the thyroid hormone thyroxin, whose chief function is to increase the rate of metabolism, thereby raising energy levels and fat burning.

The most noticeable early sign of a vitamin C deficiency is seen in the maintenance of blood-vessel integrity, resulting in bleeding gums around the teeth and dotted hemorrhaging due to pinpoint subcutaneous bleeding. These symptoms occur because of malformation of collagen due to a lack of hydroxylation of either proline or lysine to their hydroxyl forms. In the absence of hydroxylation, the collagen fibers weaken and lose integrity. As a result, the conditions mentioned before will appear. One can easily avoid the unpleasant effects of this deficiency by consuming a diet rich in citrus fruits, strawberries, red bell pepper, and kiwi.

The Fat-Soluble Vitamins

The fat-soluble vitamins differ in a number of ways from the water-soluble vitamins. Vitamins A, D, E, and K (ADEK) are all insoluble in water, thus they require a substance that makes them available for absorption. Your body produces a substance called bile, which is central in the absorption of fats in the intestines. Since ADEK is absorbed in the presence of fat, ADEK is transported with fat. All fat is transported in the lymphatic system, which is a system like blood vessels that branch out through the entire body.

If there is an excess of any one of the ADEK vitamins, the body will store it in one of two body tissues. The liver and adipose tissue will store ADEK and when the body needs any one of the ADEK vitamins, it can obtain them from the body stores. This process has its pros and its cons. The obvious benefit is that you could consume less food than what is required to meet your RDA for ADEK because you can rely on your body stores. One could potentially do this for several days, weeks, or even months before seeing any sign of deficiency. All someone would have to do is ensure that over time they consume the average daily intakes of the vitamins. The potentially harmful drawback to this fact is that if one is not careful, the fat-soluble vitamins can accumulate to toxic levels since they are not excreted as easily as the water-soluble vitamins.

In the following discussions, the function of each fat-soluble vitamin in relation to peak physical performance and optimal health is established. In addition, the levels at which deficiencies can be avoided and where you can find the best dietary sources are addressed.

The Anabolic Fat-Soluble Vitamins

Vitamin A. Vitamin A comes from a family of chemicals called the retinoids. This family of retinoids consists of three different chemicals: retinal, retinol, and retinoic acid. Animal sources of vitamin A contain compounds called retinyl esters, which are converted into the compound retinol in the intestines. The compounds found in food derived from plants are called carotenoids. Some of the carotenoids such as alpha, beta, and beta-cryptoxanthin carotene all have vitamin A activity in the body. Different cells have different needs for the specific retinoids and each form of vitamin A performs a specific function that the other two cannot do. The body can actually convert retinol into retinal and vice versa, but once any one of these two forms get converted to retinoic acid, it cannot be converted back.

For example, retinol is used in the support of reproduction and it is the major form of vitamin A that is transported and stored in the body. Retinal plays a vital role in vision by maintaining a clear cornea and takes part in the conversion of light into nerve impulses. It is also an intermediate in the conversion of retinol to retinoic acid. Retinoic acid functions much like a hormone in regulating cellular differentiation in developing embryos and in growth. Vitamin A has a role in the process of osteoclast, or the dismantling of bone. This is a natural process that must occur during bone remodeling, which takes place during bone growth. The enzymes that aid osteoclast cells need vitamin A to assist them in taking away parts of the bone that are not needed.

Some vitamin A deficiencies are apparent in people with night blindness. This is actually the first clear indication that a person may be running out of vitamin A stores in his or her body. The retina does not have enough retinal to regenerate pigments that are bleached by the light. Another severe result of vitamin A deficiency is irreversible blindness.

Toxicity develops usually when a person supplements too much vitamin A in the form of the retinoids. If you rely on a healthy, balanced diet, this is not likely to happen. Although in cases where someone would consistently eat foods that are high in vitamin A, toxicity would be a concern, too.

The healthiest way to obtain vitamin A is through the diet. Some of the best dietary sources of vitamin A are any animal-based food sources. Beef liver is the best animal source of vitamin A since liver stores a good amount of any one of the fat-soluble vitamins. Pumpkin is the best vegetable source of vitamin A since any plant that has a deep orange or a rich yellow color contains abundant amounts of carotenoids.

Vitamin D. Vitamin D is unique among all of the other vitamins, since it not an essential nutrient. Essential nutrients are nutrients that can't be synthesized by the body, yet vitamin D can be synthesized with enough sunlight and an intermediate version of cholesterol. Vitamin D plays a critical role in body development and maintenance over one's life span.

Vitamin D is really a member of a team of nutrients that regulate the bone-making process. Yet vitamin D has a key role in that it raises blood concentrations of both calcium and phosphorus. It does this by first enhancing the absorption of the two minerals from the gastrointestinal tract. It also enhances the reabsorption of these two minerals from the kidneys, and it regulates their mobilization from the bones into the blood.

Since vitamin D is necessary for the absorption of calcium, if a deficiency in this vitamin occurs, a deficiency in calcium will occur. Osteomalacia and osteoporosis are two common effects of lack of exposure to the sun and, of course, a lack of calcium in the diet. If you rely on getting added vitamin D from the diet, toxicity is unlikely to happen. If you supplement vitamin D, you could run into some potentially serious conditions. Since the role of vitamin D is to raise the blood concentration of calcium, too much vitamin D will deposit in soft tissue. This leads to stones in the kidneys and contributes to calcification of blood vessels, such as the major arteries of the heart and lungs, which will lead to death.

Few foods contain vitamin D, which is understandable since we can manufacture it. To ensure that everyone gets enough vitamin D, milk is fortified with this essential vitamin. Other sources of vitamin D are found in veal, beef, liver, and egg yolks.

Vitamin E, the Primary Antioxidant

Vitamin E is only one of two vitamins that act as antioxidants. Yet what separates vitamin E and vitamin C is that vitamin E functions only as an antioxidant. The antioxidant function of vitamin E is to prevent the multiplication of free radicals from other free radicals, as in the case of an athlete's intense training that results in the overproduction of potentially harmful free radicals. Vitamin E does this by donating one of its own H^{+-} ions (electrons) to the free radical, thereby neutralizing it. Unfortunately, vitamin E, by this point, is neutralized itself; however, vitamin C can restore vitamin E back to its active form. A diet that is abundant in these two antioxidants will drastically minimize oxidative stress placed on the body by an athlete's training.

Vitamin E naturally occurs as a family of tocopherols. The four forms of tocopherols are alpha, beta, gamma, and delta. Yet out of all the tocopherols, alpha tocopherol is the only one with direct vitamin E activity in the body. The other tocopherols aren't as easily converted into the alpha form.

A prolonged period of inadequate vitamin E consumption leads to issues with the retina of the eye and to neuromuscular dysfunctions that involve the spinal cord. Because of this, clear signs of deficiencies will include a reduction in one's ability to see, and the diminished control of muscles, resulting in poor coordination and reflexes. Treatments of vitamin E can reverse these effects. Toxicity is rare and if it does occur, it is not as serious as the toxic effects of vitamin D or vitamin A. If toxicity does occur, an interference with the blood-clotting effects of vitamin K will occur, and one can hemorrhage. To ensure that you get enough vitamin E to avoid deficiencies and toxicity, consume a diet that has a good base in food that is adequate to meet these goals. Seeds, nuts, and various vegetable oils like safflower, peanut, olive oil, and canola oil are all fantastic sources of vitamin E and the unsaturated fats, which also have their benefits for performance and health.

Vitamin K, the Coagulant

Vitamin K is like vitamin D in the sense that it can be synthesized in the body. It cannot be synthesized directly by the body, but bacteria in the gastrointestinal tract synthesize vitamin K, and the body can absorb it in the presence of fat. Vitamin K has, quite possibly, the most important role in the body. With a deficiency of the other fat-soluble vitamins, one can live with a minimum of direct threats to one's life. Vitamin K is used for the activation of several key proteins that work along with calcium in the formation of blood clots. With a deficiency of this crucial vitamin, a simple paper cut could lead to severe hemorrhaging.

Like vitamin D, vitamin K can become deficient due to several factors that are not related to inadequate dietary intakes. Secondary deficiencies occur due to other factors. For example, in the case of vitamin K, a decreased secretion of bile will lead to a decreased absorption of fat and the fat-soluble vitamins. A deficiency may also occur because of the interaction of certain drugs with vitamin K, and with its synthesis and its activity. Antibiotics will kill the bacteria in the intestines that are responsible for synthesizing vitamin K, and certain anticoagulant drugs will interfere with the functions of vitamin K.

Toxicity is not common if vitamin K is acquired from the diet. Supplementing vitamin K may lead to conditions such as jaundice—a condition in which bilirubin, a bile pigment, spills over and gives a yellowish hue to the skin and the whites of the eyes.

As previously mentioned, vitamin K is synthesized by the bacteria that naturally inhabit the intestinal tract. Yet they can only produce about half of the vitamin K we need; a good diet can provide the rest. Significant sources of vitamin K can be found in the liver, which is the best source of the fat-soluble vitamins. Other good dietary sources of vitamin K are any green leafy vegetables, cabbages, eggs, and fruits.

MINERALS

Minerals are the other group of micronutrients the body requires. They are in a completely different class from the other micronutrients for several key reasons, including each mineral's chemical makeup, their availability through absorption from food, the interactions that take place between two or more minerals, and their roles in the body. Since minerals are a dynamic factor in a person's performance, it is essential that we review their functions in the body. In addition to discussing their functions when they are taken in the proper amounts, I describe the symptoms experienced when toxicity is reached. I also indicate which foods provide the highest amounts of the particular mineral you need to avoid toxicity.

Vitamins are carbon based and are therefore are organic compounds. Anything that is carbon based can be easily destroyed by heat, radiation, and most significantly, time. Minerals, on the other hand, never change in chemical makeup. They never undergo a change to another chemical compound such as we see in the conversion of retinol to retinoic acid. However, they can combine with another compound for a specific function, such as the iron in hemoglobin and myoglobin serves to transport and store oxygen. The only way the mineral makeup of a food can be changed is for it to be depleted from the food. For example, the minerals found in vegetables can be diffused into boiling water, and then be completely lost when the water is dumped down the drain. When you cut vegetables, you increase the rate at which the minerals are lost.

The absorption and transportation processes of minerals by the body are a lot like vitamins in the sense that some minerals, like potassium, are easily absorbed, transported, and excreted by the kidneys, and others are not. Calcium is much like a fat-soluble vitamin in the sense that it needs assistance in the form of carriers and transporters for proper utilization. Since minerals can behave like vitamins in terms of absorption, storage, and excretion, there is the possibility that an excess of certain minerals can lead to toxicity.

The bioavailability of the particular minerals present in food can vary. Bioavailability refers to the amount of the particular nutrient that is available for absorption by the body. Some foods contain compounds called binders that actually hold on to the mineral and prevent it from being absorbed. For example, the compound known as phytic acid (phytates) in legumes, grains, split peas, and parsnips can act in this manner. In foods like spinach, rhubarb, plums, blueberries, nuts, and seeds, oxalates reduce the amount of minerals available for absorption. Although all of these foods provide great health benefits, the bioavailability of the minerals they contain will be low. To lessen this disadvantage, an athlete desiring adequate amounts of minerals would follow the diet-planning principles in Macrobolic Nutrition, along with the Macrobolic Food Guide Pyramid (see Appendix B).

Secondary deficiencies can occur due to factors unrelated to deficiency in dietary intake. In the case of vitamins, such factors include other substances such as drugs and the amount of exposure to the environment. Factors producing secondary deficiencies in minerals include too high an intake of one mineral, which can inhibit the absorption of another mineral. Too much of one mineral can also have a negative impact on the metabolism and excretion of another. For example, high levels of phosphorus will bind with magnesium in the gastrointestinal tract, leading to magnesium excretion.

The Macrominerals

The class of minerals termed macrominerals is present in the body's depositories (bone and teeth), soft tissue, and circulating fluids in amounts larger than 5 grams. Of them, magnesium is present in the smallest amount, which is around 30 grams. The macrominerals are divided into two separate classes, those critical for maintaining the body's fluid balance, and those serving important roles in bone growth and bone maintenance. The minerals that play a role in the body's fluid balance are sodium, chloride, and potassium. The other macrominerals important to the athlete are magnesium, phosphorus, and calcium, all of which play key roles in the processes over the life span of bone growth and maintenance. In the following sections, I establish the amounts of each of these minerals you need to achieve optimum performance and health, and describe the symptoms associated with deficiencies and toxicity. I also identify the foods that provide the highest amounts of the particular mineral to help you avoid any real threat of deficiencies and toxicity.

Fluid Stasis Minerals

Each of these minerals plays a key role in the overall performance of the athelete by maintaining water balance and body pH. Water balance and body pH are chief concerns because, as previously discussed, water provides the proper "environment" for all metabolic reactions to take place.

Sodium. Sodium is the major positive ion (cation) in the fluid outside your cells, and it functions primarily as a volume regulator. In addition to controlling extracellular volume, sodium acts as an electrolyte in the body and assists in the maintenance of the acid/base balance and is essential to nerve transmission and muscle contraction. Foods in general contain adequate amounts of sodium, especially processed foods. Typically 75 percent of a person's sodium intake comes from processed foods. Another 15 percent comes from salt added during cooking and eating. Only the remaining 10 percent of sodium actually is found naturally in the food itself. The intestines directly absorb sodium into the blood, and it is able to travel freely in the blood without the aid of carriers or transporters. Sodium then comes in contact with the kidney, which filters and releases the exact amount that the body needs. If you eat a food with a high sodium content, your body signals thirst to make you drink more water, increasing fluid levels in the body and allowing the kidneys to process the sodium. Any excess present will be excreted along with the water.

The minimum suggested amount of sodium to be ingested is set at around 500 milligrams and reflects the amount needed in a person who is not actively sweating. The maximum amount of sodium to be ingested is set at 2,400 milligrams. This amount is enough for people who lead active lifestyles and who take part in a wide variety of physical activities in different climates.

Hypertension was considered to be related to the dietary intake of sodium for quite some time. Recent studies have shown that sodium in combination with chloride at high levels raises blood pressure. This compound is sodium chloride, also known as table salt. A point of interest is that sodium alone or chloride alone does not affect blood pressure levels in the way that salt does.

Because sodium is present in adequate amounts in most of the foods we consume, deficiencies only occur for other non-diet-related reasons. These cause conditions in which large amounts of fluid are lost, including diarrhea, vomiting, or heavy sweating during intense exercise. One will experience muscle cramps when sodium deficiencies occur because sodium functions as an electrolyte.

Toxicity resulting from too high a sodium intake can happen but is extremely rare. One of the signs of sodium toxicity is edema, which is excessive fluid buildup in the cells. Hypertension is a condition where blood pressure rises beyond healthy levels. Hypertension can be caused by a number of factors, including exercise, stress, and other existing medical conditions; it can be aggravated by an excessive intake of sodium. Both of these toxic conditions can be treated through adequate water intake.

The best source of sodium is table salt, but you should avoid consuming salt in excess. Instead, you should select foods like meat, milk, bread, and vegetables, which all provide moderate amounts of sodium. The largest amounts of sodium can be found in processed foods, but you would be wise to limit the amount of processed foods that you consume. Processed foods typically have little or no nutritional value, are often high in calories, and usually don't meet Macrobolic Nutrition's recommended 45/35/20 lean-mass equation.

Chloride. Chloride is the negatively charged anion (ion with a negative charge) used by the body to control the levels of extracellular fluids. Chloride has free access to the cell membrane, and is able to move freely in and out of the cell. Outside of the cell, it is in close association with sodium, while inside the cell it can interact with potassium, classifying chloride as an electrolyte. In addition to maintaining normal electrolyte levels in the body, chloride is a part of hydrochloric acid (HCL), which maintains the acidic levels of gastric juices. The gastric juices play an indispensable role in digestion, so any decreased production of HCL leads to weakened levels of gastric juices. A case of constant vomiting would lead to a decrease in gastric juices.

Like sodium, chloride is found in abundant amounts in foods, especially processed foods, where it is combined with sodium and other salts. Chloride deficiencies are caused by excessive fluid losses from sweating, diarrhea, or vomiting. Dehydration can cause unusually high toxic concentrations of chloride in the body and is accompanied by vomiting. Adequate food consumption and water intake will rectify the situation.

The best source of chloride is table salt, where chloride is bonded to sodium in the form of sodium chloride. Other foods providing moderate amounts of chloride are meats, milks, and eggs. Again, like sodium, the largest amounts of chloride are found in processed foods.

Potassium. Potassium is another cation used by the body to control fluid levels. Unlike sodium, the other cation, potassium is found inside the cell and serves a host of key functions including maintenance of electrolyte balance and cell integrity. Another major function of particular concern to the athlete is for nerve transmission and muscle contraction. When a nerve impulse is fired to contract a muscle tissue, potassium and sodium briefly trade places across the membrane of the cell. This is of critical interest to athletes, because proper levels of potassium and other electrolytes directly affect performance and help maintain a steady heartbeat.

Potassium deficiencies are rarely, if ever, caused by a low dietary intake. The most common route for potassium to be low is through excessive fluid loss from dehydration, vomiting, and diarrhea. Food-related toxicity is not a concern. Since potassium is found in all living cells, any food that is fresh and unprocessed will contain significant amounts of potassium, and relying on a balanced diet will provide adequate amounts of it. Sources include the potato, banana, acorn squash, sirloin steak, and chicken.

The Bone Builders

As highlighted throughout this chapter, certain vitamins and minerals can be grouped together because they are in close association with each other and because they are synergistic—in other words, one increases the effectiveness of the other(s) and vice versa. Calcium and phosphorus together play a primary role in bone health. In addition to bone health, they are individually responsible for many functions in the body.

Calcium. Calcium plays the most important role in the class of bone builders. It is the most abundant mineral found in the body; it amounts to 39 percent of the total body minerals and total calcium measures about 1.5 to 2 percent of the body weight. The majority of the calcium present in the body is found in the teeth and the bones. Calcium plays two critical roles; the most obvious is its role as the key mineral in bone structure. The second role is as a depository for calcium stores. If a drop in blood calcium levels should occur for any reason, calcium can be drawn from the bones and teeth to help raise the level of blood calcium back to its optimum levels.

Calcium appears in various roles when it is in combination with other minerals. For instance, when bones are forming, crystals of calcium and phosphorus called hydroxyapatite deposit on the matrix of collagen. When the bone is going though the process of mineralization, hydroxyapatite and other minerals become denser in their crystal structures, leading to a stronger bone. This process is constantly happening because bone is continually being torn down and remodeled.

While 99 percent of the calcium in the body is held in the body's depositories, the remaining 1 percent is circulating in body fluids. In this form, calcium is ionized and is absolutely critical to life functions. The ionized fluid calcium aids in the regulation of muscle contractions, plays a role along with vitamin K in the clotting of blood, and assists in the transmission of nerve impulses, the activation of certain enzymes, and the secretion of hormones. For example, ionized fluid calcium activates the protein calmodulin, which is responsible for relaying messages from the surface of the cell to the interior portion of the cell. Some of these messages regulate blood pressure. This has led to the suggestion that higher levels of calcium will not only help reduce the severity of hypertension, but will also provide the depositories with enough calcium to prevent osteoporosis. Because of the many critical functions it performs, maintaining proper levels of calcium in the blood is one of the top priorities that the body addresses, and several hormones and vitamin D control the blood level of calcium. Since the depositories can provide adequate amounts of blood calcium despite a low dietary intake of calcium, an important issue related to a deficient intake of calcium is reduced bone integrity. This process is long and slow, so it can take years before an incident demonstrates a lack of bone integrity.

There are instances where abnormally elevated levels of calcium in the blood can result in muscular contractions that can't be relaxed, a condition called calcium rigor. Calcium tetany, which manifests the same symptoms as calcium rigor, will occur when blood calcium levels are well below normal. In either case, the altered levels of blood calcium is caused by either a decreased production in the hormones parathormone and calcitonin, which increase or decrease the secretion of calcium from the depositories, or a decreased level of vitamin D. These two muscular contraction abnormalities do not result from dietary excesses or inadequacies of calcium.

Like the fat-soluble vitamins, the mineral calcium needs a transporter to help out with absorption. The acidity of your stomach keeps calcium in a soluble state, and vitamin D plays a role in the formation of a specialized calcium transport protein. This specialized protein is called calcium-binding protein (CBP). Whenever the body is in need of added calcium from the diet, it produces more CBP to facilitate calcium absorption.

Under some conditions, insufficient production of vitamin D inhibits the synthesis of CBP, which is why much of the available milk on the shelves of the supermarket is fortified with vitamin D. Other substances that can negatively affect the absorption of calcium are the phytates and oxalates commonly associated with the fiber in whole grains and vegetables. For this reason, whole grains and vegetables are not suitable sources for dietary calcium.

This should not be a concern for the athlete who builds his or her diet using the principles based on Macrobolic Nutrition and the Macrobolic Food Guide Pyramid (see Appendix B), which emphasizes the use of all the food groups. The best source of calcium is found in yogurt and milk. Many athletes, particularly bodybuilders, restrict dairy in their diet. This is a big mistake. True, most dairy products contain high levels of saturated fat. However, dairy sources such as skim milk, low-fat cottage cheese, and non-fat yogurt have great macronutrient profiles and are excellent low-fat protein sources. And many people don't realize that these dairy sources are relatively low glycemic (skim milk has a glycemic index of only 32) even though they contain some lactose. An athlete who is a lactovegetarian will severely limit the amount of calcium present his or her their diet. This does not take into account the fact that whole grains and vegetables, the staples of the typical vegetarian diet, bind up calcium and increase the likelihood of calcium deficiency. Calcium deficiency can also be a concern to athletes who are either lactose intolerant or allergic to milk and its associated products. This would include allergic reactions to the proteins casein and whey (both of which are cornerstones to the athlete) and an inability to break down the milk sugar lactose. In these cases, protein needs can be met elsewhere, through the use of meats and other adequate sources of protein like beans and rice, but calcium will still be missing from the diet. This can be easily remedied by the use of calcium-fortified orange juice and/or milk-based products containing added lactase to break down the lactose into the two base sugars galactose and glucose.

As I have established, any prolonged period of inadequate calcium intake

will lead to decreased bone mineral mass and density. The deficiency manifested as osteoporosis, a condition that can be easily prevented, is very prevalent in the older population. The RDA for both men and women ages
nineteen to thirty is set at 1,000 milligrams of calcium a day. In addition to the
measure for the RDA, a tolerable upper intake level (UL) has been established,
which represents the highest supplemental amount of a particular nutrient,
where toxicity is avoided and most people remain healthy. The UL for calcium
is set at 2,500 milligrams for both men and women ages nineteen to seventy
years. If calcium intakes exceed this level, the potential for toxic symptoms like
constipation, kidney dysfunctions, and urinary stones will develop. In addition
to those conditions, high levels of calcium will decrease the bioavailability of
other key minerals.

Phosphorus. Phosphorus is the second most abundant mineral based on the
amount present in the body. It operates in association with calcium in the form
of hydroxyapatite crystals in the bone mineral matrix and in the teeth. Actually about 85 percent of the body's phosphorus mass is stored in the depositories. The remaining 15 percent is present in a host of compounds found in
the body.

Adenosine triphosphate (ATP), thiamine pyrophosphate, pyridoxal-5-
phosphate, and phosphoric acid (the body's buffer system) and its various salts,
phospholipids like the chylomicrons, and the membranes of cells all contain
a phosphate group in their chemical structure. These compounds would be
rendered useless without phosphorus, so we can see that this mineral plays a
significant role in the performance of an athlete because of its major role in the
release of energy at all stages of metabolism.

Dietary deficiencies of phosphorus are unknown. The reason for this is
because phosphorus is present in adequate amounts in any diet with an adequate amount of animal tissue, and legumes and milk are also good sources of
phosphorus. In addition, phosphorus is present in processed meats and other
processed foods, and in soft drinks. Deficiencies can occur because of a drug
interaction with phosphorus. Some drugs bind to the phosphorus, making
it unavailable for any of the vital functions associated with metabolism. Phosphorus deficiency symptoms are manifested as muscle weakness, a lack of energy, and bone pain.

Magnesium, the Mighty Mineral

Although magnesium is in amounts so low that it barely qualifies to be considered a macromineral, it serves a host of indispensable functions to the athlete. Over half of the body's magnesium is stored in the bone depository, and

most of the remaining amounts are held in the soft tissue of the body. About 1 percent remains in the extracellular fluid of the body. The magnesium in the soft tissue performs a vast range of roles in the body. It is a main component in the synthesis of protein, and a major player in many of the body's enzyme reactions. It functions as a catalyst in the final role of ATP production, where the final phosphate group is added to adenosine diphosphate (ADP). Magnesium is vital for countering the effects of calcium in muscle contraction and blood clotting.

In most people's dietary intake, magnesium is one of the minerals that falls far below what is considered adequate. This potential deficiency is of particular concern to the athlete, because of magnesium's role in protein synthesis and energy production. A diet high in legumes will provide sufficient amounts of magnesium to compensate for this lack. Other significant sources of magnesium are halibut, cashews, artichokes, and millet.

Toxicity is rare when magnesium is derived from the diet. However, when taken improperly in supplemental form, excessive amounts of magnesium can lead to diarrhea, which leads to dehydration.

Sulfur, the Protein Architect

Sulfur is last in the line of the macrominerals and is not used by the body in its original form. Your body derives this mineral from certain B vitamins and amino acids. In the formation of proteins, sulfur plays an important role in protein folding. The way a protein folds determines how it functions. Insulin is the hormone that promotes glucose utilization, protein synthesis, and the formation and storage of neutral lipids. This crucial hormone is a protein created by the use of three disulfide bridges that exist between the six L-cysteine amino acids.

Cysteine is a nonessential amino acid, which means the body can manufacture it in the presence of sulfur. Therefore, there are no deficiencies associated with sulfur as long as protein intake is adequate. Adequate protein intake can be obtained by an athlete who follows the principles of Macrobolic Nutrition. When an athlete follows Macrobolic Nutrition, all of these essential macrominerals are provided in adequate amounts to ensure maximum human performance.

The Microminerals

The microminerals are as important to the body's health and functioning as the macrominerals. They are considered microminerals because of the relatively small amounts that are present in the body. These microminerals, also commonly known as trace minerals, are supplied in adequate amounts in people's diets, to both maintain health and avoid toxicity. In the discussion of the trace minerals, I determine why these elements are so important to the athlete's performance. To optimize the total bioavailability, I also determine which foods contain the greatest concentration of the particular trace mineral.

The category of trace minerals includes the minerals iron, zinc, selenium, chromium, copper, manganese, fluoride, molybdenum, and others. Most of the minerals mentioned are available in supplemental form, but you should avoid excessive use of these products, because most of the time these supplements contain amounts of the trace minerals that are in excess of what is needed to maintain health. Any amount over what is suggested will produce conditions that are undesirable, which could include organ damage, muscle pain, exhaustion, and fatigue. So, it is vital to address the toxic signs of the trace minerals and the amounts at which toxicity can be avoided.

Secondary deficiencies are another issue associated with an overabundance of trace minerals. Remember, secondary deficiencies are not cause by inadequacies of nutrients in the diet; they are caused by other nondietary factors. In the case of the trace minerals, a nondietary factor may be caused by an excess of one trace mineral that is inhibiting the absorption of another equally important trace mineral.

Iron, the Oxygen Transporter

Iron is a mineral that is needed in amounts ranging from 8 milligrams per day for men to about 18 milligrams per day for women. The importance of its role to the athlete is unmatched, despite the fact that this mineral is present in the body in relatively small amounts,

Iron exists in the body in two distinct states of charge, called ionic states. Ferrous iron has a +2 charge, while the ferric iron form has a +3 charge. Since iron has the ability to exist in two distinct states, it can participate in a wide range of enzymatic reactions, and it also plays a principal role in the production of ATP. The enzyme fumerase reduces NAD^+ to NADH in the TCA cycle of metabolism. NADH can then provide H^+ to the electron transport chain. In the electron transport chain, cytochromes, which contain iron, facilitate the movement of H^+ from the matrix to the intermembrane space of the mitochondria. Fumerase and cytochromes are thus key components involved in the production of ATP.

The most common use of iron by the body is in the compounds that transport oxygen to tissues. Hemoglobin and myoglobin are two proteins that have a heme group, which contains ferrous iron. Hemoglobin is the primary transport for oxygen, while myoglobin is used mostly for storing oxygen in the muscle.

When a muscle tissue is active, a buildup of H^+ and CO_2 are produced. Hemoglobin has a high affinity for H^+ when little oxygen is present at the site of the active tissue (conversely, when blood passes through alveoli of the lungs, oxygen concentration is higher than H^+ concentrations, so oxygen binds to hemoglobin). Due to this fact, oxygen is traded for H^+ in a muscle tissue that is actively respiring. Without iron present in hemoglobin, there is a decreased ability to transport oxygen. This has a large impact on athletic performance, and is discussed later in this section.

Since iron is used in the part of hemoglobin that actually accepts oxygen, it is understandable why the body would be designed for the conservation of iron. The body doesn't excrete iron too well because of this; in fact, one of the only ways for your body to lose iron is through bleeding. That is why premenopausal women need 10 milligrams more iron than do men. The body maintains the levels of iron primarily through the manipulation of absorption, absorbing more when it is needed and less when it is not.

Iron absorption is a process that requires three specialized proteins: mucosal ferritin, mucosal transferrin, and blood transferrin. When iron is present in the small intestines, a protein formed in the mucous lining of the intestinal cells binds to the iron. This protein is called mucosal ferritin. When the body signals for the absorption of iron, the mucosal ferritin gives up the iron to another mucus-based protein, mucosal transferrin. Blood transferrin then transports the iron to the rest of the body, where either bone marrow or other cells will use it. The cells of the intestines renew themselves every three days. When they are excreted out of the body through feces, any iron that is not needed by the body at the time will be lost. Having the ability to store some iron is vital to the body. A reasonable amount of the excess dietary iron is stored in the liver or the spleen. The liver creates specialized proteins called ferritin and hemosiderin. The body readily breaks down ferritin, so a constant blood supply of iron is always available. Hemosiderin is formed from ferritin when blood iron levels become abnormally high.

To consider which type of iron has the highest bioavailability, let's quickly examine the storage of excess carbohydrates as fats, and excess fats as fats. Which is easier (in terms of caloric expenditure) for the body to do: to take a carbohydrate and chemically convert it into a fatty acid and then chemically combine it to a glycerol backbone, or to take a fat and store it as fat? The answer is obvious. So too is the bioavailability of heme iron, which is used in hemo/myoglobin. For example, heme accounts for about 10 percent of the total iron acquired from the diet, yet 25 to 35 percent of the heme iron is actually absorbed. This is significantly more than the 10 percent that is absorbed from nonheme iron.

There are several factors to consider that contribute to the overall bioavailability of iron in the diet. Since any flesh-based source of iron is best as far as bioavailability is concerned (heme iron), it is not surprising that these sources also contain a substance that enhances the all-round absorption of iron. It is called the MFP factor, because it is associated with the digestion of meats, fish, and poultry. Vitamin C also enhances the absorption of nonheme iron. This is because ascorbic acid is able to hold on to the reduced form of iron, which is ready for absorption. These two absorption enhancers are met with a degree of opposition from phytates that naturally occur in some foods, but this can be easily compensated for by the use of a wide variety of foods, as demonstrated by the Macrobolic Food Guide Pyramid. (See Appendix B.)

When the body stores of iron fall to extremely low levels, iron deficiency anemia becomes the major concern for the athlete. In this condition, the red blood cells are small and pale, and because of their physical state, their ability to bind to oxygen in the lungs is severely diminished. Energy production is decreased since the body needs oxygen to perform metabolism at its optimal level, so symptoms of this condition manifest in the form of fatigue, weakness, headaches, and poor core-temperature regulation. Iron deficiency anemia is visibly detected by a pale complexion on a person with fair skin. It can be detected in people with a darker skin tone by checking the lining of the eye, which will become pale rather than pink. Because the body conserves iron, the main cause of iron deficiency would be excessive blood loss.

The potential for greater harm exists with the toxicities associated with iron. A condition known as hemosiderosis will develop when iron is taken in excess. Repeated blood transfusions, which completely circumvent the body's intestinal defense, and naive iron supplementation, which overwhelms the intestinal defense, cause the liver to transform ferritin into hemosiderin. Hemosiderosis is a condition in which buildup of hemosiderin in the liver and other tissues can potentially cause tissue damage. Infections are more common, not because there is a decrease in immune function, but because bacteria thrive on iron-rich blood. Athletes who rely on Macrobolic Nutrition and its associated food guide pyramid will have no associated iron deficiencies or toxic symptoms, thus ensuring optimal performance.

The best dietary sources of iron are the flesh of animals since it has iron in the same form that is used by our bodies. Ground beef, sirloin steak, and shrimp are all superior choices for iron. Kidney, garbanzo, pinto, and navy beans are also excellent legume sources of iron. Other enriched foods also provide adequate amounts of iron, including oatmeal, spaghetti, and flour tortillas (all of which are low glycemic).

Zinc, the Cofactor

Zinc is a major component of more than 100 different enzymes called metalloenzymes that carry this label because a mineral is included in their structural makeup. Zinc has the ability to stabilize the membrane of the cell, which makes it crucial in the defense against free radicals. It is a participant in the synthesis, storage, and release of the blood sugar regulating the hormone insulin. Zinc is another component of the body's blood-clotting system, and it affects the functions of thyroid hormone. It is also essential for vision, since it produces retinal, the form of vitamin A required for the visual pigments.

Zinc absorption is similar to that of iron in certain ways. When the body has enough zinc to maintain optimal performance and health, it reduces the amount of absorption that occurs. As with iron, fiber and its associated phytates bind to the excess zinc, limiting the bioavailability of the mineral.

When zinc is absorbed into the microvilli (fingerlike projections on intestinal cells), the variety of roles it can take on is great. It can be absorbed into the cell right away, where it can function as a component of either DNA or RNA polymerase. This is significant because the intestinal cells renew themselves frequently and zinc is therefore absolutely crucial to the growth of new intestinal cells. Another possible avenue for zinc is in the storage protein called metallothionein. This specialized binding protein helps regulate zinc absorption, much like iron's mucosal ferritin. Metallothionein is stored in the liver, so the body has some reserves if there is any need for more zinc.

The pancreas produces many of the enzymes with zinc in their structure that are critical for digestion. When you consume a food like steak, the dietary zinc is combined with the zinc from the pancreatic juices. The zinc derived from the pancreas can be reabsorbed into the intestinal cells for growth or return to the pancreas for further use as metalloenzymes.

To illustrate the importance of a proper diet and ill-advised supplementation, let's briefly consider the interaction between iron and zinc. Some plasma zinc binds to transferrin, which is also the preferred mode of travel for diet-derived iron in the blood. Adults who overuse iron supplements will overly saturate the transferrin-binding sites and leave them unable to absorb zinc. The converse is true too; large amounts of zinc will inhibit the absorption of iron.

Large dosages of zinc interfere with copper absorption too. This interference may occur because the two minerals compete for absorption with one another. When an abundance of zinc is ingested, the intestinal-absorbing cells produce more metallothionein, a binding protein that stores zinc in much the same way that iron is stored in mucosal ferritin. Metallothionein also binds to other microminerals, such as copper and cadmium. A higher affinity exists between copper and metallothionein than between zinc and metallothionein.

So increased levels of metallothionein, due to an abundance of ingested zinc, will bind to copper as well, and severely limit the copper that is freely available for absorption. Thus copper availability is reduced because of the larger amounts of zinc. This point illustrates the most common mistake people make with supplements. It can be avoided by relying on a sound diet and some key supplementation.

Since zinc absorption is similar in principle to iron absorption, it follows that its loss from the body occurs in the same basic fashion. Since metallothionein is produced by the microvilli, any tied-up zinc is excreted in the feces when the microvilli are replaced.

When zinc levels are all but nonexistent, growth in general will be retarded because zinc plays such a large role in the area of cellular growth and protein synthesis. Deficiencies of zinc also provoke diarrhea, which worsens not only the zinc deficiency, but also the presence of other essential nutrients. Other symptoms of deficiency include an altered thyroid function and metabolic rate, warped taste, and a lowered rate of wound healing. These zinc–deficiency related conditions can manifest even when only mild zinc deficiencies exist in the diet.

The toxic symptoms of excess zinc may include vomiting, exhaustion, muscle pain, dizziness, and drowsiness. Too much zinc interferes with the absorption of copper and its proper metabolism. When researched in test animals, excess zinc has led to degeneration of cardiac muscle. High zinc levels also reduce the production of red blood cells, which further affect performance.

It is wise to rely on a variety of healthy foods to supply the body with the right amount of zinc and avoid the pitfalls of incorrect supplementation. Zinc is found in the highest concentrations in protein-rich foods, such as sirloin steak, ground beef, ham, dark turkey meat, and yogurt.

Iodine, the Metabolic Trace Mineral

Iodine is the food-based form of the ionized form iodide used by our bodies. Although iodide is found in very small amounts in the body, its role is critical. It is a primary component of the thyroid hormones triiodothyronine (T_3) and tetraiodothyronine (T_4; thyroxin). These hormones are used to regulate cellular metabolism and other functions like body temperature, reproduction, growth, and muscular function. These critical hormones actually regulate the amount of oxygen a cell uses and therefore manipulate the amount of energy released during basal metabolism.

Iodine deficiency is not common in developed countries, so we don't have to concern ourselves with this issue in great detail. To provide a basic overview, the hypothalamus controls the production of thyroid-stimulating hormone

(TSH), which is produced by the pituitary gland. During iodine deficiencies, thyroid-hormone synthesis declines. TSH is produced in larger amounts in an attempt to increase absorption of whatever iodine is left in the thyroid gland for thyroxin synthesis. If this condition persists for an extended period of time, the cells of the thyroid gland enlarge to the extent of developing into a large lump on the neck. The symptom of a toxic iodine level is identical to the symptom of deficiency, and it is also identified by a rather large lump on the front of the neck.

To avoid any form of deficiency or toxicity, the athlete would be wise to plan a well-balanced diet with a firm basis in Macrobolic Nutrition. This diet will ensure an adequate amount of iodine from seafood and other foods cultivated in iodine-rich soil. If you are allergic to certain proteins found some seafoods, you can conservatively use iodized table salt, which contains the RDA in half a teaspoon.

Selenium, the Antioxidant

Selenium is a cofactor in the enzyme glutathione peroxidase. It facilitates the reduction of toxic hydrogen peroxide within the cells. This enzyme works in conjunction with vitamin E in the defense against free radicals, so selenium can prevent oxidative damages to the cell and block free-radical formation. When selenium can't block the formation of free radicals, vitamin E will be able to stop it. The enzyme responsible for converting tetraiodothyronine to triiodothyronine, which is the active form of the hormone, contains selenium.

A deficiency in selenium is associated with a type of heart disease that is prevalent in an area of China; this deficiency is also reported in New Zealand and Finland, areas of the world where the soil is not very rich in selenium. The cardiac muscle is enlarged in this disease of the heart, and the normal tissue that composes the middle layer of cardiac walls is replaced by fibrous tissue. Since we live in a developed part of the world, selenium deficiency is hardly a concern for us. The selenium content of the soil in North America has a significant amount of this essential mineral, so a well-balanced diet will provide enough selenium. Symptoms of selenium toxicity may include vomiting, loss of hair and nails, lesions of the skin, and diarrhea, when people ingest a milligram or higher per day.

Copper, the Oxide Eater

Copper plays a diverse role in enzymatic activities. All of the metalloenzymes containing copper in their structure have similar functional characteristics, and consume oxygen and its associated radicals. The most well-known enzyme that protects against free radicals is a compound called superoxide dismutase

(SOD). This compound facilitates the conversion of the potentially dangerous compound superoxide anion into hydrogen peroxide and oxygen ($2O_2^- + 2H \longrightarrow H_2O_2 + O_2$). Another free-radical enzyme that relies on copper for its properties is a dehydrogenase protein called ceruloplasmin. This protein is involved in the transport and storage of copper, but it also can reduce super-oxide anions without any intermediate phase, making it extremely efficient.

Another enzyme that must contain copper in order to function is an enzyme called lysyl oxidase. This protein is necessary for an essential step in the cross-linking of collagen strands and for the healing of wounds. Copper works in a similar fashion to iron in the process of energy production. Cytochrome C oxidase is associated with the pumping of H^+ protons and the resulting phosphorylation (the addition of a phosphate to an organic compound) of ADP to ATP. Even though copper is present in the body in small amounts, usually around 100 milligrams, it is evident that it performs in a wide range of vital life functions.

The issue of copper deficiency is of no real concern to people living in the United States and Canada, since the typical diet includes adequate amounts of this trace mineral. Extremely high levels of vitamin C can interfere with cop-per absorption, and if prolonged, may lead to deficiency. Deficiency can result in anemia due to the reduced hemoglobin synthesis. Copper toxicity is also a rare occurrence, and should not be a concern for any athlete who follows Macrobolic Nutrition and its associated food guide pyramid (see Appendix B) for guidelines on proper dietary practices. If copper supplementation is abused, toxicity is certainly a concern. It will bring on symptoms like vomiting and diarrhea, and if prolonged will result in liver damage.

The athlete who desires adequate amounts of copper in the diet should make sure she or he eats enough legumes, seeds, nuts, and organ meats, such as liver. Another source of copper is tap water; its value as a source depends on the hardness of the water and whether or not you have copper pipes.

Manganese, the Magnesium Substitute

This trace mineral is found in the bones and in metabolically active tissue like the liver, pancreas, and kidneys. If you were to combine all of the manganese in the body, it would measure about 20 milligrams. However, this mineral plays a role in the formation of energy with the enzyme pyruvate carboxylase in the conversion of pyruvate to oxaloacetate (an intermediate in the TCA cycle), and is a cofactor in the copper enzyme SOD. It can also substitute for magnesium in many of its associated enzymes when magnesium is needed to activate the enzyme.

If an athlete relies on proper dietary principles, a primary manganese deficiency is a rare concern, partly because of the low RDA and its relative abundance in plant-based foods. The same can't be said of secondary deficiencies, however. Overuse of iron and calcium supplements can inhibit the absorption of manganese as well as the phytates found in legumes, grains, and seeds, which, ironically, are the best sources of manganese. A deficiency may become apparent in poor growth and nervous-system disorders. Toxicity should not be a concern for athletes who rely on sound dietary practices for their RDA for manganese. If an athlete oversupplements with manganese, the toxic effects will present themselves as nervous-system disorders.

Fluoride, the Bone Hardener

This abundant trace mineral is found in soil all over the world and is also present in water, plants, and animals. Yet fluoride is found in very small amounts in the human body. However, fluoride is crucial for the formation of a harder bone-mineral matrix. The macrominerals calcium and phosphorus combine to form a crystal compound called hydroxyapatite. These crystals harden with the addition of other minerals on the protein collagen. Fluoride then replaces the OH groups of the hydroxyapatite crystals, forming fluorapatite and making it stable. This compound makes bones harder and teeth more resistant to decay. Too much fluoride will have an aesthetically damaging effect. A condition known as fluorosis causes unsightly white specks on the teeth. In the more severe cases, the enamel will become permanently stained. Toxicity can occur only in areas where fluoridated water exceeds 150 ppm (parts per million). In these cases symptoms include vomiting, associated nausea, diarrhea, pain localized in the abdomen, and tingling in the extremities. The best dietary sources for fluoride are seafoods and most regular teas.

Chromium, the Insulin Augmentation Mineral

Chromium is essential in the metabolism of carbohydrates and lipids. It is similar to iron in that it exists in several different ionic states, but the state that seems to have the most benefit to metabolism is the 3+ form of chromium. Chromium is a component of compounds called glucose-tolerance factors. It helps maintain a balance in blood sugar by improving the hormone insulin's activity in the body. Because of the improved actions of insulin, less of the hormone is needed to maintain proper blood glucose levels. If chromium is deficient diabeteslike symptoms will result, manifesting in impaired insulin response, glucose tolerance, and glucagon response. Glucagon is the counter hormone to insulin that releases stored glucose (glycogen) into the bloodstream when blood glucose levels are low. A decreased level of stamina will be noted in the athlete who is low on chromium. Toxic symptoms are unknown. The best dietary sources of this trace mineral are liver, whole grains, cheeses, and nuts.

Molybdenum, the Oxidase Mineral

Molybdenum is present in such small amounts that dietary deficiencies and toxicities have not been reported in humans. It is a component of several metalloenzymes, such as xanthine oxidase, aldehyde oxidase, and sulfite oxidase. The best dietary sources of molybdenum are legumes, green leafy vegetables, skim milk, and liver. Toxicity has been observed in test animals, where kidney damage and reproductive problems became apparent.

Notable Mentions

Other trace minerals that have been shown through research on animals to have beneficial qualities are nickel, vanadium, cobalt, silicon, and boron. However, the exact amounts of these trace minerals in the body are extremely difficult to determine, and deficiencies and toxicities are not known. Their functions are known, however. Nickel may be able to serve as a cofactor for some enzymes. Vanadium is necessary for proper bone and growth development. Cobalt is the mineral present in vitamin B_{12} (cobalamin), and silicon is used in the synthesis of collagen and its subsequent bone formation. Boron may be used to facilitate optimum brain function.

Macrobolic Nutrition is a concept that allows for optimum health. All of the essential nutrients mentioned within the preceding chapters are found within foods that are central to the Macrobolic Nutrition philosophy. Food is the ultimate transporter for all of the nutrients that are key to overall fitness. Following the principles of Macrobolic Nutrition will allow the average athlete to grow into a class all his or her own and attain maximum human performance.

CHAPTER 9

Enhancing the Macrobolic Nutrition Effect

THE PREVIOUS CHAPTERS HAVE SHOWN YOU how the Macrobolic Nutrition approach provides the core building blocks for you to experience tremendous increases in muscle building, strength, and performance, while promoting leanness. You will be extremely satisfied with the results you will get from following the core Macrobolic Nutrition program alone, but this program can be intensified by using the special Up Your MASS muscle-building nutrition products. This combination of program and nutritional product will take your body into a hyperanabolic state that you have never experienced before, and that until now has only rarely been encountered by top bodybuilders. Once your body enters into this Macrobolic-induced lean muscle-building mode, your body will undergo that Herculean transformation you are looking for, culminating in a massive, superior sculpted physique.

However, if you are like me and other champion athletes, you want to know if you are doing everything possible to pump out that extra rep, to get the results you want—*faster.* If you have the same competitive spirit that I have, it is natural to be wondering, *Is there anything else I can do to enhance the Macrobolic Nutrition effect?* For example, you may want to get bigger faster, stronger faster, and/or leaner faster. I know that is what I wanted: the fastest and best results possible. I spent years of research and development to determine if any additional ingredients and delivery-system technologies existed to enhance the Macrobolic Nutrition effect. I determined that the answer is yes, there are extra measures you can take to further enhance Macrobolic Nutrition, and now I will share the results of this massive research effort with you—my secrets of how to enhance the Macrobolic Nutrition lean muscle-building effect.

This chapter is written to give you more knowledge and some precise direction on other products to consider including as part of your Macrobolic Nutrition program. You will be interested to learn that sports nutrition product development and production technology has made significant advancements in the past several years. This means you can now get even better results with well-known, clinically proven sports nutrition ingredients. For example, we all know creatine works to increase muscle size and strength, but did you know that there are sports supplement breakthroughs that may make creatine work even better? The same is true for other research-tested sports nutrients like glutamine, and fat-metabolizing dietary supplement formulas. You will also be interested to discover that a new branch of sports nutrition, muscle-building and performance science has developed as a result of the medical insights gained from working with joint and connective-tissue health issues. It deals with certain dietary and supplement ingredients, and how we can enhance joint structure and function and help to reduce exercise-induced pain and inflammation through nutrition.

You will get an inside look into how MHP develops its top-selling sports nutrition products. You will also realize that one major indication that MHP products are top quality and the most effective available is that I use them, the MHP staff uses them, and my friends use them—so I am going to make very sure that only the best ingredients are used in precise combinations! Because of my competitive drive for excellence, I am constantly trying to improve on MHP's sports nutrition products to make sure we receive the best possible results. So get ready to experience more ways to get bigger, stronger, and leaner faster, and develop a physique of the champions.

GETTING BIGGER AND STRONGER FASTER

In the world of bodybuilding, you can never be "too big." Bigger is always better. Or at least that is the way we view it. The same applies for many other sports. Most athletes always feel they can be bigger and stronger. While we all continually strive to get bigger and stronger, we want to get these results as quickly as possible, so let's look at some supplements to help us get bigger and stronger faster.

Creatine, Creatine Cofactors, and Delivery Systems

Creatine has become one of the most popular sports supplements on the market today, due to the amount of substantiating research published beginning about 1993 that started this explosion of use. The first generation of creatine supplements was based on mimicking these scientific studies. Typically, researchers in such studies use megadoses of the substance they are researching to make sure that if the substance produces any beneficial results, they will be measurable.

The number of scientific research studies documenting the effectiveness of creatine in muscle development continues to grow. This tremendous body of knowledge has enabled us to determine many facets of creatine's effective activity in the body, and I used these insights and sports nutrition technology to determine how to create a creatine-based product that produces maximum results. These technological breakthroughs in sports supplements included getting better results with less creatine, and maximizing these results with creatine cofactors.

Here's a short overview of creatine supplementation and new research findings: To date, the major scientifically proven benefits of taking creatine supplements include those listed in Table 9.1.

TABLE 9.1 CREATINE SUPPLEMENTATION RESULTS	
Creatine Supplementation Has This Effect on the Body	**Which Results in Muscle Performance**
Increases muscle content of creatine	Increased peak muscle power output
Increases muscle content of phosphocreatine	Increased one repetition maximum
Increases lean body mass	Increased vertical jump
Increases muscle size	Increased strength and power
	Speeds short duration sprinting

The newest creatine research efforts are focused on fine-tuning our current understanding of creatine and exploring the magnitude of its use. For example, E. S. Rawson and J. S. Volek, at the Department of Exercise Science and Athletics, Bloomsburg University, Bloomsburg, Pennsylvania, conducted a review of twenty-two published research studies and reported their results in the November 2003 issue of the *Journal of Strength and Conditioning Research*. Based on this review, the overwhelming scientific evidence determined that creatine supplementation improves muscle strength and weightlifting performance when combined with resistance training. Of the twenty-two studies reviewed, the average increase in muscle strength following creatine supplementation plus resistance training, at a one-, three-, or ten-repetition maximum, was 8 percent greater than the average increase in muscle strength following placebo ingestion during resistance training. Similarly, the average increase in weightlifting performance following creatine supplementation plus resistance training was 14 percent greater than the average increase in weightlifting performance. The increase in bench press, at one-repetition maximum, ranged from 3 to 45 percent, and the improvement in weightlifting performance in the bench press ranged from 16 to 43 percent. Rawson and Volek concluded that there is substantial evidence that creatine supplementation during resistance training is more effective at increasing muscle strength and weight-lifting performance than is resistance training alone, but added that the response is highly variable.

Another research review conducted by R. B. Kreider of the Exercise and Sport Nutrition Laboratory, Center for Exercise, Nutrition and Preventive Health Research, Department of Health, Human Performance and Recreation, Baylor University, provides further evidence of creatine's effectiveness. Kreider determined that a review of the scientific literature indicates that more than 500 research studies have evaluated the effects of creatine supplementation on muscle physiology and/or exercise capacity in healthy, trained, and various diseased populations. Short-term creatine supplementation has typically been reported to increase total creatine content by 10 to 30 percent and phospho-creatine stores by 10 to 40 percent. About 70 percent of the approximately 300 studies that have evaluated the potential ergogenic (performance-increasing) value of creatine supplementation report statistically significant results, while the remaining studies generally report nonsignificant gains in performance. For example, creatine supplementation has been shown to improve short-term physical performance activities such as peak power and strength muscle output and all-out-effort sprint performance, and to increase the number of sets and reps performed during resistance-type training. Furthermore, creatine supplementation combined with training has been reported to promote significantly greater gains in strength, fat-free mass, and performance, primarily in high-intensity exercise tasks. Kreider goes on to add that the preponderance of scientific evidence indicates that creatine supplementation appears to be a generally effective nutritional ergogenic aid for a variety of exercise tasks in a number of athletic and clinical populations.

The research results support the use of creatine supplementation for improving muscle strength, size, and power—that is, as a nutrition enhancer for strength athletes and bodybuilders. Creatine increases energy during maximum muscle contraction. During the very first millisecond of a grueling all-out muscle contraction, the ATP is quickly depleted in type 2 muscle fibers. Creatine phosphate (CP) is standing ready in the muscle cells to regenerate new ATP. This process happens in just a few seconds. Once CP is depleted it takes glycolytic energy systems to regenerate ATP and CP; and muscle-energy output decreases, lactic acid builds up, and fatigue sets in, so having a plentiful supply of creatine during those very strenuous short-rep workouts can ensure a maximum supply of CP at the cellular level. This is one main reason why muscle fibers increase in size to become stronger. When fibers increase in size, they increase their storage capacity to hold more ATP and CP. This gives the muscles more energy to increase starting strength and capacity to maintain contractions for longer periods of time. This is, of course, an oversimplification of the hypertrophy process, but it serves to underscore creatine's role in muscle strength and muscle-fiber content.

The form of creatine that research studies have determined works best is creatine monohydrate, and this is MHP's ingredient of choice, with one improvement. The early research studies used just pure creatine monohydrate, but eventually researchers wanted to determine if there were cofactors that would improve creatine utilization by the body. They first mixed creatine with other nutrients, such as carbohydrates, to see if the insulin boost would increase creatine uptake and delivery to the muscle fibers, and it did. Studies by A. L. Green, in 1996, demonstrated that combining creatine with a simple carbohydrate, such as glucose, will increase creatine transport into the muscle. The solution tested consisted of 5 grams of creatine and 90 grams of glucose, consumed four times per day. When tested against creatine alone, which increased total muscle creatine and creatine phosphate levels, the creatine carbohydrate supplement increased total muscle creatine and creatine phosphate levels significantly more. However, the overconsumption of simple carbohydrates can have detrimental effects on your lean muscle-building progress, as you learned from reading about Macrobolic Nutrition in previous chapters. This is one example where blindly jumping on the scientific bandwagon is not justified. Bodybuilders and strength athletes who use sugar-loaded creatine add more than 150 grams of pure sugar to their diets per day in the loading phases alone! That amounts to 600 daily calories from sugar alone, and equals the amount of sugar found in four cans of soda! Does that sound like the kind of nutrition you want to feed *your* body? There are other ways to make creatine delivery more effective without overloading the body with simple carbohydrates that only serve to increase your insulin levels too much, as you shall see shortly.

I also wanted to determine if there were ways of reducing the conversion of creatine to creatinine, which is basically useless. Ironically, acid conditions like those found in the stomach stimulate the conversion of creatine to creatinine. This is one reason some researchers have believed that large amounts of creatine had to be ingested to see beneficial results. In fact, a few interesting insights have revealed how creatine behaves in the body. A large portion of the creatine you ingest gets converted to creatinine in the stomach. Additionally, your body can only effectively absorb about 2 grams of creatine into the bloodstream from the intestines, and any excess creatine is excreted. Other nutrients can help to maximize creatine's effects and boost creatine's content in your muscle fibers once creatine is in your body, however.

This information led to the development of MHP's unique proprietary TRT™ (Time Release Technology) microencapsulation process, which produces a unique release profile for its creatine monohydrate and other ingredients. This new delivery system accomplished these benefits for creatine users: the microencapsulation protects the creatine from being converted to creatinine in your stomach. In your intestines, the creatine is time released to allow for maximum utilization and minimum waste. The timed release allows for convenience of use, because you need to take only one serving per day rather than several servings per day. This technological breakthrough led me to name the MHP product TRAC—Time Released Arginine/Creatine. As the name reveals, arginine is one of the key creatine cofactors that I found will produce additional benefits for creatine supplementation. Early in my research efforts I discovered that besides providing additional benefits of its own, arginine can help boost the effectiveness of creatine. I was the first to promote the use of arginine for benefits associated with improved nitric oxide production. While creatine helps promote muscle–cell volume, size, and strength, nitric oxide has a major influence on muscle physiology, because it increases vasodilation and nutrient uptake. The effect of nitric oxide's action is to help accelerate muscle velocity, amplify power output, improve recovery, and most amazingly, stimulate new muscle-fiber production.

New research shows ADNO (arginine–derived nitric oxide) to have powerful insulin-mediating effects. TRAC contains 4 grams of arginine in order to increase the production of nitric oxide (NO) and stimulate insulin output and sensitivity *without fattening sugar.* This new patent-pending approach to mediate insulin is called "nitro-loading," and it delivers much needed nutrients to your muscles for increased size, strength, and improved recovery. (See Figure 9.1.)

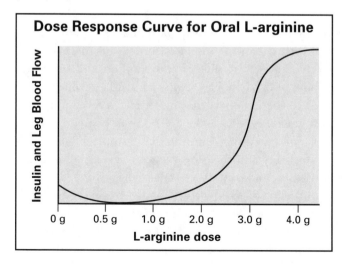

Dose Response Curve for Oral L-arginine

Insulin and Leg Blood Flow

0 g   0.5 g   1.0 g   2.0 g   3.0 g   4.0 g

L-arginine dose

Figure 9.1. Dose Response Curve for Oral L-arginine

The arginine drives insulin and leg blood flow, causing an increase in muscle perfusion and transport of creatine to muscle. A large enough dose of arginine is necessary to push nitric oxide production enough to mediate insulin and increase blood flow.

TRAC employs the patented proprietary microencapsulation process, TRT, to produce a unique release profile for its main components. The arginine and creatine are sustained release, but the L-arginine release precedes the creatine release. As can be seen in Figure 9.2, the L-arginine release is about 64 percent at the two-hour time point, whereas the creatine release is 43 percent at the same point. At the four-hour time point, the L-arginine release is about 80 percent, while the creatine release is around 66 percent. At six hours, the L-arginine release is basically complete, but the creatine is still releasing and is about 82 percent. The arginine release is always ahead of the creatine to provide the *bioactive shuttle,* stimulating IGF-1 production and facilitating the sodium/potassium channel, to increase creatine production, transport, and preservation. (See Figure 9.2.)

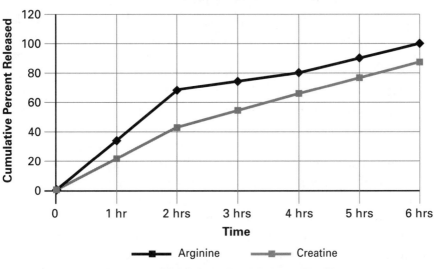

Figure 9.2. TRAC Sustained Release Profile

TRAC contains other synergistic ingredients, including one of my favorite new sports ingredients, referred to as NADH. NADH (coenzyme nicotinamide adenine dinucleotide) is present in every living cell, and is a vital biochemical that is required for production of cellular energy. NADH is involved in the production of ATP. Some research has shown that supplemental intake of NADH can also improve mental function. NADH increases the production of the neurotransmitter dopamine, which plays a role in short-term memory, concentration, and muscle function. NADH also enhances the synthesis of norepinephrine, which functions in alertness, concentration, and mental activity. Research on athletes indicates that NADH supplementation enhances work capacity. Oxygen uptake and reaction time was also observed to improve in the athletes tested. The possible increase of dopamine levels might explain improvements in reaction time, and increases in performance could be due to NADH's role in energy production. Combining NADH with creatine makes TRAC an "ATP Power Plant" for explosive strength.

A final word about how I use TRAC. I take a serving of TRAC thirty to forty-five minutes before workouts on training days, usually after work around 6:00 P.M. I also take one serving in the early evening on nontraining days to maintain muscle-creatine saturation.

Glutamine

While following the Macrobolic Nutrition program will result in the dietary intake of glutamine and other amino acids your body needs for lean muscle mass growth and performance, numerous research studies indicate that taking extra glutamine supplements can provide you with benefits above and beyond diet alone. This is especially true if you are exercising or training intensely. In addition to glutamine's benefits, which will be reviewed in this section, I find it interesting that even the military has turned its attention to the way that glutamine supplements can help improve military personnel performance. In addition to the role of glutamine in supporting immunologic defenses, a 1999 military research review by the Institute of Medicine mentioned other benefits of taking glutamine, notably: glutamine supports skeletal muscle protein synthesis; it enhances bicarbonate production, which may neutralize the acid load generated by moderate to severe exercise or catabolism; and glutamine supports glutathione synthesis, an antioxidant that attenuates the tissue damage associated with free-radical production. When it comes to improving health and physical performance the military is right on in identifying these key roles of glutamine.

Glutamine's multifunctional role and its involvement in various biochemical processes makes it one of the most important amino acids for athletes and individuals interested in maximum physique development, performance, and general health. It is a neurotransmitter and an energy source in the brain. Glutamine is a mediator of glutamic acid and GABA activity and can be converted back to glutamic acid in the brain, where it is essential for brain function. Glutamine is also vital to immunity function. New studies show that cell replication in the immune system requires glutamine. Most glutamine is stored in the muscles, however, so your muscles have to supply a large amount of glutamine to the immune system. Supplemental use of L-glutamine by athletes is known to have a strong anticatabolic effect that neutralizes the highly catabolic cortisol generated by strenuous exercise. Its anticatabolic action allows anabolism (muscle building) to take place more efficiently. L-glutamine also plays an active role in the recovery and healing process.

First generation glutamine sports nutrition products contained free-form L-glutamine, which research studies report works well. However, after reviewing the scientific research and making observations of my own, it became apparent that many of glutamine's effects can be potentiated by increasing its bioavailability and absorption. L-glutamine is very susceptible to the acid environment of the stomach, and MHP developed Effervescent Glutamine to deal with this issue. MHP's commitment to research and our willingness to go the extra mile has led to the development of some innovative and incredibly effective products. Effervescent Glutamine is at the top of this list. Studies show the utilization of a pharmaceutical-grade bicarbonate delivery system can improve glutamine uptake by almost 400 percent. Recognizing this, MHP's team of biochemists set out to find a way to neutralize the acidic gastric medium and improve bioavailability, and subsequently developed a glutamine product with an advanced bicarbonate-buffering system. Utilizing a pharmaceutically proven source for gastric alkalization (sodium bicarbonate), MHP's Effervescent Glutamine takes advantage of the acid neutralization power of the bicarbonate ion (HCO_3^-). Bicarbonate bonds with excess hydrogen ions produced by the HCL acid to form carbon dioxide and water. This process allows a buffered state to exist in the stomach, permitting more L-glutamine to pass into the intestines where it can be absorbed and utilized by intestinal cells for increased glutamine delivery to muscles. It is interesting to note that bicarbonate has been clinically proven to help increase strength and power of athletic performance on its own, making it a truly synergistic ingredient to team up with L-glutamine.

I take two servings of Effervescent Glutamine a day to ensure optimum glutamine levels, avoid catabolism, and stimulate growth hormone (GH) production. I take one serving in the morning, between my first and second meal, and the second immediately following workouts or in the early evening on nontraining days.

Testosterone Optimizers

Exploring ways of optimizing the body's production of testosterone is one of the oldest approaches to enhancing athletic performance and muscle growth. A primary goal of all bodybuilders and other strength athletes is to increase testosterone levels and optimize the anabolic effects of testosterone. MHP has focused its research efforts in two primary directions in this area:

1. providing the athlete with natural testosteronelike "prohormone" substances that are more anabolic than testosterone

2. developing a product that will optimize the body's testosterone production and utilization

T-BOMB

MHP research and expertise on prohormones resulted in what I believe is the most powerful anabolic substance legally available in the sports nutrition market today. Its chemical name is 17–beta–hydroxy–5–alpha–androst–1–ene–3–one tetrahydropyranyl ether, also known as 1–Testosterone. The fact is that 1–Testosterone has been proven to be about seven times more anabolic than the testosterone your body makes. Another benefit of 1–Testosterone is that it does not convert to estrogens in your body. There was one major challenge to overcome to make MHP's 1–Testosterone the most powerful legal anabolic supplement available, and this involved stabilizing the 1–Testosterone substance in a tablet formulation for oral ingestion. MHP's research and development team found the solution by applying a special pharmaceutical enteric coating on the tablet. This enteric coating protects the 1–Testosterone from degradation while it is in the stomach, thereby ensuring optimal stability and maximum potency. This 1–Testosterone product is so potent MHP named the finished product T-Bomb. (See Figure 9.3.)

Suggested use: 1 tablet twice daily. T-BOMB should be cycled for two months on and one month off. You may repeat the cycle on an ongoing basis.

Note: As with all testosterone formulas, T-BOMB should be used only by

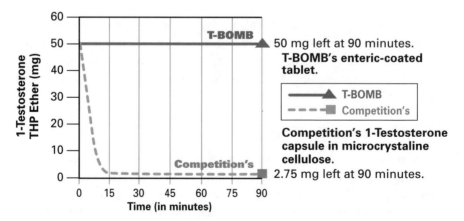

Figure 9.3. The Stability of 1-Testosterone in Enteric-Coated Tablet versus Capsule

males over the age of eighteen, and is not recommended for women or minors. Always consult your physician before taking any supplement.

T-BOMB II

Often the greatest discoveries are inspired by necessity. This is the case with MHP's T-BOMB II. The category of prohormones has been under scrutiny by the media as to whether the hormonelike compounds should be considered dietary supplements or drugs. I personally think that this scrutiny is unjust. It seems that any time supplements provide "very measurable results," they become subject to attack by the press, which forces the FDA to respond.

In any event, I decided to be proactive and looked to develop a "pro-hormone free" testosterone formula that could parallel the effectiveness of T-BOMB. This was not going to be an easy task. T-BOMB definitely set a standard that was going to be difficult to match. Hundreds of thousands of satisfied T-BOMB users reported exceptional gains from T-BOMB, making it the number-one–selling prohormone formula in America.

I knew I would need to dig my heels into some research if I was going to develop a "sequel" equal to T-BOMB. After researching thousands of compounds and examining the way they worked in the body (and consulting with scientists and endocrinologists), it became evident to me that all of the products on the market were way off the mark. Let me explain: Though some of these products do contain effective testosterone-boosting ingredients, none of them addressed the full complexity of hormone regulation by the endocrine system. The endocrine system is a complex network of checks and balances. Testosterone elevation triggers other important hormonal responses, all of which must be considered. I discovered through my research that if I was going to develop a supplement to elevate testosterone, it must also address estrogen, 5 alpha-reductase, DHT, and sex-hormone-binding globulin (SHBG).

Note: These other hormonal responses (estrogen, DHT, and SHBG) did not have to be addressed with T-BOMB, because of 1-Testosterone's unique chemical structure. Though 1-Testosterone is anabolic and attaches to the androgen receptor, it does not convert to estrogen or DHT (the testerone derivative associated with prostate enlargement). However, testosterone does make this conversion, which is why these factors must be addressed if you elevate testosterone.

Now I'm going to explain why all of these hormones come into play. As testosterone production increases, an active enzyme called *aromatase* converts a portion of testosterone to estrogen. As you already know, a high level of estrogen is definitely not what a guy wants, especially a bodybuilder. Estrogen causes increased body fat, water retention, and gynecomastia (excessive development of breasts in men). If that isn't bad enough, estrogen also stimulates the production of sex-hormone-binding globulin (SHBG), which binds testosterone. This binding process lowers free testosterone making less available to attach to the androgen receptor where it can exert its effects on sex functions and muscle building. Another enzyme, 5 alpha-reductase, converts a portion of testosterone to DHT (5-dihydrotestosterone). This compound is directly related to hair loss and prostatic hypetrophy, and can also occupy the receptor for testosterone and inhibit free testosterone from attaching. You can clearly see why you want to keep estrogen and DHT levels down.

T-BOMB II is the first formula to contain select key ingredients to do the following:

1. Increase the production of testosterone by stimulating the production of luteinizing hormone

2. Reduce DHT

3. Reduce estrogen

4. Reduce SHBG

A New Frontier—Signal Transduction: Second Messengers "Amplifying the Signal at the Receptor"

Aside from being the first and only testosterone formula to optimize endocrine functions by improving the testosterone-to-estrogen ratio and maximizing the anabolic effects of testosterone, T-BOMB II introduces a new frontier called "second messengers." This new advance in nutrition technology is going to be the biggest bodybuilding breakthrough since anabolic steroids.

In order to get the full anabolic benefits of testosterone, or any hormone, steroid or prohormone, it must first attach to the receptor cells in the body. But, so-called second messengers are responsible for actually carrying out the hormone's tasks. In other words, the binding of a hormone to the receptor initiates a series of events, which lead to the generation of second messengers within the cell (the hormone is the first messenger). The second messengers then trigger a series of molecular interactions that alter the physiological state of the target cell. This process is called "signal transduction." It sounds complicated, because it is a very complicated system.

Simply stated, second messengers amplify the signal at the receptor from a specific hormone. Therefore, a small amount of a given hormone will result in a strong hormonal response. This is why I refer to our proprietary complex as

"Second Messenger Hormone Amplifiers." Increasing signal transduction at the receptor makes the given amount of hormones like testosterone and growth hormone circulating in your body and attaching to the specific cell receptors more powerful. T-BOMB II's proprietary "Second Messenger Hormone Amplifier Complex" further increases the anabolic and androgenic effects of elevated testosterone.

T-BOMB II is by far the most advanced testosterone-booster/hormone-optimizing formula to date. The proper manipulation of endocrine function is critical if you want to improve the ratio of testosterone to estrogen. This can be achieved only by using the right amounts and combination of synergistic ingredients that are present in T-BOMB II, coupled with the groundbreaking discovery of signal transduction and second messenger hormone amplifiers. If you're looking for an anabolic edge, try T-BOMB II.

Suggested use: 3 tablets twice daily. Since T-BOMB II improves hormonal homeostasis in a natural fashion, you do not have to cycle this product. However, T-BOMB II can also be cycled for three months on and one month off and then repeat cycle.

Note: As with any testosterone formula, T-BOMB II is recommended only for males over the age of eighteen, and is not recommended for women or minors. Always consult your physician before taking any supplement.

Growth Hormone and IGF-1 Enhancers

Next in line after testosterone/anabolic steroid alternatives are human growth-hormone stimulators, which are also included in the story of how I founded MHP. As a competitive bodybuilder, I looked for every possible way to improve my progress in gaining lean muscle mass. Human growth hormone caught my attention when I looked at the medical research reports on lean body mass–enhancing substances. My path for finding natural growth-hormone stimulators led me to Vincent Giampapa, M.D. Dr. Giampapa was involved in some intriguing research involving a unique natural growth-hormone–stimulating product he had developed to use in his clinic, which specializes in anti-aging medicine and hormone replacement therapy.

Dr. Giampapa introduced me to his natural product and explained how he was using it in his clinic to optimize growth hormone levels in some of his older patients for antiaging purposes. What led him in this direction was the impressive research on the antiaging (youth-enhancing) benefits of human growth hormone. Human growth hormone or HGH (also known as somatotropin) is produced by the pituitary gland, and is essential for growth and regeneration of cells and tissues. Growth hormone has both anabolic and fat-burning effects, so it's easy to see why athletes and bodybuilders try to enhance their HGH levels.

I learned a lot about HGH while working with Dr. Giampapa during this period, both from sorting through the medical research and from experimentation. The body's production of HGH is very high during childhood and adolescence. Unfortunately, after age twenty, the pituitary gland's release of HGH falls at a rate of approximately 14 percent every ten years. A loss of 75 percent or more of HGH is not uncommon by age sixty. The usual physical symptoms of aging, such as wrinkles, increased body fat, loss of muscle mass, loss of energy, and other signs are directly related to this decrease in the production of HGH.

Research on stimulating the production of growth hormone first started with children who had inadequate growth hormone production. Researchers examined ways of increasing growth hormone production with natural and synthetic substances, and amino acids were found to be the most effective and promising substance. Some of the amino acids would actually increase the body's production of growth hormone. Yet other amino acids helped block the breakdown of the growth hormone produced by the body. From your reading so far, it is obvious that most amino acids have a few to several functions in the body. In addition to their other beneficial effects, some amino acids you've already read about, such as L-glutamine and L-arginine, are natural growth-hormone stimulators. Once researchers determined that these growth hormone-stimulating amino acids, also referred to as GH secretagogues, worked in children, they started to see how they worked in adults of all ages and activity levels. This massive research effort revealed that these GH secretagogues benefited both athletic and nonathletic adults. Of particular interest is that they benefit bodybuilding, by helping stimulate lean muscle-mass development.

But in 1990, when *The New England Journal of Medicine* published the results of a study by Daniel Rudman, M.D., the world turned its attention to the many potential benefits of HGH. Dr. Rudman led a research team that examined the effects of administering biosynthetic human growth hormone to healthy men age sixty-one to eighty-one years old with low levels of IGF-1. Note that IGF-1 is related to HGH concentrations in the human body, so when HGH levels in the body increase, IGF-1 levels also increase. The biosynthetic HGH was administered to the experimental group for six months. At the end of the study it was determined that blood levels of IGH-1 rose to that normal for a youthful range in the group of people taking the biosynthetic HGH. This would be expected from taking the biosynthetic HGH, but what shocked the medical world were the results of the increased IGF-1 levels in these older men. They increased lean body mass by about 9 percent, reduced body fat by about 14 percent, and also increased their bone density. Wow, taking this stuff really did result in a "fountain of youth" effect.

Of course, the results of the Rudman study attracted the interest of athletes, who want to increase their lean muscle mass and reduce excess body fat. It also stimulated interest in the medical community to use synthetic HGH or promote natural levels of HGH for improved general health, well-being, and longevity. Since Dr. Rudman's landmark research, hundreds of studies have been undertaken to explore the benefits of taking synthetic HGH and of using natural HGH stimulators, including the studies by Robert Goldman, M.D., and Ronald Klatz, M.D., who are authors, researchers, and founders of the American Academy of Anti-Aging Medicine. They note the following benefits that HGH has on the body:

- Reduced body fat
- Increased muscle mass
- Higher energy levels
- Faster wound healing
- Regrowth of hair
- Elevated mood
- Stronger bones

- Restoration of youthful immune function
- Lower cholesterol and blood pressure
- Enhanced sexual performance
- Regrowth of vital organs
- Smoother, firmer skin
- Improved cognition
- Sharper vision

Back to Dr. Giampapa. Once I brought myself up to date on HGH, I better appreciated why Dr. Giampapa and others were so enthralled with using HGH for antiaging, enhancing physique, and improving athletic performance. Dr. Giampapa actually created a natural, amino-acid–based HGH-stimulating formula to use in his clinic. I expressed my interest in putting this natural HGH-stimulating formula to the test by using it myself. Dr. Giampapa agreed, and established a monitoring program to track my results. To my surprise and delight, Dr. Giampapa measured a significant increase in my natural HGH and IGF-1 levels. My IGF-1 levels increased by 42 percent. Benefits to my physique became measurable after just a few weeks, and I began to increase muscle mass and decrease body fat at a faster rate than I could before taking the amino acid product.

I was blown away by these results. It is a rare occurrence for a bodybuilder at my level to be able to achieve such noticeable results in a short period of time by taking natural substances. I asked Dr. Giampapa if I could license his formula and bring it to the market for bodybuilders and other athletes, and he agreed. I incorporated MHP and launched Secretagogue-One in January 1998. The rest is history. Secretagogue-One remains the number-one–selling HGH-releasing formula in retail stores to date—because it works. You get what you pay for in this world and I believe in making an effective, quality product.

From this experience working with Dr. Giampapa, I established the foundation for MHP product development. MHP products are scientifically developed, medically validated, and bodybuilder tested to produce results fast.

As with other MHP product development, we relied on Dr. Giampapa's assistance during the product development and verification process for Secretagogue-One. Dr. Giampapa went to work in his own clinic to verify that Secretagogue-One was the best he ever used. He confirmed that it is a breakthrough in natural hormonal manipulation, designed to support the body in releasing more of its own HGH through the use of secretagogues and other precursors. Coupled with an effervescent delivery system to improve absorption, these secretagogues are delivered in a proprietary "Glucose Polymer Matrix," *providing nearly 100 percent assimilation,* as opposed to only 10 to 15 percent absorption for competing secretagogue products.

Secretagogue-One activates the pituitary gland naturally, and allows for optimum hormonal levels, while maintaining homeostasis. It is nontoxic and *does not* contain synthetic hormones, which can weaken your endocrine system. Secretagogue-One allows your body to make more of its own HGH in a balanced and natural way.

I use Secretagogue-One every day. I take one serving before bedtime on an empty stomach. This is the best way for bodybuilders and other athletes to take advantage of the natural nighttime high that occurs in HGH and IGF-1 levels, which Secretagogue-One increases even more. Note that women also produce HGH. Though HGH is anabolic, it does not have any androgenic (masculizing) effects. So, HGH supplementation is also excellent for women.

Joint Health and Reduction of Exercise-Induced Pain and Inflammation

No pain, no gain? Think again. Muscle-building progressive-resistance training requires overloading the muscles to a point where muscle fiber damage is imminent. The result is pain and inflammation, and muscle growth. Exercise physiologists use the phrase DOMS (delayed-onset muscle soreness) to describe this exercise-induced muscle pain. As an iron-pumping athlete, I wanted to discover what natural solutions existed beyond anything currently available to help relieve this exercise-induced muscle soreness. The many years of extensive training has done its share of wear and tear on my joints. I tried various types of joint remedies, such as MSM and chondroitin, and though I had some benefits, none of these products seem to address the pain and inflammation I was experiencing. I wanted to formulate a product that helped repair and minimize the pain and inflammatory response. It would then be possible to decrease recovery time physiologically and allow for greater progress. Psychologically, reducing or eliminating exercise-induced pain and inflammation translates into more frequent, better, and more pleasurable workouts. Breaking the pain barrier allows you to maximize your potential.

In search of the answer, I turned my attention to areas of medicine that have a track record of dealing with similar situations. In particular, my journey led me to the area of medicine that deals with combating the pain and inflammation of arthritis. The body tissues, especially the connective tissues of people with arthritis, are being broken down in a process that is accompanied by much pain and inflammation. Upon examination, exercise has a similar effect on the body and will eventually wear down even the healthiest joints if it is unchecked.

I began to experiment with different substances, including supplements and over-the-counter drugs like ibuprofen, in this research effort. In fact, a recent research study published in the *Journal of Strength and Conditioning Research* by S. P. Tokmakidis of the Department of Physical Education & Sports Sciences, Demoritus University of Thrace in Greece, reported on benefits of this drug. It was determined that taking ibuprofen helped reduce muscle soreness after exercise (weight resistance against muscle in the lowering motion). This motion is commonly referred to as negative rep or movement. But turning back to the lessons from my research in arthritis, I focused my attention on the inner workings of a special class of nonsteroidal anti-inflammatory drugs (NSAIDs), called COX-2 inhibitors (COX stands for cyclooxygenases).

Cyclooxygenases are enzymes needed for the synthesis of hormonelike substances called prostaglandins. There are two types of cyclooxygenases: the COX-2 enzyme that mediates inflammation and pain, and the COX-1 enzyme that helps maintain other physiological functions in the body. Traditional NSAIDs inhibit both enzymes. The new NSAIDs, however, mostly block the COX-2 enzyme, offering a new treatment option for people who have difficulty tolerating the old NSAIDs. The FDA approved the first COX-2 inhibitor, Celebrex (celecoxib), in 1998 to treat rheumatoid arthritis and osteoarthritis. Vioxx (refecoxib) became the second COX-2 inhibitor to receive approval, in 1999, for the treatment of osteoarthritis, dysmenorrhea (pain with menstrual periods), and the relief of acute pain in adults, such as that caused by dental surgery. I was amazed to find that these two are among the most frequently prescribed drugs, with billions and billion of dollars per year being spent on them. COX-2 inhibition is something people look for, sooner or later.

In the last ten years, this COX-2 paradigm has emerged as one of the most important biochemical systems of the twenty-first century. The COX-2 enzyme has become a primary model for understanding and treating numerous different conditions, including pain and inflammation. Researchers found that pain and inflammation can be dramatically reduced by inhibiting COX-2. Reducing the pain and inflammation also allows the body more resources to help speed up the muscle and connective tissue-rebuilding process. COX-2 inhibitors should be part of the daily routine of athletes and bodybuilders, who put a tremendous amount of stress and strain on their joints and cartilage. During and after every workout, damaging COX-2 is being created or induced. Daily use of COX-2 inhibitors can arrest this process and provide for long-lasting joint and overall body health.

In my search for the ideal natural COX-2 inhibitor, I reviewed the research and tried a variety of botanicals traditionally used for relieving pain and inflammation, but which also had modern scientific research proving their efficacy. I found two botanicals, boswellia and turmeric, that worked okay, but then I came across a new natural extract that boasted almost 100 percent selective COX-2 activity with almost no COX-1–inhibiting activity. This substance is called IsoOxygene™, and from the first day I used it, I experienced the best possible pain-relieving and anti-inflammatory effects ever, and I have been using it ever since.

In studies with cells, IsoOxygene has been shown to significantly reduce the production of PGE-2 produced by the COX-2 enzyme when stimulated by a mediator or cytokine. In comparison tests, IsoOxygene at a fairly low concentration was shown to reduce this degenerative chemical (PGE-2) to virtually zero. Other botanicals typically used for this purpose were inferior in both selectivity for the COX-2 enzyme, and in potency or efficacy for reducing PGE-2. Generally speaking, experts in the field agree that for an ingredient to be considered a true COX-2 inhibitor, it should selectively inhibit the COX-2 form of the enzyme five times more than the COX-1 form of the enzyme. None of the other botanical substances tested came close to the thirty times more selective ingredient in MHP's joint formula. The nearest commonly used botanical, curcumin, had a selectivity ratio of COX-1:COX-2 of about 1 to 2.8, while IsoOxygene has a selectivity ratio of 1 to 30. IsoOxygene is patent pending, which will eliminate would-be imitators and ensure authenticity of products claiming to contain this precious COX-2 inhibiting ingredient. (See Figures 9.4, 9.5, and 9.6.)

With the COX-2–inhibiting ingredient taken care of, my attention focused on including a key ingredient clinically proven to be the champion of connective-tissue rebuilding. After sorting through the research I started to

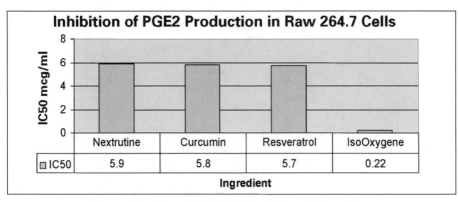

Figure 9.4. Botanical COX-2 Inhibitor Comparison

COX-2 inhibition as measured by inhibition of PGE2, a pro-inflammatory prostaglandin, in RAW 264.7 cells. The IC50 is the amount of the ingredient needed to reduce PGE2 by 50 percent.

Nextrutine™ is from Next Pharmaceuticals. Curcumin is a commonly used botanical anti-inflammatory ingredient with COX-2 to COX-1 ratios of 2:1, resveratrol is a phytoalexin found in grapes and other botanicals. IsoOxygene™ is the proprietary new COX-2 specific inhibitor. As can be seen from this graph, a much lower concentration of IsoOxygene is needed to reduce PGE2 by 50 percent than the other botanicals. Therefore, it is a much more potent COX-2 inhibitor.

Botanical COX-2 inhibitors such as curcumin have a COX-1:COX-2 ratio of about 1 to 2.8, which is called the COX-2 specificity. IsoOxygene has a COX-2 specificity of about 30.

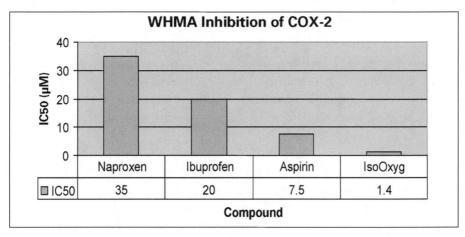

Figure 9.5. COX-2 Inhibitor Comparison: Whole Blood Assays

The potencies of the various drugs were also tested according to the William Harvey Human Modified Whole Blood Assay (WHMA) at the William Harvey Research Institute, Royal London School of Medicine in the United Kingdom.

The IC50 is in micromoles or 1×10^{-6} moles. The lower the amount (concentration) necessary to inhibit PGE2 by 50 percent (IC50), the more potent the drug. The more potent the drug, the lower the effective dose will be for reducing COX-2 activity.

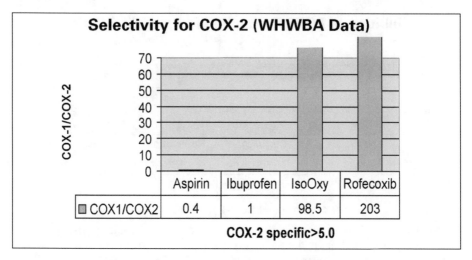

Figure 9.6. Selectivity for Cox-2 (WHWBA Data)

When compared to the OTC pain relievers aspirin, ibuprofen, and naproxen, IsoOxygene™ appears to be more selective for COX-2 than COX-1 and has a lower IC50 value for COX-2 than any of the OTC pain relievers. The selectivity for COX-2 exhibited by IsoOxygene appears to be comparable to the prescription COX-2 pain relievers Rofecoxib and Colexocib. Conversely, the COX-1/COX-2 IC50 ratio for IsoOxygene using the WHMA protocol is about 92.85, which qualifies it as a selective COX-2 inhibitor in the topmost category of those select compounds that have greater than fifty-fold selectivity for COX-2 over COX-1. Since IsoOxygene inhibits COX-2 at the level of gene transcription, the results in the A549 cells were even more significant than in blood alone.

examine how I personally responded to the top candidate ingredients supported by good research studies: chondroitin sulfate, MSM, and glucosamine sulfate. Glucosamine sulfate was my first choice, following several months of comparison and successful use, and because it was the most clinically proven of the three.

What really convinced me to use glucosamine sulfate in my new MHP products was, in addition to its being the most clinically proven for rebuilding connective tissues in people with arthritis, my discovery of a study in which glucosamine sulfate was effective in young athletes with athletic-induced wear and tear of the cartilage of the knee. A group of researchers in Germany headed by D. Bohmer examined the effects of glucosamine sulfate in young athletes with an exercise-induced knee problem. In the young athletes taking the glucosamine supplements, the knee pain was almost gone after just four weeks, and completely gone after twelve weeks of supplementation. Glucosamine's repair and rebuilding of the knees of young athletes' connective tissues allowed them to recover to the point of resuming an intense-training program.

A short review of glucosamine and related topics will explain how it works in your body to produce numerous benefits. There are several types of connective tissues. Cartilage, tendons, ligaments, intervertebral discs, the pads between joints, and cellular membranes are all composed of connective tissue. All connective tissues have two common components, chief of which is collagen. One-third of your body's total protein volume is composed of collagen, making it the most common protein in the body. The other component is proteoglycans (PGs). PGs form the "framework" for collagenous tissue. These huge structural "macromolecules" are composed mainly of glycosaminoglycans (GAGs), which are long chains of modified sugars. The principal sugar in PGs is hyaluronic acid, 50 percent of which is composed of glucosamine. The principal amino acids that form collagen are proline, glycine, and lysine. Collagen and PGs must somehow "get together" during the production of new connective tissue. Of the multitude of biochemical reactions that take place during the synthesis of connective tissue, there is one critical "rate-limiting" step, which, once reached, guarantees that new connective tissue will be successfully synthesized. That rate-limiting step is the conversion of glucose to glucosamine, so glucosamine is the single most important substance in the synthesis of connective tissue. Over thirty years of research has gone into understanding how glucosamine acts as the precursor of GAG synthesis. Scientists have long known that simply ingesting purified glucosamine from connective tissue allows the body to bypass the critical rate-limiting step of converting glucose to glucosamine. In human clinical trials, glucosamine taken orally was observed to initiate a reversal of degenerative osteoarthritis of the knee after two months. Normalization of cartilage was documented by taking biopsies of the tissues and scrutinizing them with an electron microscope. Of greater interest to athletes, glucosamine aids in feeding GAG to your injured connective tissues. GAG is the most critical precursor for rebuilding the collagenous matrix, which forms connective tissue; glucosamine is the preferred substance in synthesizing PGs, your connective tissue's framework. Glucosamine as a supplement clearly aids in connective-tissue synthesis. All athletes need such a substance, because the repair and growth of connective tissue is never-ending.

After more use of this prototype formula, I found that adding a few more ingredients improved the total effects. The formula was further enhanced with baikal skullcap, N-acetylcysteine, and alpha lipoic acid, a synergistic combination of ingredients that work together to provide fast-acting relief and anti-inflammatory action.

The resultant formula worked so well to reduce exercise-induced pain and inflammation, I decided to call it RELEVE. In order to stimulate muscle growth, you have to train heavy and hard. This training is sure to cause joint pain, inflammation, and/or injury over time. If you're looking to make serious progress in your training without suffering debilitating soreness, consider trying RELEVE.

GETTING LEANER FASTER

Meal-Replacement Powders (MRPs)

As was previously discussed, a primary goal of Macrobolic Nutrition is to give your body the tools it needs to grow lean muscle. You have learned the enormous impact food has on your body, and how Macrobolic Nutrition is scientifically developed and bodybuilder-tested to provide the nutrients you need for optimum lean muscle growth.

However, putting any nutrition plan into practice is not always as easy as one, two, three. While this book contains thorough nutrition plans and convenient recipes, you don't always have the time to plan and prepare meals and snacks that meet the Macrobolic Nutrition criteria. The same is true for me, too. That's why I developed the Up Your MASS products. The first generation of Up Your MASS products consists of the Up Your MASS Muscle Building Macrobolic Nutrition Formula in the form of nutrient dense, delicious meal-replacement powders. The Up Your MASS formulations are no ordinary MRPs, as you will soon discover from the following overview of how they were developed and of their special muscle-building characteristics.

Meal-replacement powders have a long history of use in the United States to help people with weight control and to serve as a quick meal or meal/snack on the go. The MRPs you are most familiar with are the low-calorie mass-market products used by millions to get slim fast. These and the so-called more advanced MRPs designed for athletes fall short on quality nutrition. On the surface, the mass-market MRPs offer some weight-loss benefits for the general population. However, when you examine these products with a more sophisticated eye, they are nothing more than sugar drinks, with a minimal amount of protein and essential vitamins and minerals. The weight-loss MRPs are definitely not the first choice for anyone, especially the health-conscious athlete. Although using these mass-market MRPs may result in weight loss from a reduction in daily calorie intake, there is no focus on the quality of the weight lost and the future negative impact that these unbalanced, high sugar content, poor-quality nutrition products may have on your health. The sports nutrition MRPs are not much better. When you examine sports nutrition MRP products, especially those in the weight-gain category, you will commonly discover that many of these products are loaded with sugar and are deficient in the protein-content department. These formulas are also devoid of another major group of macronutrients that you have learned are very essential: carbohydrates and fiber.

So, to keep us on track with our Macrobolic Nutrition plans, I developed Up Your MASS meal replacement powders, which are based on the 45/35/20 lean-mass equation. Following is a summary of some of the exciting lean muscle-building, nutritional technological breakthroughs found in the Up Your MASS MRPs.

The first goal was to develop a natural-based, low-glycemic–index blend of carbohydrates, because carbohydrates are the primary source of energy and are vital to exercise performance and health. To accomplish this daunting task, I directed my research team to conduct a rigorous examination of the scientific research. We discovered that the secret was to develop a virtually sugar-free natural-based blend of low-glycemic–index carbohydrates from barley, oats, and oat fiber. I call this low-glycemic–index carbohydrate blend Glycemix LGI™. When you ingest MHP products containing Glycemix LGI, you get a sustained release of energy into your body, and keep your blood-sugar levels in the anabolic zone.

In addition to increasing sustained energy, Glycemix LGI increases glycogen storage, stablizes blood sugar levels, and improves your "hormonal profile" of glucagon and insulin, for accelerated muscle building and fat burning. Glycemix LGI is also high in heart-healthy fiber. The special soluble fibers contained in Glycemix LGI help to lower your cholesterol levels, and may even help reduce your risk of developing cardiovascular diseases. Fiber also helps prolong the supply of nutrients to muscle.

The second goal was to design a protein blend that works best for muscle building. The fact is that all proteins are not created equal. Furthermore, your body experiences different protein needs, based not only on the extent of physical activity, but also on the type of physical activity or exercise. This means that weight-lifting, lean muscle-building athletes have different protein needs, or more exactly, different amino needs. After years of researching and experimenting to learn how to best meet the protein/amino acid needs for optimal lean muscle building, MHP's Probolic protein was developed. Probolic, as discussed in Chapter 3, is a proprietary amino acid–enhanced, sustained-release blend of high-quality proteins sources including proteins derived from choice, high-quality whey concentrate, casein, and soy protein isolates, fortified with crucial amino acids. As Figure 3.1 and Table 3.10 in Chapter 3 illustrate, this makes Probolic win in amino acid content, including arginine, BCAAs, and glutamine. The other key development was to make Probolic contain the ideal amino acid profile while displaying the precise release rate. This dynamic protein-delivery matrix thus provides a fast, medium, and slow release to feed your muscles over hours and help to improve nitrogen balance, growth, and recovery.

The third major goal was to develop a precise blend of lipids that best meet the Macrobolic Nutrition criteria, which demanded the inclusion of healthy, performance-enhancing fatty acids. This was no easy task, as there are many variables to conquer when attempting to contain healthy lipids in a dry, meal-replacement powder environment. The resulting Lipid Complex™ includes some of the healthiest and most sought-after lipids on the market today, such as conjugated linoleic acid (CLA), borage seed-oil powder, evening primrose oil, flaxseed powder, omega-3s, and medium-chain triglycerides. The Lipid Complex is, therefore, a synergistic blend of lipids that are vital for muscle growth, promote a desirable hormonal balance, improve nitrogen balance, provide the body with a high-energy source, and help stabilize insulin release.

All of this nutrition research and technology has resulted in making the Up Your MASS meal-replacement products a major advancement in lean muscle-building science. I usually take two servings of Up Your MASS a day; one between breakfast and lunch, and another about one hour before workouts. I find that this helps fuel my muscles during my grueling workouts, as well as being an easy-to-digest premeal workout. For added convenience, MHP has also developed Up Your MASS nutrition bars. They are also nutrient dense and based on the 45/35/20 lean-mass equation. These bars taste awesome and are great on-the-go meals or snacks.

Thermogenic Fat-Loss Aids

In addition to wanting faster improvements in muscle size and strength, most of the people I encounter also want to get leaner faster. While following the Macrobolic Nutrition program will intrinsically get you leaner, you may want to move this process along at a more rapid rate. If so, this section will bring you up-to-date on what has been termed the thermogenic fat-loss aids.

When you read this and other sections of this book regarding losing body fat, you will note that losing too much weight too fast is not the healthy way, nor is it the Macrobolic Nutrition way. A safe rate is a few pounds of *fat loss* a week. Don't confuse weight loss with fat loss. Fat loss is what you want, and not at the expense of losing any lean body mass, which includes muscle mass. When you go on a fat-loss program that results in losing too much weight too fast, most of this fast weight loss comes from water and muscle mass. My intention here is not to turn your fat-loss efforts into a race, but for you to realize that sometimes your body needs a boost in its fat-burning metabolism to better release fatty acids from body fat stores and use them for energy. This is typ-

Testimonial

"When I was an Olympic wrestler, putting on a ton of muscle mass wasn't a concern because I needed to stay in my weight class. But once I entered the WWE, I found myself going against 300-pound monsters. So, I needed to pack on serious size, but I didn't want to put on body fat or screw up my endurance and quickness. Macrobolic Nutrition has allowed me to pack on over 20 lbs of lean body mass."

—*Kurt Angle,* Olympic and Professional Wrestler

ically the case if you are overfat and inactive. Being overfat and inactive makes your body develop a fat-building metabolism. What you want to do is reverse this condition, or better yet, prevent it from occurring in the first place. Macrobolic Nutrition helps you make your metabolism a fat-burning and muscle-building metabolism.

There are many supplements that help improve your body's fat-metabolizing rate. Sometimes just ingesting certain essential vitamins and minerals you are deficient in helps improve your body's use of stored body fat for energy. For example, chromium is a trace mineral shown to help many people turn ingested nutrients into energy instead of storing them as body fat. Chromium is a cofactor for the proper function of insulin, the hormone that signals cells to let in nutrients that are circulating in bloodstream after a meal. Adequate intake of chromium allows insulin to function at full capacity. Other studies have shown that for some individuals, just ingesting calcium and magnesium supplements along with following a weight-loss diet and exercise program helps improve their rate of fat loss. There is also derived banaba leaf, a botanical ingredient with insulinlike function that I like to use to help get as much of the ingested nutrients into your cells as possible. Banaba contains a substance called corosolic acid. Scientists who have conducted clinical research on products containing corosolic acid found that it promotes improvements in lean body mass. It is believed that corosolic acid has a pseudo-insulin effect, working independently of insulin to help stimulate the cells in your body, including muscle cells, to actively take in nutrients like amino acids, essential fatty acids, and glucose. I was so impressed with the research on corosolic acid and the benefits I directly observed that I added it to the Up Your MASS products.

Fat-loss science has also turned its attention to exploring other ways to optimize your fat-loss metabolism. What has become known as the thermogenic fat-loss aids work to stimulate your body to use and metabolize body fat and ingested fats beyond what a healthy body, fortified with essential nutrients, would otherwise experience. The positive impact essential nutrient intake has on losing body fat underscores the importance of maintaining an adequate, nutrient-dense eating program like Macrobolic Nutrition, because thermogenic fat-loss aids work even better when you are well nourished. So first and foremost, get your Macrobolic Nutrition program perfected and stick to it. Only then should you try using thermogenic fat-loss aids. When discussing thermogenics, I contend that ephedra is hands-down number one. Regardless of all the negative press on ephedra, I personally think that when it is used properly by healthy individuals it is the most effective thermogenic fat-loss aid available. The most recent research results agree with my position. For example, the results of one of the highest quality research studies on ephedra-containing products was recently published. In 2002, C. N. Boozer and co-workers of the New York Obesity Research Center, at St. Luke's–Roosevelt Hospital and Columbia University, found that during a six-month period, healthy, obese people taking the herbal ephedrine/caffeine product lost more weight than those taking a placebo pill.

Research Findings Concerning the Safety and Effectiveness of Ephedrine/Ephedra Products

The results of research from a Harvard Medical Research team headed by Diane R. Krieger on how thermogenic aids can stimulate significant losses in body-fat mass got the attention of the medical community. Krieger reported the results of this study in an article titled "Ephedrine, Caffeine and Aspirin Promote Weight Loss in Obese Subjects," in *Transactions of the Association of American Physicians.*

It was in this research article that Krieger revealed the model of how the ECA (ephedrine, caffeine, and aspirin) combination might work in conjunction with a reduced-calorie diet to increase fat loss by stimulating the thermogenic effect. Ephedrine stimulates the production of norepinephrine release in the nervous system. This increased release of norepinephrine causes a chain reaction, which results in increasing the activity of a substance in the mitochondria called uncoupling protein that stimulates the release of energy from fatty acids. However, due to the fact that the body has to regulate overproduction of substances, the ephedrine-stimulated increase of norepinephrine production causes the release of two substances that work to reduce it: adenosine and prostaglandins. This is where aspirin and caffeine come in. Aspirin works to inhibit the prostaglandin synthesis, and caffeine to reduce adenosine activity. The result is prolonged stimulation of increased norepinephrine release and the thermogenic fat-burning process.

Supplement companies, inspired by the results of this research, sought to create herbal EC and ECA products, with ephedra as the cornerstone ingredient to supply herbal ephedrine and guarana, kola nut, green tea, and maté being the primary source of herbal caffeine. Willow bark is an herbal source of naturally occurring aspirinlike substances called salicin.

Unfortunately, all of the controversy spearheaded by the irresponsible media regarding ephedra-based products led to public uncertainty regarding its safety. As the debate continued, I decided that we should start researching options other than ephedra (even though it continues to be my favorite thermogenic fat-loss aid). MHP product development was steered toward formulating an ephedra-free thermogenic fat-loss aid that would duplicate the thermogenic effects of ephedra. MHP was at the forefront in developing a safe and effective alternative. When the FDA banned ephedra's use in dietary supplements, MHP already had an excellent substitute available.

The Next Generation Thermogenic Fat-Loss Aids

Once again, I directed MHP's research efforts toward examining the scientific research and what traditional natural medicine had to offer as ephedra substitutes. I was impressed with the botanical candidates we identified, and narrowed it down to two of the substances that I found worked best for me, along with the time- and research-tested guarana. These new substances included synephrine from bitter orange (*Citrus aurantium*), and certain polyphenols from green tea (*Camellia sinensis*). As it turns out, synephrine works like ephedrine in that it stimulates the body's use of fats for energy and increases caloric-burning rate. But, unlike ephedrine, it does not have the potent central nervous system and heart-stimulating effects. Simply put, synephrine works in the brain and in the body to increase the use of fatty acids for energy.

Medical studies on overweight people have demonstrated that they have a slow metabolic rate and do not use much fat for energy. This citrus solution takes care of these two major weight-loss obstacles, stimulating the use of fats for energy, and increasing the number of calories the body uses each day. Synephrine selectively turns up the switches in the body that control the rate at which fat is released from body stores (lipolysis) and the metabolic rate. This results in more fat and more calories being used for energy. In a 2002 issue of *Journal of Medicine,* researchers H. G. Preuss and coworkers from the Department of Physiology, Medicine and Pathology of Georgetown University reviewed the existing published research on *Citrus aurantium* products in their article titled "*Citrus Aurantium* as a Thermogenic, Weight Reduction Replacement for Ephedra: An Overview." They reached a similar conclusion to mine; there is scientific evidence that *Citrus aurantium* can stimulate thermogenesis and promote a significant increase in the reduction of body-fat mass.

Research is also available regarding the green tea polyphenols. A. G. Dullo, one of the ephedra researchers previously mentioned, has taken the lead in proving that substances in green tea extract can increase energy expenditure and fat oxidation in humans. The neurochemical (brain chemical) norepinephrine (noradrenaline) is a key player in stimulating thermogenesis, energy, and appetite control. The green tea polyphenols block an enzyme (catechol O-methyltranferase) that normally degrades norepinephrine and helps maintain and prolong its thermogenic effect. MHP's TakeOFF formula also contains caffeine from guarana to further help stimulate and maintain the thermogenic effect, since caffeine has synergistic properties. Caffeine on its own is thermogenic and promotes lipolysis; it also helps maintain the release of norepinephrine by inhibiting adenosine, another substance that breaks down norepinephrine in the neuroeffector junction.

With the ECA activity taken care of, additional synergistic ingredients were considered for addition to the TakeOFF formula. We developed a special triple ginseng concentrate—Chinese ginseng (*Panax ginseng*), American ginseng (*Panax quinquefolius*), and Siberian ginseng (*Eleutherococcus senticosus; eleutherosides*)—to include in the TakeOFF thermogenic fat-loss aid formula for a few reasons, but the main one centered around MHP's holistic product development philosophy. We recognized that although the *Citrus aurantium*, guarana, and green-tea extracts maximize the body's thermogenic effects, such prolonged, stimulated production of norepinephrine could lead to stress of the adrenal glands. One of the ways these ginsengs help promote health and energy in the body is by supporting adrenal gland function. It is through this activity that ginsengs are thought to exert their adaptogenic effects. The term "adaptogen" was coined by researchers to describe a substance that helps to increase the body's resistance to adverse physical and environmental influences, that is, a cure-all. To be a true adaptogen, the substance must prove safe for daily use, increase the body's resistance to a wide variety of harmful factors, and have a normalizing action in the body. Adaptogens are useful to healthy individuals as a method of coping with daily stresses and workload, and also as a tonic support to help the body normalize when it is ill (in addition to primary medical treatment). Ginseng is an example of one of the more popular adaptogenic herbs.

The "active" substances of ginseng are a group of sponin compounds called ginsenosides/panaxosides, and eleutherosides in Siberian ginseng. Ginseng also contains the trace mineral germanium, which has been shown to exhibit overall beneficial health effects and to increase the body's supply of oxygen.

Recent research has also determined that taking ginseng on a regular basis helps to keep blood sugar levels within a healthy range. Keeping your blood sugar levels under control is an important factor when trying to lose body fat. On average, when daily blood sugar levels are elevated, the body can't liberate and use its stored fat as well as it can when blood sugar levels are lower. In fact, high average blood sugar levels put you in a fat-building mode. The Macrobolic Nutrition program helps you keep you blood sugars in the right range for maximum energy and fat loss, but some ginseng each day can help this process.

I was pleased with the initial results in the TakeOFF prototype formula at this point in product development. But I wanted to further enhance the effects and duplicate the boost in physical and mental energy I got from my ephedra-containing formulas. After some further research and development, we concluded that the addition of ginkgo and L-tyrosine does the trick, with both possessing multiple functions. Ginkgo improves mental focus, concentration, and memory. It also improves circulation, which further enhances the fat-metabolizing effects of the other ingredients. L-tyrosine is involved in nervous system function and supports the thyroid to stimulate weight loss, thermogenesis, and energy production, and to improve mental focus. TakeOFF's synergistic ingredients work together to provide an immediate burst of energy to fuel you through an intense workout and keep you on the go through your busy day. Its scientifically balanced performance formula was designed to increase energy levels and boost metabolism—*without ephedra!* This revolutionary formula maximizes thermogenic fat burning, improves concentration and physical performance, and dramatically increases energy. TakeOFF really gets me energized and focused for my workouts, and helps increase the fat-burning effects of exercise.

Nighttime Lean Muscle-Building Requirements

An important part of the Macrobolic Nutrition approach is nutritional consideration of your nighttime metabolic needs. In Chapter 3, I reviewed how protein intake must be staggered throughout the day to deliver a steady supply of amino acids in the blood to keep your body in an anabolic muscle-building state. Satisfying the metabolic needs during sleep can be tricky, however. As previously mentioned, this is one time we depart from the 45/35/20 rule, because it is more advantageous to consume a supplement that is high in protein and lower in carbohydrates at bedtime. Having decent levels of "good fats" at a ratio of 4 to 8 grams per 20 grams of protein is also beneficial, as they will further prolong nitrogen retention. The goal is to provide a steady supply of amino acids, keep insulin levels down, and help raise growth hormone and glucagon levels. Since you are not working out in your sleep, you do not require carbohydrates for glycogen replenishment at night.

Developing a nighttime protein supplement to maximize anabolic and fat-metabolizing processes during sleep became the most recent research challenge of the MHP product-development team. In fact, it was during the writing and completion of this book that I signed off on the final formulation. This new formula is called Probolic SR. It contains the same highly effective Probolic-engineered protein found in Up Your MASS, but in a special base nutrient matrix compatible with your nighttime metabolic needs. Therefore, including Probolic SR in your Macrobolic Nutrition program will help maximize your lean muscle-building efforts and help you experience faster results.

A Final Word about Enhancing the Macrobolic Nutrition Effect

Macrobolic Nutrition will provide the core of your nutritional needs. However, additional supplementation with key ingredients can help enhance your muscle-building and fat-burning efforts. The supplements described in this chapter are the ones I think are the most important to consider adding to your program. In addition to these performance-enhancing supplements, I also recommend a well-formulated multivitamin/mineral supplement. I reviewed the importance of these supplements earlier in the book. Be sure to choose a high-quality brand. I also recommend taking 2,000 to 3,000 extra milligrams of vitamin C and a good antioxidant formula to combat the free radicals produced by your intense training program.

If this chapter comes off as hype for some of my products, believe me, it's not. I am conveying my passion, commitment, and confidence in these formulas. Keep in mind that the reason I started MHP was to find ways to improve the quality of supplements available. As a bodybuilder, I relied heavily on supplements to enhance my physique. The supplements I used prior to MHP did work, but I knew they could be better.

Unlike most supplement companies, which are owned by people who never compete (or even touch a weight, for that matter), MHP supplements are backed by science from leading experts and universities, and proven by a bodybuilder—me—and many other world-class athletes. Every MHP product described in this book was inspired by my own personal quest to find a better means of supplementation, to improve my physique as well as yours. I'm not bashing all other supplements or supplement companies, because there are a few good companies out there who make good products. Unfortunately, however, there are some poor-quality products out there that are "all hype." It can be difficult, as a sports nutrition consumer, to determine and choose which products are best for you. Hopefully, this overview on supplements has shown you that you can't go wrong with MHP when it comes to sports nutrition.

It is very rewarding to hear the positive feedback I get from satisfied customers. MHP receives thousands of calls and e-mails from customers, telling us about the gains and progress they have made by using MHP products. There is nothing more rewarding than receiving these testimonials. Helping others achieve maximum human performance has been and will remain my commitment to all athletes and fitness enthusiasts.

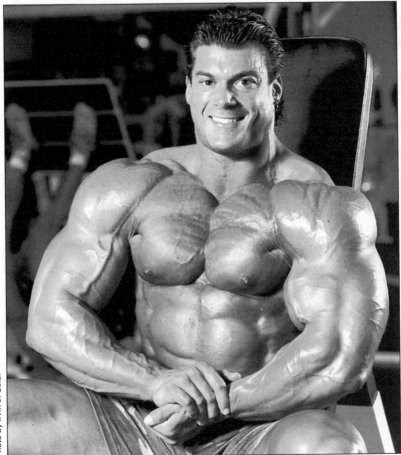

Photo by Irvin J. Gelb.

CHAPTER 10

Macrobolic Meals

AN ADDED BENEFIT OF THE MACROBOLIC 45/35/20 ratio is that it allows you to choose from a wide variety and great selection of foods. The more flexibility and variety in a diet, the easier it is for people to follow. Knowing this, I teamed up with Roger Warn, a nutritionist from Montclair State University, to create some delicious Macrobolic meals. These meals taste great—from my personal favorite, Mexican Omelet with Granola for breakfast, to King Crab Roll Sushi for dinner.

The sample meals I include offer a great variety. Some are quick and easy to prepare, while others take a little more time. You can try to create some of your own favorites; it's not that hard. Just read the nutrition information label on the foods you prepare and try to stay within the 45/35/20 ratio. You don't have to be exact; you will see from my sample meals that I sometimes am a little off in the ratio numbers. It is nearly impossible to prepare meals to the exact ratio, but try to stay within the range of 42 to 48 percent carbohydrates, 32 to 38 percent protein, and 17 to 24 percent fat.

The meals I have provided and the ones that you create will probably need to be adjusted to meet your calculated calorie requirements for each meal. Choose your favorite meals, prepare and enjoy!

BREAKFAST

Mexican Omelet with Macrobolic Granola

Yield: 1 Serving

5 large eggs, whites only

¼ cup chopped sweet green pepper

¼ cup chopped sweet red pepper

2 tablespoons chopped onions

1 ounce shredded low-fat cheddar cheese

1 serving Macrobolic Granola*

1 cup Skim Plus Milk or skim milk

1. Preheat an 8-by-12-inch skillet over medium-low heat.

2. Place egg whites in a bowl and beat with a fork until blended.

3. Spray preheated pan with nonstick cooking spray and pour in the egg whites. Flip eggs when the underside starts to get firm or it reaches the desired consistency (about 2–3 minutes).

4. Place the vegetables and cheese on top of one side of the omelet. When the underside reaches desired consistency, fold one half neatly over the other and allow the cheese to melt.

5. Serve with a side of Macrobolic Granola mixed with milk.

See recipe for Macrobolic Granola in this chapter.

Food Item	Quantity	Energy (kcal)	Carbs (g)	Protein (g)	Fat (g)	Fiber (g)
Egg whites	5 large	83	1.70	17.36	—	—
Sweet green pepper	¼ cup	10	2.40	0.33	0.07	0.70
Sweet red pepper	¼ cup	10	2.40	0.33	0.07	0.70
Onions	2 tbs	8	1.73	0.23	0.03	—
Cheddar cheese, low fat	1 oz	49	0.54	6.90	1.98	—
Macrobolic Granola	1 serving	218	29.34	9.42	8.10	6.22
Skim Plus Milk	1 cup	101	13.68	9.74	0.62	—
	TOTALS	**479**	**51.79**	**44.31**	**10.89**	**7.62**
			43%	**37%**	**20%**	

Egg White Omelet with Macrobolic Granola

YIELD: 1 SERVING

5 large eggs, whites only

2 tablespoons chopped onions

1 serving Macrobolic Granola*

1½ cups Skim Plus Milk or skim milk

1. Preheat an 8-by-12-inch skillet over medium heat.

2. Place egg whites in a bowl and beat with a fork until blended.

3. Mix half of the onions into the egg whites.

4. Spray preheated pan with nonstick cooking spray and pour in the egg whites. Flip eggs when the underside starts to get firm or it reaches the desired consistency (about 2–3 minutes).

5. Place the remaining onions on top of one side of the omelet and fold one half neatly over the other.

6. Serve with a side of Macrobolic Granola mixed with milk.

See recipe for Macrobolic Granola in this chapter.

Food Item	Quantity	Energy (kcal)	Carbs (g)	Protein (g)	Fat (g)	Fiber (g)
Egg whites	5 large	83	1.70	17.36	—	—
Onions	2 tbs	8	1.73	0.23	0.03	
Macrobolic Granola	1 serving	218	29.34	9.42	8.10	6.22
Skim Plus Milk	1½ cups	151	20.52	14.61	0.92	—
	TOTALS	460	52.63	41.62	9.07	6.22
			46%	36%	18%	

Macrobolic Granola Mix with Side of Eggs

YIELD: 1 SERVING

4 large eggs

½ cup Macrobolic Granola*

½ cup nonfat, plain yogurt

1 scoop Up Your MASS CinnaBun (measuring scoop included)

1. Boil the eggs until they are hard–boiled (approximately 15 minutes after the water comes to a boil and the heat is reduced). Peel the eggs, cut them in half, and discard the egg yolks. Place the egg whites in a bowl.

2. Mix the Macrobolic Granola with the yogurt and one scoop of Up Your MASS CinnaBun in a separate bowl. Serve.

   See recipe for Macrobolic Granola in this chapter.

Food Item	Quantity	Energy (kcal)	Carbs (g)	Protein (g)	Fat (g)	Fiber (g)
Macrobolic Granola	½ cup	218.0	29.34	9.42	8.10	6.22
Plain nonfat yogurt	½ cup	64.0	8.27	6.50	0.20	—
Up Your MASS CinnaBun	1 scoop	127.5	14.50	11.00	2.75	0.30
Hard-boiled egg whites	4 large	66.0	1.36	13.89	—	—
	TOTALS	475.5	53.47	40.81	11.07	6.52
			45%	34%	21%	

Macrobolic Morning Mix

YIELD: 1 SERVING

½ cup low-sodium instant oatmeal, cooked

1 ¼ cup low-fat (1 percent fat) cottage cheese

1 small apple, chopped

1 tablespoon flaxseed

1 cup Skim Plus Milk or skim milk

1. Place the oatmeal in a cereal bowl and mix in the cottage cheese, chopped apple, and flaxseed.

2. Serve the milk on the side.

Food Item	Quantity	Energy (kcal)	Carbs (g)	Protein (g)	Fat (g)	Fiber (g)
Low-sodium oatmeal	100 g	93	16.67	3.95	1.79	2.3
Low-fat cottage cheese	1¼ cup	203	7.68	35.00	2.88	—
Apple	small	63	16.16	0.20	0.38	2.9
Flaxseed	1 tbs	59	4.11	2.34	4.08	3.3
Skim Plus Milk	1 cup	101	13.68	9.74	0.62	—
	TOTALS	**519**	**58.30**	**51.23**	**9.74**	**8.5**
			45%	38%	17%	

Macrobolic Pancakes

YIELD: 8 SERVINGS

1 cup whole-wheat flour

4 scoops Up Your MASS CinnaBun

⅓ cup wheat germ

½ teaspoon baking soda

2 large whole eggs

7 large eggs, whites only

2½ cups Skim Plus Milk or skim milk

1 tablespoon safflower oil

Water, as needed*

1. Mix the whole-wheat flour, Up Your MASS CinnaBun, wheat germ, and baking soda together in a bowl.

2. Mix the whole eggs and egg whites together in a separate bowl.

3. Add the Skim Plus Milk to the dry mixture and place in a blender. Set the blender on low and blend for 3 minutes.

4. Add the egg mixture to the blender mixture and blend for 2 minutes.

5. Add the safflower oil and increase the blender speed. Add water until the batter reaches the desired thickness, approximately 2 minutes.

6. Lightly coat a pan with nonstick cooking spray and heat.

7. Pour some of the mixture into the heated pan and allow to cook until a corner of the pancake lifts easily. Flip the pancake and cook other side. Repeat with the remaining mixture.

Note: For thicker pancakes, use less water. For thinner pancakes, use more water.

Macrobolic Pancake—per serving
(Suggested Serving Size: 2 pancakes and 1 cup of Skim Plus Milk)

Food Item	Quantity	Energy (kcal)	Carbs (g)	Protein (g)	Fat (g)	Fiber (g)
Macrobolic Pancake	2 pancakes	389	45.80	30.40	9.60	3.64
Skim Plus Milk	1 cup	101	13.68	9.74	0.62	—
	TOTALS	490	59.48	40.14	10.22	3.64
			48%	33%	19%	

Macrobolic Pancakes—full recipe ■ 8 servings

Food Item	Quantity	Energy (kcal)	Carbs (g)	Protein (g)	Fat (g)	Fiber (g)
Whole-wheat flour	1 cup	407	87.08	16.44	2.24	14.6
Up Your MASS CinnaBun	4 scoops	510	58.00	44.00	11.00	10.5
Wheat germ	1/3 cup	1	0.17	0.08	0.03	5.0
Baking soda	1/2 tsp	—	—	—	—	—
Skim Plus Milk	2 1/2 cups	252	34.20	24.35	1.54	—
Eggs, whole	2 large	149	1.22	12.49	10.02	—
Eggs, white	7 large	116	2.38	20.30	—	—
Oil, safflower	1 tbs	120	—	—	13.60	—
	TOTALS	1,555	183.05	121.66	38.43	30.1
	per pancake	194.39	22.90	15.20	4.80	3.76
			47%	31%	22%	

Macrobolic Granola

YIELD: 24 HALF-CUP SERVINGS

7 cups quick oats

1 1/2 cups wheat germ, crude

1 1/2 cups wheat bran, crude

6 scoops Up Your MASS CinnaBun

1/4 cup safflower seed oil

1/2 cup water

1 tablespoon vanilla extract

$\frac{1}{4}$ cup honey

1 teaspoon ground cinnamon

1 teaspoon ground nutmeg

$\frac{1}{2}$ cup chopped pecans

$\frac{1}{2}$ cup sliced or chopped almonds

1. Preheat oven to 275°F.

2. In a large bowl, mix the oats, wheat germ, wheat bran, and Up Your MASS CinnaBun.

3. In a separate bowl, mix together the remaining ingredients except the pecans and almonds. Combine with the oat mixture and place into a shallow baking dish.

4. Bake for 30 minutes, stirring every 15 minutes. After 30 minutes, stir in the pecans and almonds, and continue baking for 15 minutes more, or until the mixture is lightly brown. Remove and cool and store in an airtight container.

Note: Macrobolic Granola is nutritionally enhanced, but does not meet the 45/35/20 ratio. Macrobolic Granola should be used with other high-protein food sources as part of a meal to balance the ratios to 45/35/20. (See breakfast omelet with Macrobolic Granola recipes.)

Food Item	Quantity	Energy (kcal)	Carbs (g)	Protein (g)	Fat (g)	Fiber (g)
Quick oats	7 cups	2,177	379.89	9.77	35.72	60.1
Wheat germ, crude	1½ cups	621	89.36	39.93	16.77	22.8
Wheat bran, crude	1½ cups	188	56.12	13.53	3.70	37.2
Up Your MASS CinnaBun	6 scoops	765	87.00	66.00	16.50	18.0
Safflower seed oil	¼ cup	482	—	—	54.50	—
Water	½ cup	—	—	—	—	—
Vanilla extract	1 tbs	37	1.64	0.01	0.01	—
Honey	¼ cup	258	69.83	0.25	—	—
Cinnamon	1 tsp	6	—	0.09	0.07	—

Nutmeg	1 tsp	12	1.08	0.13	0.80	—
Pecans	½ cup	411	8.25	5.46	42.82	5.7
Almonds	½ cup	275	9.38	10.10	24.05	5.6
	TOTALS	**5,232**	**704.39**	**226.27**	**194.90**	**149.4**
	per ½ cup serving	*218*	*29.34*	*9.42*	*8.10*	*6.2*
			51%	**17%**	**32%**	

══ Scrambled Eggs with Oatmeal and Strawberries ══

Yield: 1 Serving

½ cup quick oats

4–8 ounces water

6 large eggs, whites only

1 large whole egg

1 cup fresh strawberry slices

1. Place the oats in a microwavable container. Add water and place in the microwave. Cook for about 1 minute or until the oatmeal reaches desired consistency.

2. Preheat a skillet over medium heat.

3. In a bowl, beat the whole eggs and egg whites with a fork until well blended.

4. Coat the skillet with nonstick cooking spray and pour in the eggs. Gently mix the eggs with a wooden spoon until cooked.

5. Serve the eggs alongside the bowl of oatmeal and the strawberry slices.

Food Item	Quantity	Energy (kcal)	Carbs (g)	Protein (g)	Fat (g)	Fiber (g)
Quick oats	½ cup	156	27.00	6.00	2.50	4.3
Egg whites	6 large	99	2.04	20.38	—	—
Whole egg	1 large	75	—	6.25	5.00	—
Strawberries	1 cup	50	11.65	1.01	0.61	3.8
	TOTALS	**380**	**40.69**	**33.64**	**8.11**	**8.1**
			44%	**36%**	**20%**	

LUNCH

Chicken Parm Pasta Salad

YIELD: 1 SERVING

2 ounces melted shredded mozzarella

1 cup cooked whole-wheat spaghetti

2 large ripe tomatoes, sliced

2 large raw mushrooms, sliced

1 teaspoon dried parsley

½ teaspoon minced garlic

2 ounces sliced roasted chicken breast,
meat only, skin and visible fat removed

1. Mix the mozzarella cheese into the cooked spaghetti.

2. Mix the sliced vegetables into the spaghetti and add the parsley and garlic.

3. Place the roasted chicken breast slices over the spaghetti.

4. Serve either hot or chilled.

Food Item	Quantity	Energy (kcal)	Carbs (g)	Protein (g)	Fat (g)	Fiber (g)
Mozzarella	2 oz	144	1.58	13.76	9.02	—
Whole-wheat spaghetti	1 cup	174	37.16	7.46	0.76	6.3
Tomatoes	2 large	76	16.89	3.09	1.20	4.0
Mushrooms	2 large	12	1.88	1.33	0.15	—
Parsley	1 tsp	1	0.15	0.07	—	—
Garlic	½ tsp	1	0.23	0.04	—	—
Roast chicken breast, meat only	2 oz	94	—	17.59	2.02	—
	TOTALS	**502**	**57.89**	**43.34**	**13.15**	**10.3**
			44%	**33%**	**23%**	

Grilled Chicken–Bean Salad

YIELD: 1 SERVING

1/2 cup chopped grilled chicken breast,
meat only, skin and visible fat removed

1/2 cup canned black beans

1/2 cup canned kidney beans

1/2 cup chopped sweet green peppers

1/2 cup chopped sweet red peppers

1 teaspoon olive oil

1/8 teaspoon dried ground basil

1/8 teaspoon dried ground oregano

1 tablespoon grated Parmesan cheese

1. Place chicken, beans, and peppers in a bowl, and toss. Mix in the olive oil, basil, and oregano.

2. Sprinkle with the cheese.

3. Serve either hot or chilled.

Food Item	Quantity	Energy (kcal)	Carbs (g)	Protein (g)	Fat (g)	Fiber (g)
Grilled chicken breast, meat only	1/2 cup	116	—	21.71	2.50	—
Black beans	1/2 cup	114	20.39	7.62	0.49	7.5
Kidney beans	1/2 cup	112	20.19	7.67	0.44	5.7
Sweet green pepper	1/2 cup	20	4.79	0.66	0.14	1.3
Sweet red pepper	1/2 cup	20	4.79	0.66	0.14	1.5
Olive oil	1 tsp	40	—	—	4.50	—
Basil	1/8 tsp	—	—	—	—	—
Oregano	1/8 tsp	1	0.12	0.02	0.02	—
Parmesan cheese	1 tbs	23	0.19	2.08	1.50	—
	TOTALS	**446**	**50.47**	**40.42**	**9.73**	**16.0**
			45%	**36%**	**19%**	

Tuna Salad Sandwich

YIELD: 1 SERVING

1 6-ounce can white tuna in water, drained

½ cup chopped carrots

½ cup sliced cucumber

1 teaspoon flaxseed

½ cup sliced celery

½ cup chopped onion

2 tablespoons lemon juice

1 cup shredded loose-leaf lettuce

3 tablespoons fat-free mayonnaise

2 slices pumpernickel bread

1. In a large bowl, mix together all of ingredients except the bread.

2. Place the salad between the slices of bread and serve.

   Note: If there is any extra, place on a side dish and serve with the sandwich.

Food Item	Quantity	Energy (kcal)	Carbs (g)	Protein (g)	Fat (g)	Fiber (g)
Tuna, white, canned in water	6 oz	220	—	40.63	5.11	—
Carrots	½ cup	28	6.49	0.66	0.12	1.9
Cucumber	½ cup	7	1.44	0.36	0.07	0.4
Flaxseed	1 tsp	19	1.36	0.77	1.35	1.1
Celery	½ cup	10	2.19	0.45	0.08	1.1
Onions	½ cup	30	6.90	0.93	0.13	1.4
Lemon juice	2 tbs	6	1.94	0.12	0.09	—
Loose-leaf lettuce	1 cup	10	1.96	0.73	0.17	—
Fat-free mayo	3 tbs	34	5.95	0.10	1.30	2.0
Pumpernickel bread	2 slices	160	30.28	5.50	1.98	4.2
	TOTALS	**524**	**58.51**	**50.25**	**10.40**	**12.1**
			44%	**38%**	**18%**	

Beef Mass Burger

Yield: 2 Servings

8 ounces lean ground beef or turkey

¼ cup shredded low-fat cheddar cheese

⅛ teaspoon parsley

⅛ teaspoon basil

2 rolls whole-wheat hamburger rolls

2 leaves loose-leaf lettuce

4 medium slices ripe tomato

1. Preheat a skillet or grill to desired heat range (145°F for rare; 160°F for medium; 170°F for well-done).

2. Mix the beef or turkey with the cheese and spices in a large bowl. Form into two equal patties.

3. Coat skillet or griddle with nonstick cooking spray and cook patties until desired doneness.

4. Place on whole-wheat roll with lettuce and tomato. Serve.

Per 2 servings

Food Item	Quantity	Energy (kcal)	Carbs (g)	Protein (g)	Fat (g)	Fiber (g)
Lean ground beef	8 oz	311	—	48.60	11.35	—
Low-fat cheddar cheese	¼ cup	49	0.54	6.88	1.98	—
Whole-wheat hamburger rolls	2 rolls	532	102.20	17.40	4.04	15.08
Parsley	⅛ tsp	—	—	0.01	—	—
Basil	⅛ tsp	—	0.11	0.03	0.01	—
Loose-leaf lettuce	2 leaves	4	0.70	0.26	0.06	—
Tomato	4 slices	14	3.71	0.68	0.26	0.90
	TOTALS	**910**	**107.26**	**73.86**	**17.70**	**15.98**
	per serving	*455*	*53.63*	*36.93*	*8.85*	*7.99*
			49%	**33%**	**18%**	

Steak Pita Pocket

Yield: 1 Serving

4 ounces beef chuck cubes

$1/8$ teaspoon salt

$1/8$ teaspoon ground cumin

$1/4$ clove garlic, diced

1 cup chopped tomatoes

1 ounce shredded low-fat
cheddar cheese

$1/2$ cup shredded loose-leaf lettuce

5 thin slices onion

3 jalapeño peppers, chopped

1 cup sliced sweet red pepper

$1/8$ cup prepared (commercial) salsa

1 large whole-wheat pita

1. Preheat a skillet over high heat.

2. Slice each of the beef chuck cubes in half.

3. Coat the skillet with nonstick cooking spray and immediately add the beef chuck halves.

4. Stir-fry for about 3–5 minutes, or until the beef chuck halves brown on all sides.

5. While the beef chuck is cooking, mix the salt with the cumin and place in a bowl with the remaining ingredients except for the pita. Mix together if desired.

6. When the beef chuck is fully cooked, place it on a dish or a cutting board. Slice the beef chuck halves into smaller slices. Then place in the bowl with the other ingredients and stir until well mixed.

7. Cut a pocket into the whole-wheat pita. Place the shredded beef mixture into the pita pocket with a large spoon. Serve.

   Note: If there is any extra, place on a side dish and serve with the sandwich.

Food Item	Quantity	Energy (kcal)	Carbs (g)	Protein (g)	Fat (g)	Fiber (g)
Beef chuck	4 oz	181	—	29.32	6.26	—
Salt	⅛ tsp	—	—	—	—	—
Garlic	¼ clove	1	0.25	0.05	—	—
Cumin	⅛ tsp	1	0.12	0.05	0.06	—
Tomato	1 cup	38	8.35	1.53	0.59	2.0
Low-fat cheddar cheese	1 oz	49	0.54	6.90	1.98	—
Loose-leaf lettuce	½ cup	5	0.98	0.36	0.08	—
Onions	5 slices	17	3.88	0.52	0.07	0.8
Jalapeño peppers	3	13	2.48	0.57	0.26	—
Sweet red pepper	1 cup	25	5.92	0.82	0.17	3.0
Salsa	⅛ cup	9	2.02	0.41	0.08	—
Whole-wheat pita	1 large	170	35.20	6.27	1.66	4.7
TOTALS		**509**	**59.74**	**46.80**	**11.21**	**10.5**
			45%	**36%**	**19%**	

DINNER

Mixed-Meat Teriyaki

Yield: 4 Servings

1 roast or grilled, sliced chicken breast, meat only, skin and visible fat removed

8 ounces grilled, sliced, lean top-round or short-loin porterhouse ($\frac{1}{4}$" fat)

2 cups cooked medium brown rice

1$\frac{1}{4}$ cup teriyaki sauce

1 large onion, chopped

1 large sweet green pepper, chopped

1 small zucchini, sliced

1 large sweet yellow pepper, chopped

2 tablespoons olive oil

1$\frac{1}{2}$ tablespoons soy sauce

2 teaspoons garlic powder

1 teaspoon ground black pepper

1. Place the chicken, beef, and cooked rice into a bowl with the teriyaki sauce.

2. Mix the vegetables with the olive oil, soy sauce, and garlic powder. Place mixture into the bowl with the chicken, beef, and rice. Add the black pepper.

3. Divide into four equal servings. Refrigerate the leftover servings in separate containers for the rest of the week.

Per 4 servings

Food Item	Quantity	Energy (kcal)	Carbs (g)	Protein (g)	Fat (g)	Fiber (g)
Roast chicken breast, meat only	1 breast	284	—	53.35	6.14	—
Top round, lean only, $\frac{1}{4}$" fat	8 oz	272	—	51.96	5.67	—
Medium brown rice	2 cups	437	91.96	9.05	3.24	7.0

Teriyaki sauce	1¼ cup	302	57.42	21.53	—	—
Onion	1 large	57	12.59	1.74	0.24	2.7
Sweet green pepper	1 large	44	10.55	1.46	0.31	3.0
Zucchini	1 small	17	3.42	1.37	0.17	1.4
Sweet yellow pepper	1 large	50	11.76	1.86	0.39	1.7
Olive oil	2 tbs	239	—	—	27.00	—
Soy sauce, low-sodium	1½ tbs	14	2.30	1.40	—	—
Garlic powder	2 tsp	9	2.04	0.47	0.02	—
Black pepper	1 tsp	5	1.36	0.23	0.07	—
	TOTALS	**1,730**	**193.40**	**144.42**	**43.25**	**15.8**
	per serving	*433*	*48.35*	*36.10*	*10.81*	*4.0*
			45%	33%	22%	

Lemon Sole with Broccoli

Yield: 4 Servings

1 pound sole or flounder fillets (4-ounces each)

2 tablespoons lemon juice

Black pepper to taste

10 ounces broccoli spears

1 cup whole-wheat pasta

4 ounces melted low-fat cheddar cheese

¼ cup skim milk

½ teaspoon grated lemon peel

¼ teaspoon fresh dill

1½ teaspoons olive oil

4 slices toasted pumpernickel bread

1. Fill a large pot three-quarters with water and bring the water to a boil.

2. Sprinkle each fillet with juice and pepper. Place the broccoli spears on the narrow end of each fish fillet. Roll up the fillet starting at the end with the broccoli, so the broccoli ends up in the center of the roll. Secure the roll with toothpicks. Place the roll seam side down on a microwavable dish and cover.

3. Microwave on high for 5–7 minutes until the fish flakes easily with a fork.

4. Place whole-wheat pasta in the boiling water. (Note: individual pasta manufacturers may indicate the length of time the pasta should be cooked.)

5. Place the remaining ingredients (except the bread and the olive oil) in a microwavable bowl and mix together until blended. Microwave 2–3 minutes or until the sauce reaches a smooth consistency. (Stir the sauce after each minute to ensure even melting.)

6. Drain the water from the pasta when done and immediately mix the olive oil into the pasta.

7. Remove fillets and discard the toothpicks. Place on top of pasta (1 cup per fillet) and serve with sauce and bread.

Per 4 servings (without pasta and bread)

Food Item	Quantity	Energy (kcal)	Carbs (g)	Protein (g)	Fat (g)	Fiber (g)
Sole fillets	1 lb	530	—	109.53	6.94	—
Lemon juice	2 tbs	6	1.94	0.12	0.90	—
Broccoli spears	10 oz	70	13.38	7.75	0.28	7.5
Low-fat cheddar cheese	4 oz	196	2.17	27.61	7.94	—
Skim milk	¼ cup	23	3.07	2.19	0.15	—
Lemon peel	½ tsp	—	0.16	0.01	—	—
Fresh dill	¼ tsp	—	—	—	—	—
	TOTALS	**825**	**20.72**	**147.21**	**16.21**	**7.5**

Per serving (with pasta and bread)

Food Item	Quantity	Energy (kcal)	Carbs (g)	Protein (g)	Fat (g)	Fiber (g)
Lemon Broccoli of Sole	1 serving	206.25	5.18	36.80	4.10	1.87
Whole-wheat pasta	1 cup	174.00	37.16	7.46	0.76	6.30
Olive oil	1½ tsp	60.00	—	—	6.75	—
Pumpernickel bread, toasted	1 slice	80.00	15.14	2.75	0.99	2.10
	TOTALS	**520.25**	**57.48**	**47.01**	**12.62**	**10.27**
			44%	**35%**	**21%**	

══════════ Lemon Salmon with Spinach ══════════

YIELD: 1 SERVING

5 ounces farm-fresh salmon

3 tablespoons lemon juice

2 cups raw spinach, rinsed and dried

1 medium potato

1. Preheat a large skillet over medium-high heat.

2. Coat the skillet with nonfat cooking spray, and add the salmon.

3. Cook for 10 minutes for each inch of thickness.

4. Flip the fillet halfway through cooking to brown both sides.

5. When the fillet is brown on both sides, place on a dish and sprinkle the lemon juice over salmon.

6. Place the spinach on the dish with the lemon salmon, and serve with the baked potato (recipe follows).

Baked Potato

1. Preheat oven to 350°F.

2. Wash potato thoroughly with water and dry.

3. Prick the skin of the potato with a fork several times to prevent steam buildup during cooking.

4. Bake the potato for approximately 90 minutes, or until it is slightly soft (fork will pierce the potato easily) and golden brown.

Food Item	Quantity	Energy (kcal)	Carbs (g)	Protein (g)	Fat (g)	Fiber (g)
Salmon	5 oz	201	—	28.11	8.89	—
Lemon juice	3 tbs	13	3.89	0.24	0.17	—
Spinach	2 cups	14	2.10	1.72	0.22	1.6
Baked potato with skin	1 medium	145	33.63	3.06	0.16	3.8
	TOTALS	**380**	**40.67**	**33.99**	**9.55**	**4.6**
			43%	**36%**	**21%**	

Macrobolic Sushi Menu

Yield: 2 Rolls

Yellowfin Tuna Roll

$\frac{1}{3}$ cup uncooked white short-grain rice

1$\frac{1}{2}$ teaspoons cider vinegar

$\frac{1}{4}$ medium cucumber, peeled and sliced into strips

$\frac{1}{3}$ cup avocado, sliced into strips

2$\frac{1}{2}$ sheets nori seaweed

6 ounces yellowfin tuna, sliced into strips

King Crab Roll

$\frac{1}{3}$ cup uncooked white short-grain rice

1$\frac{1}{2}$ tablespoons cider vinegar

$\frac{1}{2}$ medium cucumber, peeled and sliced into strips

$\frac{1}{3}$ cup avocado, sliced into strips

2$\frac{1}{2}$ sheets nori seaweed

8 ounces Alaskan king crab strips

Shrimp Roll

$\frac{1}{3}$ cup uncooked white short-grain rice

1$\frac{1}{2}$ tablespoons cider vinegar

$\frac{1}{4}$ medium cucumber, peeled and sliced into strips

$\frac{1}{3}$ cup sliced avocado, sliced into strips

2 sheets nori seaweed

7 ounces shrimp

Rice

1. Wash the rice repeatedly under running water to remove all of the starch and until the water is clear.

2. As a rule of thumb, use twice the amount of water as rice for cooking the rice (for example, 2 cups water to 1 cup rice).

3. Place the measured water into a pot and bring to a boil.

4. Add the washed rice and return the water to a boil.

5. Add the vinegar to the rice.

6. Once the water has returned to a boil, lower the heat until it is barely simmering. Stir the rice occasionally (this makes the rice sticky, which is essential for sushi).

7. Let the pot simmer until all the water is absorbed, then take pot off heat and let it cool for an additional 10 minutes.

Sushi

1. Preheat the oven to 300°F. Heat the nori sheets on a medium baking sheet in the oven for 1 to 2 minutes, or until the sheets are warm.

2. Place the warm nori sheets on a clean dish towel. This will be used to roll the sushi.

3. Wet your hands. Then spread and press a thin layer of rice on the nori sheet.

4. Arrange and place other ingredients so that a piece of each is placed together in a single straight line, pressing gently as you go.

5. Using the dish towel, gently roll the nori sheet and press it over the ingredients.

6. Roll it forward until you make a complete roll. Repeat with the other prepared sheets.

7. Unravel the dish towel, to be reused. Cut each roll to your desired size using a wet, sharp knife.

Yellowfin Tuna Roll

Food Item	Quantity	Energy (kcal)	Carbs (g)	Protein (g)	Fat (g)	Fiber (g)
White, short-grain rice	⅓ cup	215	47.49	3.90	0.31	1.8
Cider vinegar	1½ tbs	3	0.07	—	—	—
Cucumber, peeled	¼ medium	6	1.26	0.29	0.08	0.4
Avocado	⅓ cup	71	3.24	0.87	6.71	2.4
Nori seaweed sushi sheets	2½ sheets	25	5.00	2.50	—	2.5
Tuna, yellowfin, raw	6 oz	184	—	39.75	1.67	—
	TOTALS	**504**	**57.06**	**47.31**	**8.77**	**7.1**
			46%	**38%**	**16%**	

King Crab Roll

Food Item	Quantity	Energy (kcal)	Carbs (g)	Protein (g)	Fat (g)	Fiber (g)
White, short-grain rice	⅓ cup	215	47.49	3.90	0.31	1.8
Cider vinegar	1½ tbs	3	0.07	—	—	
Cucumber, peeled	¼ medium	6	1.26	0.29	0.08	0.4
Avocado, raw	⅓ cup	71	3.24	0.87	6.71	2.4
Nori seaweed sushi sheets	2.5 sheets	25	5.00	2.50	—	2.5
Alaskan king crab, raw	8 oz	190	—	41.46	1.36	—
	TOTALS	**510**	**57.06**	**49.02**	**8.46**	**7.1**
			46%	**39%**	**15%**	

Shrimp Roll

Food Item	Quantity	Energy (kcal)	Carbs (g)	Protein (g)	Fat (g)	Fiber (g)
White, short-grain rice	⅓ cup	215	47.49	3.90	0.31	1.8
Cider vinegar	1½ tbs	3	0.07	—	—	—
Cucumber, peeled	¼ medium	6	1.26	0.29	0.08	0.4
Avocado, raw	⅓ cup	71	3.24	0.87	6.71	2.4
Nori seaweed sushi sheets	2.5 sheets	25	5.00	2.50	—	2.5
Shrimp, raw	7 oz	210	1.80	40.28	3.43	—
	TOTALS	**530**	**58.86**	**47.84**	**10.53**	**7.1**
			45%	**37%**	**18%**	

SHAKES, BARS, AND DESSERTS

Up Your MASS Shake

YIELD: 1 SERVING

4 scoops Up Your MASS
(CinnaBun or Chocolate Fudge Brownie)

15–18 ounces water

1. Mix 4 scoops of Up Your MASS with 15–18 ounces of water.

Food Item	Quantity	Energy (kcal)	Carbs (g)	Protein (g)	Fat (g)	Fiber (g)
Up Your MASS Shake	4 scoops	510	58	44	11	12
Water	15–18 oz	—	—	—	—	—
	TOTALS	510	58	44	11	12
			45%	35%	20%	

Up Your MASS Bar

1 BAR

Food Item	Quantity	Energy (kcal)	Carbs (g)	Protein (g)	Fat (g)	Fiber (g)
Up Your MASS bar (crunchy peanut or fudge)	1 bar	380	44	30	11	1
	TOTALS	380	44	30	11	1
			46%	32%	22%	

Fruit Salad

YIELD: 1 SERVING

½ cup diced mandarin orange sections

½ cup diced strawberries

½ cup grapes

½ cup chopped apples with skin

½ cup peaches

1½ cups low-fat cottage cheese
(not packed)

2 tablespoons flaxseed

1. Combine all of the fruit in a dish.

2. Mix in cottage cheese and sprinkle with flaxseed.

Food Item	Quantity	Energy (kcal)	Carbs (g)	Protein (g)	Fat (g)	Fiber (g)
Mandarin orange	½ cup	43	10.91	0.61	0.19	2.2
Strawberries	½ cup	25	5.83	0.51	0.31	1.9
Grapes	½ cup	31	7.89	0.29	0.16	0.5
Apples, raw, with skin	½ cup	37	9.53	0.12	0.22	1.7
Peaches	½ cup	37	9.43	0.59	0.08	1.7
Low-fat cottage cheese	1½ cup	244	9.22	42.00	3.46	—
Flaxseed	2 tbs	118	8.22	4.68	8.16	6.7
	TOTALS	**535**	**61.03**	**48.80**	**12.58**	**14.7**
			44%	**35%**	**21%**	

Macrobolic Instant Chocolate Pudding

YIELD: 3 SERVINGS

4½ cups cold skim milk

2 packets Jell-O Brand
Instant Chocolate Pudding
(or other instant chocolate pudding)

4 scoops Up Your MASS: Fudge Brownie

1. In a bowl, combine milk and pudding mix.

2. Add 4 scoops of Up Your MASS: Fudge Brownie.

3. Using a handheld blender, begin blending mix at a low setting.

4. As the pudding gets thicker, increase the blender speed and blend for about 2 to 3 minutes, or until the pudding mix reaches a smooth consistency.

5. Cover the bowl with plastic wrap and refrigerate until firm.

Note: This dessert can also be prepared with vanilla pudding instead of chocolate, or Up Your MASS CinnaBun instead of Fudge Brownie.

Per 3 servings

Food Item	Quantity	Energy (kcal)	Carbs (g)	Protein (g)	Fat (g)	Fiber (g)
Jell-O Brand Instant Chocolate Pudding	2 packets	70	8	—	—	—
Up Your MASS: Fudge Brownie	4 scoops	510	58	46	11.0	12
Skim Milk	4½ cups	531	63	45	13.5	—
	TOTALS	**1,111**	**129**	**91**	**24.5**	**12**
	per serving	*370*	*43*	*30*	*8.2*	*4*
			45%	**33%**	**22%**	

Progress Is the Great Motivator

AS I MENTIONED EARLY IN THIS BOOK, seeing people just like you working hard in the gym and frustrated because of their lack of progress is what inspired me to write about Macrobolic Nutrition. Like anything in life, when you feel like you are rowing against the tide, it is easy to lose interest, throw in the oars, and quit. Yet, when you are rowing with the tide and you experience progress and results, it motivates you to row even harder and faster to go further! Continual progress and motivation are residual benefits of Macrobolic Nutrition.

What I describe as "Macrobolic Momentum" is the net effect of Macrobolic Nutrition's 45/35/20 lean-mass equation. To sum it up, Macrobolic Nutrition creates the ideal hormonal and anabolic environment to build muscle and burn body fat. Over time, as your body composition shifts to increased muscle mass and less body fat, your body's metabolism becomes even more efficient at building muscle and burning body fat. So, you will continue to get bigger and leaner as you follow Macrobolic Nutrition. These continual gains will keep you motivated not only to eat properly, but also to push your body to its limits when you train.

Macrobolic Nutrition has taught you the powerful effects food has on your body. And now you understand how Macrobolic Nutrition's 45/35/20 lean-mass equation will optimize key hormones and supply the nutrients you need and is customized so you can reach your goals and achieve your full genetic potential.

The days of frustration and lack of progress are over. From this day forward, you can continue to make gains in lean body mass. I am confident that, if you follow the Macrobolic Nutrition program, you will break through plateaus and reach levels of size and performance you never imagined possible.

Macrobolic Caloric Requirements Tables

In Chapter 7, you learned how to use the Macroblic caloric equation:

$$(\text{Bodyweight} \times \text{MGV*}) + (\text{Bodyweight} \times \text{Lifestyle}) + (\text{Exercise Expenditure}) = \text{Total Caloric Requirements}$$

Macrobolic Goal Variables

If you're pressed for time or if you simply don't want to do the calculations yourself, this appendix provides you with the exact amount of total calories, carbohydrates, protein, and fat you need to maximize muscle mass and target your goals based on your current body weight, goal, lifestyle, and workout schedules. This appendix will also break out separate daily and nighttime nutrient and caloric intake for you. First, determine your goal:

Gain, Maintain, Lose

- Gain Body Fat/Increase Muscle
- Maintain Body Fat/Increase Muscle
- Lose Body Fat/Increase Muscle
- Lose Body Fat/Increase Muscle—Over 15% Body Fat

Then, simply locate the table that best matches your profile. For example, if your goal is to lose body fat and increase muscle, your workout is 90 minutes, you weigh 215 pounds, your body fat percentage is over 15%, and you lead an active lifestyle, you'll find your target nutrient and caloric intake for workout days in the table on page 187 and for non–workout days on page 189.

*You can also go to **www.macrobolicnutrition.com** and the Macrobolic Calculator program I have developed will do the math for you, providing the precise amount of calories and nutrients you'll need to live the Macrobolic Nutrition lifestyle.*

GOAL: LOSE BODY FAT/INCREASE MUSCLE (BODY FAT UNDER 15%) • 60 MINUTE WORKOUTS

BW	SED Kcal	Total Carbs	Total Prot	Total Fat	Day Carbs	Day Prot	Day Fat	Day Kcal	Night Carbs	Night Prot	Night Fat	Night Kcal	MOD Kcal	Total Carbs	Total Prot	Total Fat
130	1900	196	179	44	188	146	37	1673	8	33	7	228	2160	226	202	49
135	1950	201	184	45	193	150	38	1714	8	34	7	236	2220	232	207	51
140	2000	206	189	46	197	154	39	1755	9	35	7	245	2280	238	213	52
145	2050	211	193	47	202	157	40	1796	9	36	7	254	2340	244	219	54
150	2100	216	198	48	207	161	41	1838	9	38	8	263	2400	250	225	55
155	2150	221	203	50	211	164	42	1879	10	39	8	271	2460	256	230	56
160	2200	226	208	51	216	168	43	1920	10	40	8	280	2520	262	236	58
165	2250	231	213	52	221	172	44	1961	10	41	8	289	2580	268	242	59
170	2300	236	218	53	225	175	45	2003	11	43	9	298	2640	274	247	61
175	2350	241	223	54	230	179	45	2044	11	44	9	306	2700	280	253	62
180	2400	246	227	55	235	182	46	2085	11	45	9	315	2760	286	259	63
185	2450	251	232	57	239	186	47	2126	12	46	9	324	2820	292	265	65
190	2500	256	237	58	244	190	48	2168	12	48	10	333	2880	298	270	66
195	2550	261	242	59	248	193	49	2209	12	49	10	341	2940	305	276	68
200	2600	266	247	60	253	197	50	2250	13	50	10	350	3000	311	282	69
205	2650	271	252	61	258	200	51	2291	13	51	10	359	3060	317	288	70
210	2700	276	257	62	262	204	52	2333	13	53	11	368	3120	323	293	72
215	2750	280	261	64	267	208	53	2374	13	54	11	376	3180	329	299	73
220	2800	285	266	65	272	211	54	2415	14	55	11	385	3240	335	305	74
225	2850	290	271	66	276	215	55	2456	14	56	11	394	3300	341	311	76
230	2900	295	276	67	281	219	56	2498	14	58	12	403	3360	347	316	77
235	2950	300	281	68	286	222	56	2539	15	59	12	411	3420	353	322	79
240	3000	305	286	69	290	226	57	2580	15	60	12	420	3480	359	328	80
245	3050	310	291	71	295	229	58	2621	15	61	12	429	3540	365	333	81
250	3100	315	295	72	300	233	59	2663	16	63	13	438	3600	371	339	83
255	3150	320	300	73	304	237	60	2704	16	64	13	446	3660	377	345	84
260	3200	325	305	74	309	240	61	2745	16	65	13	455	3720	384	351	86
265	3250	330	310	75	313	244	62	2786	17	66	13	464	3780	390	356	87
270	3300	335	315	76	318	247	63	2828	17	68	14	473	3840	396	362	88

BW = Body Weight   SED = Sedentary   MOD = Moderately Active   ACT = Active

GOAL: LOSE BODY FAT/INCREASE MUSCLE (BODY FAT UNDER 15%) • 60 MINUTE WORKOUTS (cont.)

BW	Day Carbs	Day Prot	Day Fat	Day Kcal	Night Carbs	Night Prot	Night Fat	Night Kcal	ACT Kcal	Total Carbs	Total Prot	Total Fat	Day Carbs	Day Prot	Day Fat	Day Kcal	Night Carbs	Night Prot	Night Fat	Night Kcal
130	217	169	43	1933	8	33	7	228	2810	299	258	64	291	226	57	2583	8	33	7	228
135	223	174	44	1984	8	34	7	236	2895	308	266	66	299	233	59	2659	8	34	7	236
140	229	178	45	2035	9	35	7	245	2980	316	274	68	308	239	61	2735	9	35	7	245
145	235	183	46	2086	9	36	7	254	3065	325	282	70	316	246	62	2811	9	36	7	254
150	240	187	48	2138	9	38	8	263	3150	334	290	72	325	253	64	2888	9	38	8	263
155	246	192	49	2189	10	39	8	271	3235	343	298	74	333	259	66	2964	10	39	8	271
160	252	196	50	2240	10	40	8	280	3320	352	306	76	342	266	68	3040	10	40	8	280
165	258	200	51	2291	10	41	8	289	3405	361	314	78	351	273	69	3116	10	41	8	289
170	264	205	52	2343	11	43	9	298	3490	370	322	79	359	279	71	3193	11	43	9	298
175	269	209	53	2394	11	44	9	306	3575	379	330	81	368	286	73	3269	11	44	9	306
180	275	214	54	2445	11	45	9	315	3660	388	338	83	376	293	74	3345	11	45	9	315
185	281	218	55	2496	12	46	9	324	3745	396	346	85	385	299	76	3421	12	46	9	324
190	287	223	57	2548	12	48	10	333	3830	405	354	87	393	306	78	3498	12	48	10	333
195	292	227	58	2599	12	49	10	341	3915	414	361	89	402	313	79	3574	12	49	10	341
200	298	232	59	2650	13	50	10	350	4000	423	369	91	411	319	81	3650	13	50	10	350
205	304	236	60	2701	13	51	10	359	4085	432	377	93	419	326	83	3726	13	51	10	359
210	310	241	61	2753	13	53	11	368	4170	441	385	95	428	333	85	3803	13	53	11	368
215	315	245	62	2804	13	54	11	376	4255	450	393	97	436	339	86	3879	13	54	11	376
220	321	250	63	2855	14	55	11	385	4340	459	401	99	445	346	88	3955	14	55	11	385
225	327	254	65	2906	14	56	11	394	4425	468	409	101	454	353	90	4031	14	56	11	394
230	333	259	66	2958	14	58	12	403	4510	476	417	103	462	359	91	4108	14	58	12	403
235	338	263	67	3009	15	59	12	411	4595	485	425	105	471	366	93	4184	15	59	12	411
240	344	268	68	3060	15	60	12	420	4680	494	433	107	479	373	95	4260	15	60	12	420
245	350	272	69	3111	15	61	12	429	4765	503	441	109	488	379	96	4336	15	61	12	429
250	356	277	70	3163	16	63	13	438	4850	512	449	111	496	386	98	4413	16	63	13	438
255	362	281	71	3214	16	64	13	446	4935	521	457	113	505	393	100	4489	16	64	13	446
260	367	286	73	3265	16	65	13	455	5020	530	464	114	514	399	101	4565	16	65	13	455
265	373	290	74	3316	17	66	13	464	5105	539	472	116	522	406	103	4641	17	66	13	464
270	379	295	75	3368	17	68	14	473	5190	548	480	118	531	413	105	4718	17	68	14	473

BW = Body Weight   SED = Sedentary   MOD = Moderately Active   ACT = Active

GOAL: LOSE BODY FAT/INCREASE MUSCLE (BODY FAT UNDER 15%) • 90 MINUTE WORKOUTS

BW	SED Kcal	Total Carbs	Total Prot	Total Fat	Day Carbs	Day Prot	Day Fat	Day Kcal	Night Carbs	Night Prot	Night Fat	Night Kcal	MOD Kcal	Total Carbs	Total Prot	Total Fat
130	2200	230	205	50	222	173	44	1973	8	33	7	228	2460	259	228	56
135	2250	235	210	52	227	176	45	2014	8	34	7	236	2520	265	234	58
140	2300	240	215	53	231	180	46	2055	9	35	7	245	2580	271	239	58
145	2350	245	220	54	236	183	47	2096	9	36	7	254	2640	278	245	59
150	2400	250	225	55	240	187	48	2138	9	38	8	263	2700	284	251	60
155	2450	255	229	56	245	191	48	2179	10	39	8	271	2760	290	257	62
160	2500	260	234	57	250	194	49	2220	10	40	8	280	2820	296	262	63
165	2550	265	239	59	254	198	50	2261	10	41	8	289	2880	302	268	64
170	2600	270	244	60	259	201	51	2303	11	43	9	298	2940	308	274	66
175	2650	275	249	61	264	205	52	2344	11	44	9	306	3000	314	279	67
180	2700	280	254	62	268	209	53	2385	11	45	9	315	3060	320	285	69
185	2750	285	259	63	273	212	54	2426	12	46	9	324	3120	326	291	70
190	2800	289	263	64	278	216	55	2468	12	48	10	333	3180	332	297	71
195	2850	294	268	66	282	220	56	2509	12	49	10	341	3240	338	302	73
200	2900	299	273	67	287	223	57	2550	13	50	10	350	3300	344	308	74
205	2950	304	278	68	292	227	58	2591	13	51	10	359	3360	350	314	76
210	3000	309	283	69	296	230	59	2633	13	53	11	368	3420	357	320	77
215	3050	314	288	70	301	234	59	2674	13	54	11	376	3480	363	325	78
220	3100	319	293	71	305	238	60	2715	14	55	11	385	3540	369	331	80
225	3150	324	297	73	310	241	61	2756	14	56	11	394	3600	375	337	81
230	3200	329	302	74	315	245	62	2798	14	58	12	403	3660	381	343	83
235	3250	334	307	75	319	248	63	2839	15	59	12	411	3720	387	348	84
240	3300	339	312	76	324	252	64	2880	15	60	12	420	3780	393	354	85
245	3350	344	317	77	329	256	65	2921	15	61	12	429	3840	399	360	87
250	3400	349	322	78	333	259	66	2963	16	63	13	438	3900	405	365	88
255	3450	354	327	80	338	263	67	3004	16	64	13	446	3960	411	371	89
260	3500	359	331	81	343	266	68	3045	16	65	13	455	4020	417	377	91
265	3550	364	336	82	347	270	69	3086	17	66	13	464	4080	423	383	94
270	3600	369	341	83	352	274	70	3128	17	68	14	473	4140	429	388	95

BW = Body Weight   SED = Sedentary   MOD = Moderately Active   ACT = Active

GOAL: LOSE BODY FAT/INCREASE MUSCLE (BODY FAT UNDER 15%) • 90 MINUTE WORKOUTS (cont.)

BW	Day Carbs	Day Prot	Day Fat	Day Kcal	Night Carbs	Night Prot	Night Fat	Night Kcal	ACT Kcal	Total Carbs	Total Prot	Total Fat	Day Carbs	Day Prot	Day Fat	Day Kcal	Night Carbs	Night Prot	Night Fat	Night Kcal
130	251	195	50	2233	8	33	7	228	3110	332	285	71	324	252	64	2883	8	33	7	228
135	257	200	51	2284	8	34	7	236	3195	341	293	73	333	259	66	2959	8	34	7	236
140	263	204	52	2335	9	35	7	245	3280	350	301	74	341	266	67	3035	9	35	7	245
145	268	209	53	2386	9	36	7	254	3365	359	308	76	350	272	69	3111	9	36	7	254
150	274	213	54	2438	9	38	8	263	3450	368	316	78	359	279	71	3188	9	38	8	263
155	280	218	55	2489	10	39	8	271	3535	377	324	80	367	286	73	3264	10	39	8	271
160	286	222	56	2540	10	40	8	280	3620	386	332	82	376	292	74	3340	10	40	8	280
165	292	227	58	2591	10	41	8	289	3705	395	340	84	384	299	76	3416	10	41	8	289
170	297	231	59	2643	11	43	9	298	3790	404	348	86	393	306	78	3493	11	43	9	298
175	303	236	60	2694	11	44	9	306	3875	412	356	88	401	312	79	3569	11	44	9	306
180	309	240	61	2745	11	45	9	315	3960	421	364	90	410	319	81	3645	11	45	9	315
185	315	245	62	2796	12	46	9	324	4045	430	372	92	419	326	83	3721	12	46	9	324
190	320	249	63	2848	12	48	10	333	4130	439	380	94	427	332	84	3798	12	48	10	333
195	326	254	64	2899	12	49	10	341	4215	448	388	96	436	339	86	3874	12	49	10	341
200	332	258	66	2950	13	50	10	350	4300	457	396	98	444	346	88	3950	13	50	10	350
205	338	263	67	3001	13	51	10	359	4385	466	404	100	453	352	89	4026	13	51	10	359
210	343	267	68	3053	13	53	11	368	4470	475	411	102	462	359	91	4103	13	53	11	368
215	349	272	69	3104	13	54	11	376	4555	484	419	104	470	366	93	4179	13	54	11	376
220	355	276	70	3155	14	55	11	385	4640	492	427	106	479	372	95	4255	14	55	11	385
225	361	281	71	3206	14	56	11	394	4725	501	435	108	487	379	96	4331	14	56	11	394
230	366	285	72	3258	14	58	12	403	4810	510	443	109	496	386	98	4408	14	58	12	403
235	372	290	74	3309	15	59	12	411	4895	519	451	111	504	392	100	4484	15	59	12	411
240	378	294	75	3360	15	60	12	420	4980	528	459	113	513	399	101	4560	15	60	12	420
245	384	298	76	3411	15	61	12	429	5065	537	467	115	522	406	103	4636	15	61	12	429
250	390	303	77	3463	16	63	13	438	5150	546	475	117	530	412	105	4713	16	63	13	438
255	395	307	78	3514	16	64	13	446	5235	555	483	119	539	419	106	4789	16	64	13	446
260	401	312	79	3565	16	65	13	455	5320	564	491	121	547	426	108	4865	16	65	13	455
265	407	316	80	3616	17	66	13	464	5405	572	499	123	556	432	110	4941	17	66	13	464
270	413	321	82	3668	17	68	14	473	5490	581	507	125	564	439	112	5018	17	68	14	473

BW = Body Weight   SED = Sedentary   MOD = Moderately Active   ACT = Active

GOAL: LOSE BODY FAT/INCREASE MUSCLE (BODY FAT UNDER 15%) • Non-Workout

BW	SED Kcal	Total Carbs	Total Prot	Total Fat	Day Carbs	Day Prot	Day Fat	Day Kcal	Night Carbs	Night Prot	Night Fat	Night Kcal	MOD Kcal	Total Carbs	Total Prot	Total Fat
130	1300	129	126	30	121	94	24	1073	8	33	7	228	1560	158	149	36
135	1350	134	131	32	125	97	25	1114	8	34	7	236	1620	164	155	38
140	1400	139	136	33	130	101	26	1155	9	35	7	245	1680	170	161	39
145	1450	144	141	34	135	105	27	1196	9	36	7	254	1740	176	166	40
150	1500	149	146	35	139	108	28	1238	9	38	8	263	1800	182	172	42
155	1550	154	151	36	144	112	28	1279	10	39	8	271	1860	188	178	43
160	1600	159	156	37	149	116	29	1320	10	40	8	280	1920	195	184	44
165	1650	163	160	39	153	119	30	1361	10	41	8	289	1980	201	189	46
170	1700	168	165	40	158	123	31	1403	11	43	9	298	2040	207	195	47
175	1750	173	170	41	162	126	32	1444	11	44	9	306	2100	213	201	49
180	1800	178	175	42	167	130	33	1485	11	45	9	315	2160	219	206	50
185	1850	183	180	43	172	134	34	1526	12	46	9	324	2220	225	212	51
190	1900	188	185	44	176	137	35	1568	12	48	10	333	2280	231	218	53
195	1950	193	190	46	181	141	36	1609	12	49	10	341	2340	237	224	54
200	2000	198	194	47	186	144	37	1650	13	50	10	350	2400	243	229	56
205	2050	203	199	48	190	148	38	1691	13	51	10	359	2460	249	235	57
210	2100	208	204	49	195	152	39	1733	13	53	11	368	2520	255	241	58
215	2150	213	209	50	200	155	39	1774	13	54	11	376	2580	261	247	60
220	2200	218	214	51	204	159	40	1815	14	55	11	385	2640	267	252	61
225	2250	223	219	53	209	162	41	1856	14	56	11	394	2700	274	258	63
230	2300	228	224	54	213	166	42	1898	14	58	12	403	2760	280	264	64
235	2350	233	228	55	218	170	43	1939	15	59	12	411	2820	286	270	65
240	2400	238	233	56	223	173	44	1980	15	60	12	420	2880	292	275	67
245	2450	243	238	57	227	177	45	2021	15	61	12	429	2940	298	281	68
250	2500	248	243	58	232	180	46	2063	16	63	13	438	3000	304	287	69
255	2550	253	248	60	237	184	47	2104	16	64	13	446	3060	310	292	71
260	2600	258	253	61	241	188	48	2145	16	65	13	455	3120	316	298	72
265	2650	263	258	62	246	191	49	2186	17	66	13	464	3180	322	304	74
270	2700	267	262	63	251	195	50	2228	17	68	14	473	3240	328	310	75

BW = Body Weight   SED = Sedentary   MOD = Moderately Active   ACT = Active

GOAL: LOSE BODY FAT/INCREASE MUSCLE (BODY FAT UNDER 15%) • Non-Workout (cont.)

BW	Day Carbs	Day Prot	Day Fat	Day Kcal	Night Carbs	Night Prot	Night Fat	Night Kcal	ACT Kcal	Total Carbs	Total Prot	Total Fat	Day Carbs	Day Prot	Day Fat	Day Kcal	Night Carbs	Night Prot	Night Fat	Night Kcal
130	150	117	30	1333	8	33	7	228	2210	231	206	51	223	173	44	1983	8	33	7	228
135	156	121	31	1384	8	34	7	236	2295	240	214	53	232	180	46	2059	8	34	7	236
140	161	126	32	1435	9	35	7	245	2380	249	222	54	240	187	47	2135	9	35	7	245
145	167	130	33	1486	9	36	7	254	2465	258	230	56	249	193	49	2211	9	36	7	254
150	173	135	34	1538	9	38	8	263	2550	267	238	58	257	200	51	2288	9	38	8	263
155	179	139	35	1589	10	39	8	271	2635	276	246	60	266	207	53	2364	10	39	8	271
160	185	144	36	1640	10	40	8	280	2720	285	254	62	275	214	54	2440	10	40	8	280
165	190	148	38	1691	10	41	8	289	2805	293	261	64	283	220	56	2516	10	41	8	289
170	196	152	39	1743	11	43	9	298	2890	302	269	66	292	227	58	2593	11	43	9	298
175	202	157	40	1794	11	44	9	306	2975	311	277	68	300	234	59	2669	11	44	9	306
180	208	161	41	1845	11	45	9	315	3060	320	285	70	309	240	61	2745	11	45	9	315
185	213	166	42	1896	12	46	9	324	3145	329	293	72	317	247	63	2821	12	46	9	324
190	219	170	43	1948	12	48	10	333	3230	338	301	74	326	254	64	2898	12	48	10	333
195	225	175	44	1999	12	49	10	341	3315	347	309	76	335	260	66	2974	12	49	10	341
200	231	179	46	2050	13	50	10	350	3400	356	317	78	343	267	68	3050	13	50	10	350
205	236	184	47	2101	13	51	10	359	3485	365	325	80	352	274	69	3126	13	51	10	359
210	242	188	48	2153	13	53	11	368	3570	373	333	82	360	280	71	3203	13	53	11	368
215	248	193	49	2204	13	54	11	376	3655	382	341	84	369	287	73	3279	13	54	11	376
220	254	197	50	2255	14	55	11	385	3740	391	349	86	377	294	75	3355	14	55	11	385
225	259	202	51	2306	14	56	11	394	3825	400	356	88	386	300	76	3431	14	56	11	394
230	265	206	52	2358	14	58	12	403	3910	409	364	89	395	307	78	3508	14	58	12	403
235	271	211	54	2409	15	59	12	411	3995	418	372	91	403	314	80	3584	15	59	12	411
240	277	215	55	2460	15	60	12	420	4080	427	380	93	412	320	81	3660	15	60	12	420
245	283	220	56	2511	15	61	12	429	4165	436	388	95	420	327	83	3736	15	61	12	429
250	288	224	57	2563	16	63	13	438	4250	445	396	97	429	334	85	3813	16	63	13	438
255	294	229	58	2614	16	64	13	446	4335	453	404	99	437	340	86	3889	16	64	13	446
260	300	233	59	2665	16	65	13	455	4420	462	412	101	446	347	88	3965	16	65	13	455
265	306	238	60	2716	17	66	13	464	4505	471	420	103	455	354	90	4041	17	66	13	464
270	311	242	62	2768	17	68	14	473	4590	480	428	105	463	360	92	4118	17	68	14	473

BW = Body Weight   SED = Sedentary   MOD = Moderately Active   ACT = Active

GOAL: LOSE BODY FAT/INCREASE MUSCLE (BODY FAT OVER 15%) • 60-Minute Workouts

BW	SED Kcal	Total Carbs	Total Prot	Total Fat	Day Carbs	Day Prot	Day Fat	Day Kcal	Night Carbs	Night Prot	Night Fat	Night Kcal	MOD Kcal	Total Carbs	Total Prot	Total Fat
130	1770	182	167	41	174	135	34	1543	8	33	7	228	2030	211	190	47
135	1815	186	172	42	178	138	35	1579	8	34	7	236	2085	216	196	48
140	1860	190	176	43	182	141	36	1615	9	35	7	245	2140	222	201	49
145	1905	195	181	44	186	144	37	1651	9	36	7	254	2195	227	206	50
150	1950	199	185	45	190	148	38	1688	9	38	8	263	2250	233	211	52
155	1995	204	190	46	194	151	38	1724	10	39	8	271	2305	238	217	53
160	2040	208	194	47	198	154	39	1760	10	40	8	280	2360	244	222	54
165	2085	212	198	48	202	157	40	1796	10	41	8	289	2415	250	227	56
170	2130	217	203	49	206	160	41	1833	11	43	9	298	2470	255	233	57
175	2175	221	207	50	210	164	42	1869	11	44	9	306	2525	261	238	58
180	2220	226	212	51	214	167	42	1905	11	45	9	315	2580	266	243	59
185	2265	230	216	52	218	170	43	1941	12	46	9	324	2635	272	248	61
190	2310	234	221	53	222	173	44	1978	12	48	10	333	2690	277	254	62
195	2355	239	225	55	227	176	45	2014	12	49	10	341	2745	283	259	63
200	2400	243	229	56	231	179	46	2050	13	50	10	350	2800	288	264	64
205	2445	248	234	57	235	183	46	2086	13	51	10	359	2855	294	270	66
210	2490	252	238	58	239	186	47	2123	13	53	11	368	2910	299	275	67
215	2535	256	243	59	243	189	48	2159	13	54	11	376	2965	305	280	68
220	2580	261	247	60	247	192	49	2195	14	55	11	385	3020	310	286	70
225	2625	265	251	61	251	195	50	2231	14	56	11	394	3075	316	291	71
230	2670	269	256	62	255	198	50	2268	14	58	12	403	3130	321	296	72
235	2715	274	260	63	259	202	51	2304	15	59	12	411	3185	327	301	73
240	2760	278	265	64	263	205	52	2340	15	60	12	420	3240	332	307	75
245	2805	283	269	65	267	208	53	2376	15	61	12	429	3295	338	312	76
250	2850	287	274	66	271	211	54	2413	16	63	13	438	3350	343	317	77
255	2895	291	278	67	275	214	54	2449	16	64	13	446	3405	349	323	79
260	2940	296	282	68	280	217	55	2485	16	65	13	455	3460	354	328	80
265	2985	300	287	69	284	221	56	2521	17	66	13	464	3515	360	333	81
270	3030	305	291	70	288	224	57	2558	17	68	14	473	3570	365	339	82

BW = Body Weight   SED = Sedentary   MOD = Moderately Active   ACT = Active

GOAL: LOSE BODY FAT/INCREASE MUSCLE (BODY FAT OVER 15%) • 60-Minute Workouts (cont.)

BW	Day Carbs	Day Prot	Day Fat	Day Kcal	Night Carbs	Night Prot	Night Fat	Night Kcal	ACT Kcal	Total Carbs	Total Prot	Total Fat	Day Carbs	Day Prot	Day Fat	Day Kcal	Night Carbs	Night Prot	Night Fat	Night Kcal
130	203	158	40	1803	8	33	7	228	2680	284	247	61	276	215	55	2453	8	33	7	228
135	208	162	41	1849	8	34	7	236	2760	292	255	63	284	221	56	2524	8	34	7	236
140	213	166	42	1895	9	35	7	245	2840	301	262	65	292	227	58	2595	9	35	7	245
145	218	170	43	1941	9	36	7	254	2920	309	270	67	300	233	59	2666	9	36	7	254
150	224	174	44	1988	9	38	8	263	3000	317	277	68	308	240	61	2738	9	38	8	263
155	229	178	45	2034	10	39	8	271	3080	326	285	70	316	246	62	2809	10	39	8	271
160	234	182	46	2080	10	40	8	280	3160	334	292	72	324	252	64	2880	10	40	8	280
165	239	186	47	2126	10	41	8	289	3240	342	299	74	332	258	66	2951	10	41	8	289
170	244	190	48	2173	11	43	9	298	3320	351	307	76	340	264	67	3023	11	43	9	298
175	250	194	49	2219	11	44	9	306	3400	359	314	78	348	271	69	3094	11	44	9	306
180	255	198	50	2265	11	45	9	315	3480	367	322	79	356	277	70	3165	11	45	9	315
185	260	202	51	2311	12	46	9	324	3560	376	329	81	364	283	72	3236	12	46	9	324
190	265	206	52	2358	12	48	10	333	3640	384	337	83	372	289	74	3308	12	48	10	333
195	270	210	53	2404	12	49	10	341	3720	392	344	85	380	296	75	3379	12	49	10	341
200	276	214	54	2450	13	50	10	350	3800	401	352	87	388	302	77	3450	13	50	10	350
205	281	218	55	2496	13	51	10	359	3880	409	359	89	396	308	78	3521	13	51	10	359
210	286	222	57	2543	13	53	11	368	3960	417	367	90	404	314	80	3593	13	53	11	368
215	291	227	58	2589	13	54	11	376	4040	426	374	92	412	321	81	3664	13	54	11	376
220	296	231	59	2635	14	55	11	385	4120	434	382	94	420	327	83	3735	14	55	11	385
225	302	235	60	2681	14	56	11	394	4200	442	389	96	428	333	85	3806	14	56	11	394
230	307	239	61	2728	14	58	12	403	4280	451	397	98	436	339	86	3878	14	58	12	403
235	312	243	62	2774	15	59	12	411	4360	459	404	100	444	346	88	3949	15	59	12	411
240	317	247	63	2820	15	60	12	420	4440	467	412	101	452	352	89	4020	15	60	12	420
245	322	251	64	2866	15	61	12	429	4520	476	419	103	460	358	91	4091	15	61	12	429
250	328	255	65	2913	16	63	13	438	4600	484	427	105	468	364	93	4163	16	63	13	438
255	333	259	66	2959	16	64	13	446	4680	492	434	107	476	370	94	4234	16	64	13	446
260	338	263	67	3005	16	65	13	455	4760	501	442	109	484	377	96	4305	16	65	13	455
265	343	267	68	3051	17	66	13	464	4840	509	449	111	492	383	97	4376	17	66	13	464
270	348	271	69	3098	17	68	14	473	4920	517	457	112	500	389	99	4448	17	68	14	473

BW = Body Weight   SED = Sedentary   MOD = Moderately Active   ACT = Active

GOAL: LOSE BODY FAT/INCREASE MUSCLE (BODY FAT OVER 15%) • 90-Minute Workouts

BW	SED Kcal	Total Carbs	Total Prot	Total Fat	Day Carbs	Day Prot	Day Fat	Day Kcal	Night Carbs	Night Prot	Night Fat	Night Kcal	MOD Kcal	Total Carbs	Total Prot	Total Fat
130	2070	215	194	47	207	161	41	1843	8	33	7	228	2330	245	216	53
135	2115	220	198	49	211	164	42	1879	8	34	7	236	2385	250	222	55
140	2160	224	203	50	215	168	43	1915	9	35	7	245	2440	256	227	56
145	2205	229	207	51	220	171	43	1951	9	36	7	254	2495	261	232	57
150	2250	233	211	52	224	174	44	1988	9	38	8	263	2550	267	238	58
155	2295	237	216	53	228	177	45	2024	10	39	8	271	2605	272	243	60
160	2340	242	220	54	232	180	46	2060	10	40	8	280	2660	278	248	61
165	2385	246	225	55	236	183	47	2096	10	41	8	289	2715	283	254	62
170	2430	251	229	56	240	187	47	2133	11	43	9	298	2770	289	259	63
175	2475	255	234	57	244	190	48	2169	11	44	9	306	2825	294	264	65
180	2520	259	238	58	248	193	49	2205	11	45	9	315	2880	300	269	66
185	2565	264	242	59	252	196	50	2241	12	46	9	324	2935	305	275	67
190	2610	268	247	60	256	199	51	2278	12	48	10	333	2990	311	280	69
195	2655	272	251	61	260	202	51	2314	12	49	10	341	3045	316	285	70
200	2700	277	256	62	264	206	52	2350	13	50	10	350	3100	322	291	71
205	2745	281	260	63	268	209	53	2386	13	51	10	359	3155	327	296	72
210	2790	286	264	64	273	212	54	2423	13	53	11	368	3210	333	301	74
215	2835	290	269	65	277	215	55	2459	13	54	11	376	3265	338	307	75
220	2880	294	273	66	281	218	55	2495	14	55	11	385	3320	344	312	76
225	2925	299	278	68	285	221	56	2531	14	56	11	394	3375	349	317	78
230	2970	303	282	69	289	225	57	2568	14	58	12	403	3430	355	322	79
235	3015	308	287	70	293	228	58	2604	15	59	12	411	3485	360	328	80
240	3060	312	291	71	297	231	59	2640	15	60	12	420	3540	366	333	81
245	3105	316	295	72	301	234	59	2676	15	61	12	429	3595	372	338	83
250	3150	321	300	73	305	237	60	2713	16	63	13	438	3650	377	344	84
255	3195	325	304	74	309	241	61	2749	16	64	13	446	3705	383	349	85
260	3240	330	309	75	313	244	62	2785	16	65	13	455	3760	388	354	86
265	3285	334	313	76	317	247	63	2821	17	66	13	464	3815	394	359	88
270	3330	338	318	77	321	250	64	2858	17	68	14	473	3870	399	365	89

BW = Body Weight   SED = Sedentary   MOD = Moderately Active   ACT = Active

GOAL: LOSE BODY FAT/INCREASE MUSCLE (BODY FAT OVER 15%) • 90-Minute Workouts (cont.)

BW	Day Carbs	Day Prot	Day Fat	Day Kcal	Night Carbs	Night Prot	Night Fat	Night Kcal	ACT Kcal	Total Carbs	Total Prot	Total Fat	Day Carbs	Day Prot	Day Fat	Day Kcal	Night Carbs	Night Prot	Night Fat	Night Kcal
130	237	184	47	2103	8	33	7	228	2980	318	273	68	310	241	61	2753	8	33	7	228
135	242	188	48	2149	8	34	7	236	3060	326	281	70	318	247	63	2824	8	34	7	236
140	247	192	49	2195	9	35	7	245	3140	334	288	71	326	253	64	2895	9	35	7	245
145	252	196	50	2241	9	36	7	254	3220	343	296	73	334	260	66	2966	9	36	7	254
150	257	200	51	2288	9	38	8	263	3300	351	303	75	342	266	68	3038	9	38	8	263
155	263	204	52	2334	10	39	8	271	3380	359	311	77	350	272	69	3109	10	39	8	271
160	268	208	53	2380	10	40	8	280	3460	368	318	79	358	278	71	3180	10	40	8	280
165	273	212	54	2426	10	41	8	289	3540	376	326	81	366	284	72	3251	10	41	8	289
170	278	216	55	2473	11	43	9	298	3620	384	333	82	374	291	74	3323	11	43	9	298
175	283	220	56	2519	11	44	9	306	3700	393	341	84	382	297	75	3394	11	44	9	306
180	289	224	57	2565	11	45	9	315	3780	401	348	86	390	303	77	3465	11	45	9	315
185	294	228	58	2611	12	46	9	324	3860	409	356	88	398	309	79	3536	12	46	9	324
190	299	233	59	2658	12	48	10	333	3940	418	363	90	406	316	80	3608	12	48	10	333
195	304	237	60	2704	12	49	10	341	4020	426	371	92	414	322	82	3679	12	49	10	341
200	309	241	61	2750	13	50	10	350	4100	434	378	93	422	328	83	3750	13	50	10	350
205	315	245	62	2796	13	51	10	359	4180	443	386	95	430	334	85	3821	13	51	10	359
210	320	249	63	2843	13	53	11	368	4260	451	393	97	438	341	87	3893	13	53	11	368
215	325	253	64	2889	13	54	11	376	4340	459	401	99	446	347	88	3964	13	54	11	376
220	330	257	65	2935	14	55	11	385	4420	468	408	101	454	353	90	4035	14	55	11	385
225	335	261	66	2981	14	56	11	394	4500	476	416	103	462	359	91	4106	14	56	11	394
230	341	265	67	3028	14	58	12	403	4580	484	423	104	470	366	93	4178	14	58	12	403
235	346	269	68	3074	15	59	12	411	4660	493	431	106	478	372	94	4249	15	59	12	411
240	351	273	69	3120	15	60	12	420	4740	501	438	108	486	378	96	4320	15	60	12	420
245	356	277	70	3166	15	61	12	429	4820	509	445	110	494	384	98	4391	15	61	12	429
250	361	281	71	3213	16	63	13	438	4900	518	453	112	502	390	99	4463	16	63	13	438
255	367	285	72	3259	16	64	13	446	4980	526	460	114	510	397	101	4534	16	64	13	446
260	372	289	73	3305	16	65	13	455	5060	534	468	115	518	403	102	4605	16	65	13	455
265	377	293	74	3351	17	66	13	464	5140	543	475	117	526	409	104	4676	17	66	13	464
270	382	297	76	3398	17	68	14	473	5220	551	483	119	534	415	106	4748	17	68	14	473

BW = Body Weight   SED = Sedentary   MOD = Moderately Active   ACT = Active

GOAL: LOSE BODY FAT/INCREASE MUSCLE (BODY FAT OVER 15%) • Non-Workout

BW	SED Kcal	Total Carbs	Total Prot	Total Fat	Day Carbs	Day Prot	Day Fat	Day Kcal	Night Carbs	Night Prot	Night Fat	Night Kcal	MOD Kcal	Total Carbs	Total Prot	Total Fat
130	1170	114	115	27	106	82	21	943	8	33	7	228	1430	143	138	33
135	1215	119	119	29	110	86	22	979	8	34	7	236	1485	149	143	35
140	1260	123	124	30	114	89	23	1015	9	35	7	245	1540	154	148	36
145	1305	127	128	31	118	92	23	1051	9	36	7	254	1595	160	154	37
150	1350	132	133	32	122	95	24	1088	9	38	8	263	1650	165	159	38
155	1395	136	137	33	126	98	25	1124	10	39	8	271	1705	171	164	40
160	1440	141	142	34	131	102	26	1160	10	40	8	280	1760	177	170	41
165	1485	145	146	35	135	105	27	1196	10	41	8	289	1815	182	175	42
170	1530	149	150	36	139	108	27	1233	11	43	9	298	1870	188	180	43
175	1575	154	155	37	143	111	28	1269	11	44	9	306	1925	193	185	45
180	1620	158	159	38	147	114	29	1305	11	45	9	315	1980	199	191	46
185	1665	162	164	39	151	117	30	1341	12	46	9	324	2035	204	196	47
190	1710	167	168	40	155	121	31	1378	12	48	10	333	2090	210	201	49
195	1755	171	172	41	159	124	31	1414	12	49	10	341	2145	215	207	50
200	1800	176	177	42	163	127	32	1450	13	50	10	350	2200	221	212	51
205	1845	180	181	43	167	130	33	1486	13	51	10	359	2255	226	217	52
210	1890	184	186	44	171	133	34	1523	13	53	11	368	2310	232	222	54
215	1935	189	190	45	175	136	35	1559	13	54	11	376	2365	237	228	55
220	1980	193	195	46	179	140	35	1595	14	55	11	385	2420	243	233	56
225	2025	198	199	48	184	143	36	1631	14	56	11	394	2475	248	238	58
230	2070	202	203	49	188	146	37	1668	14	58	12	403	2530	254	244	59
235	2115	206	208	50	192	149	38	1704	15	59	12	411	2585	259	249	60
240	2160	211	212	51	196	152	39	1740	15	60	12	420	2640	265	254	61
245	2205	215	217	52	200	155	39	1776	15	61	12	429	2695	270	260	63
250	2250	220	221	53	204	159	40	1813	16	63	13	438	2750	276	265	64
255	2295	224	226	54	208	162	41	1849	16	64	13	446	2805	281	270	65
260	2340	228	230	55	212	165	42	1885	16	65	13	455	2860	287	275	66
265	2385	233	234	56	216	168	43	1921	17	66	13	464	2915	292	281	68
270	2430	237	239	57	220	171	44	1958	17	68	14	473	2970	298	286	69

BW = Body Weight   SED = Sedentary   MOD = Moderately Active   ACT = Active

GOAL: LOSE BODY FAT/INCREASE MUSCLE (BODY FAT OVER 15%) • Non-Workout (cont.)

BW	Day Carbs	Day Prot	Day Fat	Day Kcal	Night Carbs	Night Prot	Night Fat	Night Kcal	ACT Kcal	Total Carbs	Total Prot	Total Fat	Day Carbs	Day Prot	Day Fat	Day Kcal	Night Carbs	Night Prot	Night Fat	Night Kcal
130	135	105	27	1203	8	33	7	228	2080	217	195	48	208	162	41	1853	8	33	7	228
135	140	109	28	1249	8	34	7	236	2160	225	202	50	216	168	43	1924	8	34	7	236
140	146	113	29	1295	9	35	7	245	2240	233	210	51	224	175	44	1995	9	35	7	245
145	151	117	30	1341	9	36	7	254	2320	242	217	53	232	181	46	2066	9	36	7	254
150	156	121	31	1388	9	38	8	263	2400	250	225	55	240	187	48	2138	9	38	8	263
155	161	125	32	1434	10	39	8	271	2480	258	232	57	248	193	49	2209	10	39	8	271
160	167	130	33	1480	10	40	8	280	2560	267	240	59	257	200	51	2280	10	40	8	280
165	172	134	34	1526	10	41	8	289	2640	275	247	61	265	206	52	2351	10	41	8	289
170	177	138	35	1573	11	43	9	298	2720	283	254	62	273	212	54	2423	11	43	9	298
175	182	142	36	1619	11	44	9	306	2800	291	262	64	281	218	55	2494	11	44	9	306
180	187	146	37	1665	11	45	9	315	2880	300	269	66	289	224	57	2565	11	45	9	315
185	193	150	38	1711	12	46	9	324	2960	308	277	68	297	231	59	2636	12	46	9	324
190	198	154	39	1758	12	48	10	333	3040	316	284	70	305	237	60	2708	12	48	10	333
195	203	158	40	1804	12	49	10	341	3120	325	292	72	313	243	62	2779	12	49	10	341
200	208	162	41	1850	13	50	10	350	3200	333	299	73	321	249	63	2850	13	50	10	350
205	213	166	42	1896	13	51	10	359	3280	341	307	75	329	256	65	2921	13	51	10	359
210	219	170	43	1943	13	53	11	368	3360	350	314	77	337	262	67	2993	13	53	11	368
215	224	174	44	1989	14	54	11	376	3440	358	322	79	345	268	68	3064	14	54	11	376
220	229	178	45	2035	14	55	11	385	3520	366	329	81	353	274	70	3135	14	55	11	385
225	234	182	46	2081	14	56	11	394	3600	375	337	83	361	281	71	3206	14	56	11	394
230	239	186	47	2128	15	58	12	403	3680	383	344	84	369	287	73	3278	15	58	12	403
235	245	190	48	2174	15	59	12	411	3760	391	352	86	377	293	74	3349	15	59	12	411
240	250	194	49	2220	15	60	12	420	3840	400	359	88	385	299	76	3420	15	60	12	420
245	255	198	50	2266	16	61	12	429	3920	408	367	90	393	305	78	3491	16	61	12	429
250	260	202	51	2313	16	63	13	438	4000	416	374	92	401	312	79	3563	16	63	13	438
255	265	206	52	2359	16	64	13	446	4080	425	382	94	409	318	81	3634	16	64	13	446
260	271	210	53	2405	17	65	13	455	4160	433	389	95	417	324	82	3705	17	65	13	455
265	276	214	54	2451	17	66	13	464	4240	441	397	97	425	330	84	3776	17	66	13	464
270	281	219	56	2498	17	68	14	473	4320	450	404	99	433	337	86	3848	17	68	14	473

BW = Body Weight   SED = Sedentary   MOD = Moderately Active   ACT = Active

GOAL: MAINTAIN BODY FAT/INCREASE MUSCLE • 60-Minute Workouts

BW	SED Kcal	Total Carbs	Total Prot	Total Fat	Day Carbs	Day Prot	Day Fat	Day Kcal	Night Carbs	Night Prot	Night Fat	Night Kcal	MOD Kcal	Total Carbs	Total Prot	Total Fat
130	2290	240	213	52	232	180	46	2063	8	33	7	228	2550	269	236	58
135	2355	247	219	54	238	185	47	2119	8	34	7	236	2625	277	243	60
140	2420	253	225	55	245	190	48	2175	9	35	7	245	2700	285	250	62
145	2485	260	231	57	251	195	50	2231	9	36	7	254	2775	293	257	63
150	2550	267	238	58	257	200	51	2288	9	38	8	263	2850	300	264	65
155	2615	273	244	60	264	205	52	2344	10	39	8	271	2925	308	271	67
160	2680	280	250	61	270	210	53	2400	10	40	8	280	3000	316	278	68
165	2745	287	256	63	276	215	55	2456	10	41	8	289	3075	324	285	70
170	2810	293	262	64	283	220	56	2513	11	43	9	298	3150	332	292	72
175	2875	300	269	66	289	225	57	2569	11	44	9	306	3225	339	299	74
180	2940	307	275	67	295	230	58	2625	11	45	9	315	3300	347	306	75
185	3005	313	281	69	302	235	60	2681	12	46	9	324	3375	355	313	77
190	3070	320	287	70	308	240	61	2738	12	48	10	333	3450	363	320	79
195	3135	326	293	72	314	244	62	2794	12	49	10	341	3525	370	327	81
200	3200	333	299	73	321	249	63	2850	13	50	10	350	3600	378	334	82
205	3265	340	306	75	327	254	65	2906	13	51	10	359	3675	386	341	84
210	3330	346	312	76	333	259	66	2963	13	53	11	368	3750	394	348	86
215	3395	353	318	78	340	264	67	3019	13	54	11	376	3825	401	356	87
220	3460	360	324	79	346	269	68	3075	14	55	11	385	3900	409	363	89
225	3525	366	330	81	352	274	70	3131	14	56	11	394	3975	417	370	91
230	3590	373	336	82	359	279	71	3188	14	58	12	403	4050	425	377	93
235	3655	380	343	84	365	284	72	3244	15	59	12	411	4125	432	384	94
240	3720	386	349	85	371	289	73	3300	15	60	12	420	4200	440	391	96
245	3785	393	355	87	378	294	75	3356	15	61	12	429	4275	448	398	98
250	3850	400	361	88	384	299	76	3413	16	63	13	438	4350	456	405	99
255	3915	406	367	90	390	304	77	3469	16	64	13	446	4425	464	412	101
260	3980	413	373	91	397	308	78	3525	16	65	13	455	4500	471	419	103
265	4045	419	380	93	403	313	80	3581	17	66	13	464	4575	479	426	105
270	4110	426	386	94	409	318	81	3638	17	68	14	473	4650	487	433	106

BW = Body Weight   SED = Sedentary   MOD = Moderately Active   ACT = Active

GOAL: MAINTAIN BODY FAT/INCREASE MUSCLE • 60-Minute Workouts (cont.)

BW	Day Carbs	Day Prot	Day Fat	Day Kcal	Night Carbs	Night Prot	Night Fat	Night Kcal	ACT Kcal	Total Carbs	Total Prot	Total Fat	Day Carbs	Day Prot	Day Fat	Day Kcal	Night Carbs	Night Prot	Night Fat	Night Kcal
130	261	203	52	2323	8	33	7	228	3200	343	293	73	334	260	66	2973	8	33	7	228
135	269	209	53	2389	8	34	7	236	3300	353	302	75	345	268	68	3064	8	34	7	236
140	276	215	55	2455	9	35	7	245	3400	364	311	77	355	276	70	3155	9	35	7	245
145	284	221	56	2521	9	36	7	254	3500	374	320	79	365	284	72	3246	9	36	7	254
150	291	226	58	2588	9	38	8	263	3600	385	330	82	375	292	74	3338	9	38	8	263
155	299	232	59	2654	10	39	8	271	3700	395	339	84	386	300	76	3429	10	39	8	271
160	306	238	60	2720	10	40	8	280	3800	406	348	86	396	308	78	3520	10	40	8	280
165	313	244	62	2786	10	41	8	289	3900	417	357	89	406	316	80	3611	10	41	8	289
170	321	250	63	2853	11	43	9	298	4000	427	366	91	417	324	82	3703	11	43	9	298
175	328	255	65	2919	11	44	9	306	4100	438	376	93	427	332	84	3794	11	44	9	306
180	336	261	66	2985	11	45	9	315	4200	448	385	95	437	340	86	3885	11	45	9	315
185	343	267	68	3051	12	46	9	324	4300	459	394	98	447	348	88	3976	12	46	9	324
190	351	273	69	3118	12	48	10	333	4400	469	403	100	458	356	90	4068	12	48	10	333
195	358	279	71	3184	12	49	10	341	4500	480	413	102	468	364	92	4159	12	49	10	341
200	366	284	72	3250	13	50	10	350	4600	491	422	104	478	372	94	4250	13	50	10	350
205	373	290	74	3316	13	51	10	359	4700	501	431	107	488	380	96	4341	13	51	10	359
210	381	296	75	3383	13	53	11	368	4800	512	440	109	499	388	99	4433	13	53	11	368
215	388	302	77	3449	13	54	11	376	4900	522	450	111	509	396	101	4524	13	54	11	376
220	395	308	78	3515	14	55	11	385	5000	533	459	114	519	404	103	4615	14	55	11	385
225	403	313	80	3581	14	56	11	394	5100	544	468	116	529	412	105	4706	14	56	11	394
230	410	319	81	3648	14	58	12	403	5200	554	477	118	540	420	107	4798	14	58	12	403
235	418	325	83	3714	15	59	12	411	5300	565	487	120	550	428	109	4889	15	59	12	411
240	425	331	84	3780	15	60	12	420	5400	575	496	123	560	436	111	4980	15	60	12	420
245	433	337	85	3846	15	61	12	429	5500	586	505	125	571	444	113	5071	15	61	12	429
250	440	342	87	3913	16	63	13	438	5600	596	514	127	581	452	115	5163	16	63	13	438
255	448	348	88	3979	16	64	13	446	5700	607	523	130	591	460	117	5254	16	64	13	446
260	455	354	90	4045	16	65	13	455	5800	618	533	132	601	468	119	5345	16	65	13	455
265	463	360	91	4111	17	66	13	464	5900	628	542	134	612	476	121	5436	17	66	13	464
270	470	366	93	4178	17	68	14	473	6000	639	551	136	622	484	123	5528	17	68	14	473

BW = Body Weight   SED = Sedentary   MOD = Moderately Active   ACT = Active

GOAL: MAINTAIN BODY FAT/INCREASE MUSCLE • 90-Minute Workouts

BW	SED Kcal	Total Carbs	Total Prot	Total Fat	Day Carbs	Day Prot	Day Fat	Day Kcal	Night Carbs	Night Prot	Night Fat	Night Kcal	MOD Kcal	Total Carbs	Total Prot	Total Fat
130	2590	274	239	59	266	207	53	2363	8	33	7	228	2850	303	262	65
135	2655	281	245	61	272	212	54	2419	8	34	7	236	2925	311	269	67
140	2720	287	252	62	278	217	55	2475	9	35	7	245	3000	319	276	68
145	2785	294	258	64	285	221	56	2531	9	36	7	254	3075	326	283	70
150	2850	300	264	65	291	226	58	2588	9	38	8	263	3150	334	290	72
155	2915	307	270	67	297	231	59	2644	10	39	8	271	3225	342	297	73
160	2980	314	276	68	304	236	60	2700	10	40	8	280	3300	350	304	75
165	3045	320	282	70	310	241	61	2756	10	41	8	289	3375	358	311	77
170	3110	327	289	71	316	246	63	2813	11	43	9	298	3450	365	318	79
175	3175	334	295	73	323	251	64	2869	11	44	9	306	3525	373	325	80
180	3240	340	301	74	329	256	65	2925	11	45	9	315	3600	381	332	82
185	3305	347	307	76	335	261	66	2981	12	46	9	324	3675	389	339	84
190	3370	354	313	77	342	266	68	3038	12	48	10	333	3750	396	347	85
195	3435	360	319	79	348	271	69	3094	12	49	10	341	3825	404	354	87
200	3500	367	326	80	354	276	70	3150	13	50	10	350	3900	412	361	89
205	3565	374	332	82	361	281	71	3206	13	51	10	359	3975	420	368	91
210	3630	380	338	83	367	285	73	3263	13	53	11	368	4050	427	375	92
215	3695	387	344	85	373	290	74	3319	13	54	11	376	4125	435	382	94
220	3760	393	350	86	380	295	75	3375	14	55	11	385	4200	443	389	96
225	3825	400	356	88	386	300	76	3431	14	56	11	394	4275	451	396	98
230	3890	407	363	89	392	305	78	3488	14	58	12	403	4350	458	403	99
235	3955	413	369	91	399	310	79	3544	15	59	12	411	4425	466	410	101
240	4020	420	375	92	405	315	80	3600	15	60	12	420	4500	474	417	103
245	4085	427	381	94	411	320	81	3656	15	61	12	429	4575	482	424	104
250	4150	433	387	95	418	325	83	3713	16	63	13	438	4650	490	431	106
255	4215	440	394	97	424	330	84	3769	16	64	13	446	4725	497	438	108
260	4280	447	400	98	430	335	85	3825	16	65	13	455	4800	505	445	110
265	4345	453	406	100	437	340	86	3881	17	66	13	464	4875	513	452	111
270	4410	460	412	101	443	345	88	3938	17	68	14	473	4950	521	459	113

BW = Body Weight   SED = Sedentary   MOD = Moderately Active   ACT = Active

GOAL: MAINTAIN BODY FAT/INCREASE MUSCLE • 90-Minute Workouts (cont.)

BW	Day Carbs	Day Prot	Day Fat	Day Kcal	Night Carbs	Night Prot	Night Fat	Night Kcal	ACT Total Kcal	Total Carbs	Total Prot	Total Fat	Day Carbs	Day Prot	Day Fat	Day Kcal	Night Carbs	Night Prot	Night Fat	Night Kcal
130	295	229	58	2623	8	33	7	228	3500	376	319	79	368	286	73	3273	8	33	7	228
135	302	235	60	2689	8	34	7	236	3600	387	328	82	378	294	75	3364	8	34	7	236
140	310	241	61	2755	9	35	7	245	3700	397	337	84	389	302	77	3455	9	35	7	245
145	317	247	63	2821	9	36	7	254	3800	408	347	86	399	310	79	3546	9	36	7	254
150	325	253	64	2888	9	38	8	263	3900	419	356	88	409	318	81	3638	9	38	8	263
155	332	258	66	2954	10	39	8	271	4000	429	365	91	419	326	83	3729	10	39	8	271
160	340	264	67	3020	10	40	8	280	4100	440	374	93	430	334	85	3820	10	40	8	280
165	347	270	69	3086	10	41	8	289	4200	450	383	95	440	342	87	3911	10	41	8	289
170	355	276	70	3153	11	43	9	298	4300	461	393	97	450	350	89	4003	11	43	9	298
175	362	282	72	3219	11	44	9	306	4400	471	402	100	461	358	91	4094	11	44	9	306
180	370	287	73	3285	11	45	9	315	4500	482	411	102	471	366	93	4185	11	45	9	315
185	377	293	74	3351	12	46	9	324	4600	493	420	104	481	374	95	4276	12	46	9	324
190	384	299	76	3418	12	48	10	333	4700	503	430	107	491	382	97	4368	12	48	10	333
195	392	305	77	3484	12	49	10	341	4800	514	439	109	502	390	99	4459	12	49	10	341
200	399	311	79	3550	13	50	10	350	4900	524	448	111	512	398	101	4550	13	50	10	350
205	407	316	80	3616	13	51	10	359	5000	535	457	113	522	406	103	4641	13	51	10	359
210	414	322	82	3683	13	53	11	368	5100	546	467	116	532	414	105	4733	13	53	11	368
215	422	328	83	3749	13	54	11	376	5200	556	476	118	543	422	107	4824	13	54	11	376
220	429	334	85	3815	14	55	11	385	5300	567	485	120	553	430	109	4915	14	55	11	385
225	437	340	86	3881	14	56	11	394	5400	577	494	123	563	438	111	5006	14	56	11	394
230	444	345	88	3948	14	58	12	403	5500	588	504	125	573	446	113	5098	14	58	12	403
235	452	351	89	4014	15	59	12	411	5600	598	513	127	584	454	115	5189	15	59	12	411
240	459	357	91	4080	15	60	12	420	5700	609	522	129	594	462	117	5280	15	60	12	420
245	466	363	92	4146	15	61	12	429	5800	620	531	132	604	470	119	5371	15	61	12	429
250	474	369	94	4213	16	63	13	438	5900	630	540	134	615	478	121	5463	16	63	13	438
255	481	374	95	4279	16	64	13	446	6000	641	550	136	625	486	123	5554	16	64	13	446
260	489	380	97	4345	16	65	13	455	6100	651	559	138	635	494	125	5645	16	65	13	455
265	496	386	98	4411	17	66	13	464	6200	662	568	141	645	502	127	5736	17	66	13	464
270	504	392	100	4478	17	68	14	473	6300	672	577	143	656	510	130	5828	17	68	14	473

BW = Body Weight   SED = Sedentary   MOD = Moderately Active   ACT = Active

GOAL: MAINTAIN BODY FAT/INCREASE MUSCLE • Non-Workout

BW	SED Kcal	Total Carbs	Total Prot	Total Fat	Day Carbs	Day Prot	Day Fat	Day Kcal	Night Carbs	Night Prot	Night Fat	Night Kcal	MOD Kcal	Total Carbs	Total Prot	Total Fat
130	1690	173	160	39	165	128	33	1463	8	33	7	228	1950	202	183	45
135	1755	179	167	41	171	133	34	1519	8	34	7	236	2025	210	190	47
140	1820	186	173	42	177	138	35	1575	9	35	7	245	2100	217	197	48
145	1885	193	179	44	184	143	36	1631	9	36	7	254	2175	225	204	50
150	1950	199	185	45	190	148	38	1688	9	38	8	263	2250	233	211	52
155	2015	206	191	47	196	153	39	1744	10	39	8	271	2325	241	218	53
160	2080	213	198	48	203	158	40	1800	10	40	8	280	2400	249	226	55
165	2145	219	204	50	209	162	41	1856	10	41	8	289	2475	256	233	57
170	2210	226	210	51	215	167	43	1913	11	43	9	298	2550	264	240	59
175	2275	232	216	53	221	172	44	1969	11	44	9	306	2625	272	247	60
180	2340	239	222	54	228	177	45	2025	11	45	9	315	2700	280	254	62
185	2405	246	228	56	234	182	46	2081	12	46	9	324	2775	287	261	64
190	2470	252	235	57	240	187	48	2138	12	48	10	333	2850	295	268	65
195	2535	259	241	59	247	192	49	2194	12	49	10	341	2925	303	275	67
200	2600	266	247	60	253	197	50	2250	13	50	10	350	3000	311	282	69
205	2665	272	253	62	259	202	51	2306	13	51	10	359	3075	318	289	71
210	2730	279	259	63	266	207	53	2363	13	53	11	368	3150	326	296	72
215	2795	286	265	65	272	212	54	2419	13	54	11	376	3225	334	303	74
220	2860	292	272	66	278	217	55	2475	14	55	11	385	3300	342	310	76
225	2925	299	278	68	285	221	56	2531	14	56	11	394	3375	349	317	78
230	2990	305	284	69	291	226	58	2588	14	58	12	403	3450	357	324	79
235	3055	312	290	71	297	231	59	2644	15	59	12	411	3525	365	331	81
240	3120	319	296	72	304	236	60	2700	15	60	12	420	3600	373	338	83
245	3185	325	302	74	310	241	61	2756	15	61	12	429	3675	381	345	84
250	3250	332	309	75	316	246	63	2813	16	63	13	438	3750	388	352	86
255	3315	339	315	77	323	251	64	2869	16	64	13	446	3825	396	359	88
260	3380	345	321	78	329	256	65	2925	16	65	13	455	3900	404	366	90
265	3445	352	327	80	335	261	66	2981	17	66	13	464	3975	412	373	91
270	3510	359	333	81	342	266	68	3038	17	68	14	473	4050	419	381	93

BW = Body Weight   SED = Sedentary   MOD = Moderately Active   ACT = Active

GOAL: MAINTAIN BODY FAT/INCREASE MUSCLE • Non-Workout (cont.)

BW	Day Carbs	Day Prot	Day Fat	Day Kcal	Night Carbs	Night Prot	Night Fat	Night Kcal	ACT Kcal	Total Carbs	Total Prot	Total Fat	Day Carbs	Day Prot	Day Fat	Day Kcal	Night Carbs	Night Prot	Night Fat	Night Kcal
130	194	151	38	1723	8	33	7	228	2600	275	240	59	267	208	53	2373	8	33	7	228
135	201	157	40	1789	8	34	7	236	2700	286	249	62	277	216	55	2464	8	34	7	236
140	209	162	41	1855	9	35	7	245	2800	296	259	64	287	224	57	2555	9	35	7	245
145	216	168	43	1921	9	36	7	254	2900	307	268	66	298	232	59	2646	9	36	7	254
150	224	174	44	1988	9	38	8	263	3000	317	277	68	308	240	61	2738	9	38	8	263
155	231	180	46	2054	10	39	8	271	3100	328	286	71	318	248	63	2829	10	39	8	271
160	239	186	47	2120	10	40	8	280	3200	339	296	73	329	256	65	2920	10	40	8	280
165	246	191	49	2186	10	41	8	289	3300	349	305	75	339	263	67	3011	10	41	8	289
170	253	197	50	2253	11	43	9	298	3400	360	314	77	349	271	69	3103	11	43	9	298
175	261	203	52	2319	11	44	9	306	3500	370	323	80	359	279	71	3194	11	44	9	306
180	268	209	53	2385	11	45	9	315	3600	381	332	82	370	287	73	3285	11	45	9	315
185	276	214	54	2451	12	46	9	324	3700	391	342	84	380	295	75	3376	12	46	9	324
190	283	220	56	2518	12	48	10	333	3800	402	351	87	390	303	77	3468	12	48	10	333
195	291	226	57	2584	12	49	10	341	3900	413	360	89	400	311	79	3559	12	49	10	341
200	298	232	59	2650	13	50	10	350	4000	423	369	91	411	319	81	3650	13	50	10	350
205	306	238	60	2716	13	51	10	359	4100	434	379	93	421	327	83	3741	13	51	10	359
210	313	243	62	2783	13	53	11	368	4200	444	388	96	431	335	85	3833	13	53	11	368
215	320	249	63	2849	13	54	11	376	4300	455	397	98	441	343	87	3924	13	54	11	376
220	328	255	65	2915	14	55	11	385	4400	465	406	100	452	351	89	4015	14	55	11	385
225	335	261	66	2981	14	56	11	394	4500	476	416	103	462	359	91	4106	14	56	11	394
230	343	267	68	3048	14	58	12	403	4600	487	425	105	472	367	93	4198	14	58	12	403
235	350	272	69	3114	15	59	12	411	4700	497	434	107	482	375	95	4289	15	59	12	411
240	358	278	71	3180	15	60	12	420	4800	508	443	109	493	383	97	4380	15	60	12	420
245	365	284	72	3246	15	61	12	429	4900	518	452	112	503	391	99	4471	15	61	12	429
250	373	290	74	3313	16	63	13	438	5000	529	462	114	513	399	101	4563	16	63	13	438
255	380	296	75	3379	16	64	13	446	5100	539	471	116	524	407	103	4654	16	64	13	446
260	388	301	77	3445	16	65	13	455	5200	550	480	118	534	415	105	4745	16	65	13	455
265	395	307	78	3511	17	66	13	464	5300	561	489	121	544	423	107	4836	17	66	13	464
270	402	313	80	3578	17	68	14	473	5400	571	499	123	554	431	110	4928	17	68	14	473

BW = Body Weight   SED = Sedentary   MOD = Moderately Active   ACT = Active

GOAL: GAIN BODY FAT/INCREASE MUSCLE • 60-Minute Workouts

BW	SED Kcal	Total Carbs	Total Prot	Total Fat	Day Carbs	Day Prot	Day Fat	Day Kcal	Night Carbs	Night Prot	Night Fat	Night Kcal	MOD Kcal	Total Carbs	Total Prot	Total Fat
130	2680	284	247	61	276	215	55	2453	8	33	7	228	2940	313	270	67
135	2760	292	255	63	284	221	56	2524	8	34	7	236	3030	323	278	69
140	2840	301	262	65	292	227	58	2595	9	35	7	245	3120	332	287	71
145	2920	309	270	67	300	233	59	2666	9	36	7	254	3210	342	295	73
150	3000	317	277	68	308	240	61	2738	9	38	8	263	3300	351	303	75
155	3080	326	285	70	316	246	62	2809	10	39	8	271	3390	361	312	77
160	3160	334	292	72	324	252	64	2880	10	40	8	280	3480	370	320	79
165	3240	342	299	74	332	258	66	2951	10	41	8	289	3570	379	328	81
170	3320	351	307	76	340	264	67	3023	11	43	9	298	3660	389	337	83
175	3400	359	314	78	348	271	69	3094	11	44	9	306	3750	398	345	85
180	3480	367	322	79	356	277	70	3165	11	45	9	315	3840	408	353	87
185	3560	376	329	81	364	283	72	3236	12	46	9	324	3930	417	362	89
190	3640	384	337	83	372	289	74	3308	12	48	10	333	4020	427	370	91
195	3720	392	344	85	380	296	75	3379	12	49	10	341	4110	436	379	94
200	3800	401	352	87	388	302	77	3450	13	50	10	350	4200	446	387	96
205	3880	409	359	89	396	308	78	3521	13	51	10	359	4290	455	395	98
210	3960	417	367	90	404	314	80	3593	13	53	11	368	4380	465	404	100
215	4040	426	374	92	412	321	81	3664	13	54	11	376	4470	474	412	102
220	4120	434	382	94	420	327	83	3735	14	55	11	385	4560	483	420	104
225	4200	442	389	96	428	333	85	3806	14	56	11	394	4650	493	429	106
230	4280	451	397	98	436	339	86	3878	14	58	12	403	4740	502	437	108
235	4360	459	404	100	444	346	88	3949	15	59	12	411	4830	512	445	110
240	4440	467	412	101	452	352	89	4020	15	60	12	420	4920	521	454	112
245	4520	476	419	103	460	358	91	4091	15	61	12	429	5010	531	462	114
250	4600	484	427	105	468	364	93	4163	16	63	13	438	5100	540	470	116
255	4680	492	434	107	476	370	94	4234	16	64	13	446	5190	550	479	118
260	4760	501	442	109	484	377	96	4305	16	65	13	455	5280	559	487	120
265	4840	509	449	111	492	383	97	4376	17	66	13	464	5370	569	496	122
270	4920	517	457	112	500	389	99	4448	17	68	14	473	5460	578	504	124

BW = Body Weight   SED = Sedentary   MOD = Moderately Active   ACT = Active

GOAL: GAIN BODY FAT/INCREASE MUSCLE • 60-Minute Workouts (cont.)

BW	Day Carbs	Day Prot	Day Fat	Day Kcal	Night Carbs	Night Prot	Night Fat	Night Kcal	ACT Kcal	Total Carbs	Total Prot	Total Fat	Day Carbs	Day Prot	Day Fat	Day Kcal	Night Carbs	Night Prot	Night Fat	Night Kcal
130	305	237	60	2713	8	33	7	228	3590	386	327	81	378	294	75	3363	8	33	7	228
135	314	244	62	2794	8	34	7	236	3705	399	337	84	390	304	77	3469	8	34	7	236
140	323	252	64	2875	9	35	7	245	3820	411	348	86	402	313	79	3575	9	35	7	245
145	333	259	66	2956	9	36	7	254	3935	423	358	89	414	322	82	3681	9	36	7	254
150	342	266	68	3038	9	38	8	263	4050	435	369	92	426	331	84	3788	9	38	8	263
155	351	273	69	3119	10	39	8	271	4165	448	379	94	438	341	87	3894	10	39	8	271
160	360	280	71	3200	10	40	8	280	4280	460	390	97	450	350	89	4000	10	40	8	280
165	369	287	73	3281	10	41	8	289	4395	472	401	100	462	359	91	4106	10	41	8	289
170	378	294	75	3363	11	43	9	298	4510	485	411	102	474	369	94	4213	11	43	9	298
175	387	301	77	3444	11	44	9	306	4625	497	422	105	486	378	96	4319	11	44	9	306
180	397	308	78	3525	11	45	9	315	4740	509	432	107	498	387	98	4425	11	45	9	315
185	406	316	80	3606	12	46	9	324	4855	521	443	110	510	396	101	4531	12	46	9	324
190	415	323	82	3688	12	48	10	333	4970	534	453	113	522	406	103	4638	12	48	10	333
195	424	330	84	3769	12	49	10	341	5085	546	464	115	534	415	105	4744	12	49	10	341
200	433	337	86	3850	13	50	10	350	5200	558	474	118	546	424	108	4850	13	50	10	350
205	442	344	87	3931	13	51	10	359	5315	570	485	120	558	434	110	4956	13	51	10	359
210	451	351	89	4013	13	53	11	368	5430	583	495	123	570	443	113	5063	13	53	11	368
215	461	358	91	4094	13	54	11	376	5545	595	506	126	581	452	115	5169	14	54	11	376
220	470	365	93	4175	14	55	11	385	5660	607	517	128	593	462	117	5275	14	55	11	385
225	479	372	95	4256	14	56	11	394	5775	619	527	131	605	471	120	5381	14	56	11	394
230	488	380	96	4338	14	58	12	403	5890	632	538	133	617	480	122	5488	14	58	12	403
235	497	387	98	4419	15	59	12	411	6005	644	548	136	629	489	124	5594	15	59	12	411
240	506	394	100	4500	15	60	12	420	6120	656	559	139	641	499	127	5700	15	60	12	420
245	515	401	102	4581	15	61	12	429	6235	669	569	141	653	508	129	5806	15	61	12	429
250	525	408	104	4663	16	63	13	438	6350	681	580	144	665	517	131	5913	16	63	13	438
255	534	415	105	4744	16	64	13	446	6465	693	590	147	677	527	134	6019	16	64	13	446
260	543	422	107	4825	16	65	13	455	6580	705	601	149	689	536	136	6125	16	65	13	455
265	552	429	109	4906	17	66	13	464	6695	718	611	152	701	545	138	6231	17	66	13	464
270	561	436	111	4988	17	68	14	473	6810	730	622	154	713	555	141	6338	17	68	14	473

GOAL: GAIN BODY FAT/INCREASE MUSCLE • 90-Minute Workouts

BW	SED Kcal	Total Carbs	Total Prot	Total Fat	Day Carbs	Day Prot	Day Fat	Day Kcal	Night Carbs	Night Prot	Night Fat	Night Kcal	MOD Kcal	Total Carbs	Total Prot	Total Fat
130	2980	318	273	68	310	241	61	2753	8	33	7	228	3240	347	296	73
135	3060	326	281	70	318	247	63	2824	8	34	7	236	3330	356	304	76
140	3140	334	288	71	326	253	64	2895	9	35	7	245	3420	366	313	78
145	3220	343	296	73	334	260	66	2966	9	36	7	254	3510	375	321	80
150	3300	351	303	75	342	266	68	3038	9	38	8	263	3600	385	330	82
155	3380	359	311	77	350	272	69	3109	10	39	8	271	3690	394	338	84
160	3460	368	318	79	358	278	71	3180	10	40	8	280	3780	404	346	86
165	3540	376	326	81	366	284	72	3251	10	41	8	289	3870	413	355	88
170	3620	384	333	82	374	291	74	3323	11	43	9	298	3960	423	363	90
175	3700	393	341	84	382	297	75	3394	11	44	9	306	4050	432	371	92
180	3780	401	348	86	390	303	77	3465	11	45	9	315	4140	442	380	94
185	3860	409	356	88	398	309	79	3536	12	46	9	324	4230	451	388	96
190	3940	418	363	90	406	316	80	3608	12	48	10	333	4320	460	396	98
195	4020	426	371	92	414	322	82	3679	12	49	10	341	4410	470	405	100
200	4100	434	378	93	422	328	83	3750	13	50	10	350	4500	479	413	102
205	4180	443	386	95	430	334	85	3821	13	51	10	359	4590	489	421	104
210	4260	451	393	97	438	341	87	3893	13	53	11	368	4680	498	430	106
215	4340	459	401	99	446	347	88	3964	13	54	11	376	4770	508	438	108
220	4420	468	408	101	454	353	90	4035	14	55	11	385	4860	517	447	110
225	4500	476	416	103	462	359	91	4106	14	56	11	394	4950	527	455	113
230	4580	484	423	104	470	366	93	4178	14	58	12	403	5040	536	463	115
235	4660	493	431	106	478	372	94	4249	15	59	12	411	5130	546	472	117
240	4740	501	438	108	486	378	96	4320	15	60	12	420	5220	555	480	119
245	4820	509	445	110	494	384	98	4391	15	61	12	429	5310	564	488	121
250	4900	518	453	112	502	390	99	4463	16	63	13	438	5400	574	497	123
255	4980	526	460	114	510	397	101	4534	16	64	13	446	5490	583	505	125
260	5060	534	468	115	518	403	102	4605	16	65	13	455	5580	593	513	127
265	5140	543	475	117	526	409	104	4676	17	66	13	464	5670	602	522	129
270	5220	551	483	119	534	415	106	4748	17	68	14	473	5760	612	530	131

BW = Body Weight   SED = Sedentary   MOD = Moderately Active   ACT = Active

GOAL: GAIN BODY FAT/INCREASE MUSCLE • 90-Minute Workouts (cont.)

BW	Day Carbs	Day Prot	Day Fat	Day Kcal	Night Carbs	Night Prot	Night Fat	Night Kcal	ACT Kcal	Total Carbs	Total Prot	Total Fat	Day Carbs	Day Prot	Day Fat	Day Kcal	Night Carbs	Night Prot	Night Fat	Night Kcal
130	339	264	67	3013	8	33	7	228	3890	420	353	88	412	320	81	3663	8	33	7	228
135	348	271	69	3094	8	34	7	236	4005	432	364	91	424	330	84	3769	8	34	7	236
140	357	278	71	3175	9	35	7	245	4120	445	374	93	436	339	86	3875	9	35	7	245
145	366	285	72	3256	9	36	7	254	4235	457	385	96	448	348	88	3981	9	36	7	254
150	375	292	74	3338	9	38	8	263	4350	469	395	98	460	358	91	4088	9	38	8	263
155	385	299	76	3419	10	39	8	271	4465	481	406	101	472	367	93	4194	10	39	8	271
160	394	306	78	3500	10	40	8	280	4580	494	416	104	484	376	96	4300	10	40	8	280
165	403	313	80	3581	10	41	8	289	4695	506	427	106	496	386	98	4406	10	41	8	289
170	412	320	81	3663	11	43	9	298	4810	518	437	109	508	395	100	4513	11	43	9	298
175	421	328	83	3744	11	44	9	306	4925	531	448	111	520	404	103	4619	11	44	9	306
180	430	335	85	3825	11	45	9	315	5040	543	458	114	532	413	105	4725	11	45	9	315
185	439	342	87	3906	12	46	9	324	5155	555	469	117	544	423	107	4831	12	46	9	324
190	449	349	89	3988	12	48	10	333	5270	567	480	119	555	432	110	4938	12	48	10	333
195	458	356	90	4069	12	49	10	341	5385	580	490	122	567	441	112	5044	12	49	10	341
200	467	363	92	4150	13	50	10	350	5500	592	501	124	579	451	114	5150	13	50	10	350
205	476	370	94	4231	13	51	10	359	5615	604	511	127	591	460	117	5256	13	51	10	359
210	485	377	96	4313	13	53	11	368	5730	616	522	130	603	469	119	5363	13	53	11	368
215	494	384	98	4394	13	54	11	376	5845	629	532	132	615	479	122	5469	13	54	11	376
220	503	392	99	4475	14	55	11	385	5960	641	543	135	627	488	124	5575	14	55	11	385
225	513	399	101	4556	14	56	11	394	6075	653	553	138	639	497	126	5681	14	56	11	394
230	522	406	103	4638	14	58	12	403	6190	665	564	140	651	506	129	5788	14	58	12	403
235	531	413	105	4719	15	59	12	411	6305	678	574	143	663	516	131	5894	15	59	12	411
240	540	420	107	4800	15	60	12	420	6420	690	585	145	675	525	133	6000	15	60	12	420
245	549	427	108	4881	15	61	12	429	6535	702	596	148	687	534	136	6106	15	61	12	429
250	558	434	110	4963	16	63	13	438	6650	715	606	151	699	544	138	6213	16	63	13	438
255	567	441	112	5044	16	64	13	446	6765	727	617	153	711	553	140	6319	16	64	13	446
260	577	448	114	5125	16	65	13	455	6880	739	627	156	723	562	143	6425	16	65	13	455
265	586	456	116	5206	17	66	13	464	6995	751	638	158	735	571	145	6531	17	66	13	464
270	595	463	118	5288	17	68	14	473	7110	764	648	161	747	581	148	6638	17	68	14	473

BW = Body Weight   SED = Sedentary   MOD = Moderately Active   ACT = Active

GOAL: GAIN BODY FAT/INCREASE MUSCLE • Non-Workout

BW	SED Kcal	Total Carbs	Total Prot	Total Fat	Day Carbs	Day Prot	Day Fat	Day Kcal	Night Carbs	Night Prot	Night Fat	Night Kcal	MOD Kcal	Total Carbs	Total Prot	Total Fat
130	2080	217	195	48	208	162	41	1853	8	33	7	228	2340	246	217	53
135	2160	225	202	50	216	168	43	1924	8	34	7	236	2430	255	226	56
140	2240	233	210	51	224	175	44	1995	9	35	7	245	2520	265	234	58
145	2320	242	217	53	232	181	46	2066	9	36	7	254	2610	274	242	60
150	2400	250	225	55	240	187	48	2138	9	38	8	263	2700	284	251	62
155	2480	258	232	57	248	193	49	2209	10	39	8	271	2790	293	259	64
160	2560	267	240	59	257	200	51	2280	10	40	8	280	2880	303	268	66
165	2640	275	247	61	265	206	52	2351	10	41	8	289	2970	312	276	68
170	2720	283	254	62	273	212	54	2423	11	43	9	298	3060	321	284	70
175	2800	291	262	64	281	218	55	2494	11	44	9	306	3150	331	293	72
180	2880	300	269	66	289	224	57	2565	11	45	9	315	3240	340	301	74
185	2960	308	277	68	297	231	59	2636	12	46	9	324	3330	350	309	76
190	3040	316	284	70	305	237	60	2708	12	48	10	333	3420	359	318	78
195	3120	325	292	72	313	243	62	2779	12	49	10	341	3510	369	326	80
200	3200	333	299	73	321	249	63	2850	13	50	10	350	3600	378	334	82
205	3280	341	307	75	329	256	65	2921	13	51	10	359	3690	388	343	84
210	3360	350	314	77	337	262	67	2993	13	53	11	368	3780	397	351	86
215	3440	358	322	79	345	268	68	3064	13	54	11	376	3870	406	359	88
220	3520	366	329	81	353	274	70	3135	14	55	11	385	3960	416	368	90
225	3600	375	337	83	361	281	71	3206	14	56	11	394	4050	425	376	93
230	3680	383	344	84	369	287	73	3278	14	58	12	403	4140	435	385	95
235	3760	391	352	86	377	293	74	3349	15	59	12	411	4230	444	393	97
240	3840	400	359	88	385	299	76	3420	15	60	12	420	4320	454	401	99
245	3920	408	367	90	393	305	78	3491	15	61	12	429	4410	463	410	101
250	4000	416	374	92	401	312	79	3563	16	63	13	438	4500	473	418	103
255	4080	425	382	94	409	318	81	3634	16	64	13	446	4590	482	426	105
260	4160	433	389	95	417	324	82	3705	16	65	13	455	4680	492	435	107
265	4240	441	397	97	425	330	84	3776	17	66	13	464	4770	501	443	109
270	4320	450	404	99	433	337	86	3848	17	68	14	473	4860	510	451	111

BW = Body Weight   SED = Sedentary   MOD = Moderately Active   ACT = Active

GOAL: GAIN BODY FAT/INCREASE MUSCLE • Non-Workout (cont.)

BW	Day Carbs	Day Prot	Day Fat	Day Kcal	Night Carbs	Night Prot	Night Fat	Night Kcal	ACT Kcal	Total Carbs	Total Prot	Total Fat	Day Carbs	Day Prot	Day Fat	Day Kcal	Night Carbs	Night Prot	Night Fat	Night Kcal
130	238	185	47	2113	8	33	7	228	2990	319	274	68	311	242	61	2763	8	33	7	228
135	247	192	49	2194	8	34	7	236	3105	331	285	71	323	251	64	2869	8	34	7	236
140	256	199	51	2275	9	35	7	245	3220	343	295	73	335	260	66	2975	9	35	7	245
145	265	206	52	2356	9	36	7	254	3335	356	306	76	347	270	68	3081	9	36	7	254
150	274	213	54	2438	9	38	8	263	3450	368	316	78	359	279	71	3188	9	38	8	263
155	283	220	56	2519	10	39	8	271	3565	380	327	81	371	288	73	3294	10	39	8	271
160	293	228	58	2600	10	40	8	280	3680	393	338	84	383	298	76	3400	10	40	8	280
165	302	235	60	2681	10	41	8	289	3795	405	348	86	394	307	78	3506	10	41	8	289
170	311	242	61	2763	11	43	9	298	3910	417	359	89	406	316	80	3613	11	43	9	298
175	320	249	63	2844	11	44	9	306	4025	429	369	91	418	325	83	3719	11	44	9	306
180	329	256	65	2925	11	45	9	315	4140	442	380	94	430	335	85	3825	11	45	9	315
185	338	263	67	3006	12	46	9	324	4255	454	390	97	442	344	87	3931	12	46	9	324
190	347	270	69	3088	12	48	10	333	4370	466	401	99	454	353	90	4038	12	48	10	333
195	356	277	70	3169	12	49	10	341	4485	478	411	102	466	363	92	4144	12	49	10	341
200	366	284	72	3250	13	50	10	350	4600	491	422	104	478	372	94	4250	13	50	10	350
205	375	291	74	3331	13	51	10	359	4715	503	432	107	490	381	97	4356	13	51	10	359
210	384	299	76	3413	13	53	11	368	4830	515	443	110	502	390	99	4463	13	53	11	368
215	393	306	78	3494	13	54	11	376	4945	527	454	112	514	400	102	4569	13	54	11	376
220	402	313	79	3575	14	55	11	385	5060	540	464	115	526	409	104	4675	14	55	11	385
225	411	320	81	3656	14	56	11	394	5175	552	475	118	538	418	106	4781	14	56	11	394
230	420	327	83	3738	14	58	12	403	5290	564	485	120	550	428	109	4888	14	58	12	403
235	430	334	85	3819	15	59	12	411	5405	576	496	123	562	437	111	4994	15	59	12	411
240	439	341	87	3900	15	60	12	420	5520	589	506	125	574	446	113	5100	15	60	12	420
245	448	348	88	3981	15	61	12	429	5635	601	517	128	586	456	116	5206	15	61	12	429
250	457	355	90	4063	16	63	13	438	5750	613	527	131	598	465	118	5313	16	63	13	438
255	466	363	92	4144	16	64	13	446	5865	626	538	133	610	474	120	5419	16	64	13	446
260	475	370	94	4225	16	65	13	455	5980	638	548	136	622	483	123	5525	16	65	13	455
265	484	377	96	4306	17	66	13	464	6095	650	559	138	634	493	125	5631	17	66	13	464
270	494	384	98	4388	17	68	14	473	6210	662	570	141	645	502	128	5738	17	68	14	473

BW = Body Weight   SED = Sedentary   MOD = Moderately Active   ACT = Active

Macrobolic Food Guide Pyramids

The following Macrobolic Food Guide Pyramids allow you to allot the proper amounts of food to meet the Macrobolic Lean-Mass Equation. Athletes who are on the lower end of the calorie range would choose the lower servings. Athletes who are on the higher end of the calorie range would choose the higher servings. The Macrobolic Food Guide Pyramids are to be used in conjunction with the Macrobolic Exchange Lists (see Appendix C). The proper serving sizes are predetermined in the Macrobolic Exchange Lists along with the different foods that are suggested for consumption.

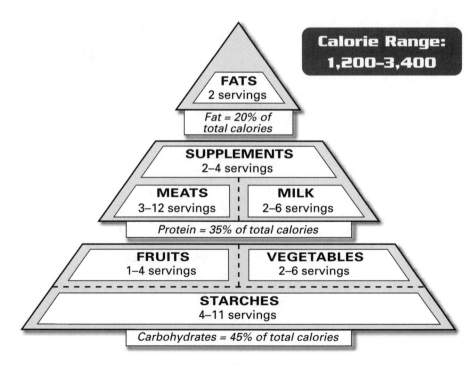

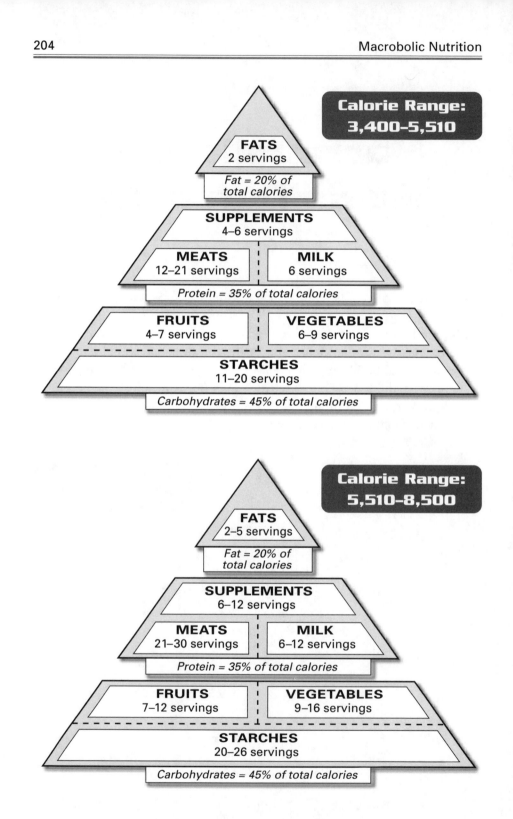

APPENDIX C

Macrobolic Exchange Lists

The Macrobolic Exchange Lists allows you to utilize the Macrobolic Food Guide Pyramids (see Appendix B) in meal planning. The Macrobolic Exchange Lists will enable you to effectively "exchange" one serving from one list for another food item on the same list. For example, 1 cup of raw mushrooms has the same nutritional value as a half cup of cooked broccoli. Everything is spelled out for you, so plan, eat, and GROW!

LOW-GLYCEMIC VEGETABLES		
Macrobolic Exchange: 1 Vegetable =		
5 g carbohydrate • 2 g protein • 0 g fat • 25 calories		
All vegetables 1 cup raw or ¹/₂ cup cooked		
Alfalfa sprouts*	Cucumbers (free)*	Radish*
Asparagus*	Eggplant*	Raw spinach (free)*
Bamboo shoots*	Green beans*	Sauerkraut*
Broccoli*	Green peppers*	Summer squash*
Brussels sprouts*	Lettuce, all varieties (free)*	Tomato*
Cabbage*	Mushrooms*	Turnip*
Cauliflower*	Onions *	Zucchini*
Celery*		
GI values not established		

LOW-GLYCEMIC ROOT VEGETABLES
Macrobolic Exchange: 1 Starch =
15 g carbohydrate • 3 g protein • 1 g fat • 80 calories

Carrots, raw ($\frac{1}{2}$ cup)	Sweet potatoes (3 oz)
New potatoes (3 oz)	White potatoes, boiled) (3 oz)
Pontiac potatoes, boiled (3 oz)	Yams, baked (2 oz)
Russet potatoes, baked w/o skin (3 oz)	

LOW-GLYCEMIC BEANS
Macrobolic Exchange: 1 Very Lean Starch =
15–20 g carbohydrate • 7–10 g protein • 1 g fat • 115 calories

All beans/peas cooked w/o salt ($\frac{1}{2}$ cup)

Baked beans	Lentils	Peas
Butter beans	Lima beans	Pinto beans
Kidney beans	Marrowfat beans	Soya bean
Kidney beans (white)	Mung beans	Split pea

LOW-GLYCEMIC FRUITS
Macrobolic Exchange: 1 Fruit =
15 g carbohydrate • 60 calories

Apple, small (4 oz)	Grapefruit, $\frac{1}{2}$ large (11 oz)	Peach, medium (6 oz)
Apples, dried (4 rings)	Grapes, small 17 (3 oz)	Pear, medium
Apricots, dried (8 halves)	Kiwi (3.5 oz)	Pineapple ($\frac{3}{4}$ cup)
Banana, small (4 oz)	Mandarin orange ($\frac{1}{2}$ cup)	Strawberries ($1\frac{1}{4}$ cup
Cherries ($\frac{1}{3}$ cup)	Mango, $\frac{1}{2}$ small (8 oz)	whole berries)

LOW-GLYCEMIC GRAINS
Macrobolic Exchange: 1 Starch =
15 g carbohydrate • 3 g protein • 1 g fat • 80 calories

Amaranth, uncooked (2 tbs)	Pasta (seminola), cooked $\frac{1}{2}$ cup
Barley, cooked ($\frac{1}{2}$ cup)	Pita, whole-wheat, six inch ($\frac{1}{2}$)
Brown rice, steamed ($\frac{3}{8}$ cup)	Pumpernickel bread (1 slice)
Buckwheat, uncooked (2 tbs)	Rye bread (1 slice)
Bulgur, cooked ($\frac{1}{3}$ cup)	Semolina, uncooked (2 tbs)
Corn tortilla, six inch	Wheat tortilla, six inch

Durum, uncooked (2 tbs)	Whole-wheat bagel, small ($\frac{1}{2}$)
Oatmeal ($\frac{1}{2}$ cup)	Whole-wheat bread (1 slice)

LOW-GLYCEMIC/LOW-FAT DAIRY/MILK
Macrobolic Exchange: 1 Dairy =
12 g carbohydrate • 8 g protein • 0–3 g fat • 90 calories

Skim Milk (1 cup)

MEATS AND MEAT SUBSTITUTES
Macrobolic Exchange: 1 Very Lean Meat =
0 g carbohydrate • 7 g protein • 0–1 g fat • 35 calories

Meats, No Beef (all 1 ounce)

Chicken or turkey (white meat only, no skin)	Clams, crab, lobster, scallops, shrimp
Buffalo, ostrich	Duck, pheasant (no skin)
Fresh cod, flounder, haddock, halibut, trout, tuna (canned in water)	

Meat Substitutes

Egg whites (2 large)	Fat–free cheese (1 oz)
Nonfat/low-fat cottage cheese ($\frac{1}{4}$ cup)	

Macrobolic Exchange: 1 Lean Meat =
0 g carbohydrate • 7 g protein • 3 g fat • 55 calories

Meats (all 1 ounce)

Goose (no skin)	Lamb, roast, chop, or leg	Rabbit
Herring, salmon, catfish	Lean pork	Veal, lean chop, roast

USDA **Select** or **Choice** grades of lean beef **trimmed of fat**.
For example: round, sirloin, flank steak, tenderloin, roast (rib, chunk, rump)
steak (T-bone, porterhouse, cubed), ground round.

Meat Substitutes

Any cheese with 3 g of fat or less per 1 oz	Grated parmesan (2 tbs)
Low-fat Cheddar cheese (1 oz)	

Macrobolic Exchange: 1 Medium Fat =
0 g carbohydrate • 7 g protein • 5 g fat • 75 calories

Meats (all 1 ounce)

Most beef products fall into this category (ground beef, meatloaf, prime grades of meat
trimmed of fat, for example, prime rib)

Chicken (dark meat, with skin)

Meat Substitutes		
Feta, mozzarella cheese (1 oz)	Ricotta cheese ($\frac{1}{4}$ cup, 2 oz)	Whole egg (1 large)

Macrobolic Exchange: 1 High-Fat Meat =
0 g carbohydrate • 7 g protein • 8 g fat • 100 calories

All regular cheeses such as American, Cheddar, Monterey Jack, and Swiss (1 oz)

Pork spareribs, ground pork (1 oz)

FAT
Macrobolic Exchange: 1 Fat =
5 g fat • 45 calories

Monounsaturated fats

Avocado, medium (1 oz)	Peanut butter (2 tsp)
Nuts: almonds, cashews (6 nuts)	Peanuts (10 nuts)
Oil: canola, olive, peanut (1 tsp)	Pecans (4 halves)
Olives, ripe, black (8 large)	Seeds: sesame seeds (1 tbs)

Polyunsaturated fats

Flaxseeds (1 tbs)	Oil: corn, safflower, soybean (1 tsp)
Mayonnaise, reduced fat (1 tsp)	Seeds: pumpkin, sunflower seeds (1 tbs)
Nuts: walnuts (4 halves)	

Saturated fats (use sparingly)

Butter, stick (1 tsp)	Reduced-fat sour cream (3 tbs)
Reduced-fat cream cheese (1 oz)	

SUPPLEMENTS
Macrobolic Exchange: 3 Very Lean Meat =
2–3 g carbohydrate • 20 g protein • 2–3 g fat • 120 calories

MHP's Probolic (any flavor): 1 scoop (approx. 30 g)

Macrobolic Exchange: Macrobolic Complete Supplement =
15 g carbohydrate • 11 g protein • 3 g fat • 130 calories

MHP's Up Your MASS (any flavor): 1 scoop (33 g)

References

Almada, A., et al. "Effects of B-BHBM Supplementation with and without Creatine during Training on Strength and Sprint Capacity." *Federation of American Societies of Experimental Biology Journal* 11 (1997): A374.

Anderson, Helen L., Mary Belle Heindel, and Hellen Linkswiler. "Effect on Nitrogen Balance of Adult Man of Varying Source of Nitrogen and Level of Calorie Intake." *Journal of Nutrition* (1969): 82–90.

Anderson J.W., B. M. Johnstone, and M. E. Cook-Newell. "Meta-Analysis of the Effects of Soy Protein Intake on Serum Lipids." *New England Journal of Medicine* 333, 5 (1995): 276–82.

Anderson, M., et al. "Pre-Exercise Meal Affects Ride Time to Fatigue in Trained Cyclists." *Journal of the American Dietetic Association* 94 (1994): 1152–1153.

Apfelbaum, Marian, Jacques Fricker, and Lawrence Igoin-Apfelbaum. "Low and Very Low Calorie Diets." *American Journal of Clinical Nutrition* 45 (1987): 1126–1134.

Armstrong, R.B. "Mechanisms of Exercise-Induced Delayed Onset Muscular Soreness: A Brief Review." *Medicine and Science in Sports and Exercise* 16 no. 6 (1984): 529–538.

————. "Muscle Damage and Endurance Events." *Sports Medicine* 3 (1986): 370–381.

Ball, T., et al. "Periodic Carbohydrate Replacement During 50 Minutes of High-Intensity Cycling Improves Subsequent Sprint Performance." *International Journal of Sport Science* 5(2) (June 1995): 151–158.

Bamman, M.M., et al. "Changes in Body Composition, Diet, and Strength of Bodybuilders During the 12 Weeks Prior to Competition." *Journal of Sports Medicine and Physical Fitness* 33 (1993): 383.

Bell, D.G., et al. "Effects of Caffeine, Ephedrine and the Combination on Time to Exhaustion during High-Intensity Exercise." *European Journal of Applied Physiology* 77 (1998): 427–433.

Bergstrom, Jonas, and Eric Hultman. "Nutrition for Maximal Sports Performance." *Journal of the American Medical Association* 221, no. 9 (1972): 999–1004.

Berning, J.R. "The Role of Medium-Chain Triglycerides in Exercise." *International Journal of Sport Nutrition* 6, no. 3 (1996): 121–133.

Bohmer, D., et al. "Treatment of Chondropathia Patellae in Young Athletes with Glucosamine Sulfate," In *Current Topics in Sports Medicine,* N. Bachl, L. Prokop, and R. Suckert, eds. Vienna: Urban & Schwarzenberg, 1984, pp. 799–803.

Boire, Y., et al. "Slow and fast dietary proteins differentially modulate postprandial protein accretion." *Proceedings of the National Academy of Science* 94(26) (Dec 1997): 14930–14935.

Bonde-Petersen, Flemming, Howard G. Knuttgen, and Jan Henriksson. "Muscle Metabolism During Exercise with Concentric and Eccentric Contractions." *Journal of Applied Physiology* 33 (1972): 792–795.

Boozer, C.N., P. A. Daly, P. Homel, et al. "Herbal Ephedra/Caffeine for Weight Loss: A 6-Month Randomized Safety and Efficacy Trial." *International Journal of Obesity Related Metabolic Disorders* 26, no. 5 (May 2002):593–604.

Boyne, P.S., and H. Medhurst. "Oral Anti-inflammatory Enzyme Therapy in Injuries in Professional Footballers." *The Practitioner* 198 (April 1967): 543–546.

Braatan, J.T., F.W. Scott, P.J. Wood, et al. "High Beta-glucan Oat Bran and Oat Grain Reduce Post-prandial Blood Glucose and Insulin in Subjects with and without Type 2 Diabetes." *Diabetic Medicine* 11 (1994): 312–318.

Braatan, J.T., P.J. Word, F.W. Scott, et al. "Oat Grain Lowers Glucose and Insulin After an Oral Glucose Load," *American Journal of Clinical Nutrition* 53 (1991): 1425–1430.

Brilla, L.R., and T. E. Landerholm. "Effect of Fish Oil Supplementation and Exercise on Serum Lipids and Aerobic Fitness." *Journal of Sports Medicine and Physical Fitness* 30, no. 2 (1990): 173–180.

Brose, A., G. Parise, and M.A. Tarnopolsky. "Creatine Supplementation Enhances Isometric Strength and Body Composition Improvements Following Strength Exercise Training in Older Adults." *Journal of Gerontology Series A: Biological Sciences and Medical Sciences* 58, no. 1 (January 2003): 9–11.

Brown, C., and Jack H. Wilmore. "The Effects of Maximal Resistance Training on the Strength and Body Composition of Women Athletes." *Medicine and Science in Sports* 6, no. 3 (1974): 174–177.

Bucci, L. *Nutrients as Ergogenic Aids for Sports and Exercise.* Boca Raton, FL: CRC Press, 1993.

———. *Nutrition Applied to Injury Rehabilitation and Sports Medicine.* Boca Raton, FL: CRC Press, 1995.

Burke D.G., P.D. Chilibeck, K.S. Davidson, et al. "The Effect of Whey Protein Supplementation with and without Creatine Monohydrate Combined with Resistance Training on Lean Tissue Mass and Muscle Strength." *International Journal of Sport Nutrition and Exercise Metabolism* 11, no. 3 (September 2001): 349–64.

Burke, D.G., P.D. Chilibeck, G. Parise, et al. "Effect of Creatine and Weight Training on Muscle Creatine and Performance in Vegetarians." *Medicine & Science in Sports and Exercise* 35, no. 11 (November 2003): 1946–55.

Burke, D.G., S. Silver, L.E. Holt, et al. "The Effect of Continuous Low Dose Creatine Supplementation on Force, Power, and Total Work." *International Journal of Sport Nutrition and Exercise Metabolism* 10, no. 3 (September 2000):235–44.

Burke, L.M., and S.D. Read. "Dietary Supplements in Sport." *Sports Medicine* 15 (1993): 43–65.

Buskirk, Elsworth R., and José Mendez. "Sports Science and Body Composition Analysis: Emphasis on Cell and Muscle Mass." *Medicine and Science in Sports and Exercise* 16, no. 6 (1984): 584–593.

Butterfield, G. "Ergogenic Aids: Evaluating Sport Nutrition Products." *International Journal of Sport Nutrition* no. 3 (1996): 191–197.

Butterfield, Gail E., and Doris H. Calloway. "Physical Activity Improves Protein Utilization in Young Men." *British Journal of Nutrition* 51 (1984): 171–184.

Calver, A., et al., "Dilator Actions of Arginine in Human Peripheral Vasculature," *Clinical Science (Colch)*, 85, no. 5 (1991): 695–700.

Casanueva, F.F., L. Villanueva, J.A. Cabranes, et al. "Cholinergic Mediation of Growth Hormone Secretion Elicited by Arginine, Clonidine, and Physical Exercise in Man." *Journal of Clinical Endocrinology and Metabolism* 59, no. 3 (1984): 526–530.

Celejowa, I., and M. Homa. "Food Intake, Nitrogen and Energy Balance in Polish Weight Lifters, During Training Camp." *Nutrition and Metabolism* 12 (1970): 259–274.

Chandalia, M., A. Garg, D. Lutjohann, et al. "Beneficial Effects of High Dietary Fiber Intake in Patients with Type 2 Diabetes Mellitus." *New England Journal of Medicine* 342 (2000): 1392–1398.

Chang, Tse Wen, and Alfred L. Goldberg. "The Metabolic Fates of Amino Acids and the Formation of Glutamine in Skeletal Muscle." *Journal of Biological Chemistry* 253, no. 10 (1978): 3685–3695.

Chin, S. "Dietary Sources of Conjugated Dienoic Isomers of Linoleic Acid, a Newly Recognized Class of Anticarcinogens." *Journal of Food Composition and Analysis* 5 (1992): 185–195.

Chin, S., J. Storkron, K. Albright, et al. "Conjugated Linoleic Acid is a Growth Factor for Rats as Shown by Enhanced Weight Gain and Improved Feed Efficiency." *Journal of Nutrition* 124 (1994): 2344–2349.

Christensen, H. "Muscle Activity and Fatigue in the Shoulder Muscles during Repetitive Work." *European Journal of Applied Physiology* 54 (1986): 596–601.

Clarkson, P., and E. Haymes. "Trace Mineral Requirements for Athletes." *International Journal of Sports Nutrition* 4 (1994): 104.

Clarkson, Priscilla M., Walter Kroll, and Thomas C. McBride. "Plantar Flexion Fatigue and Muscle Fiber Type in Power and Endurance Athletes." *Medicine and Science in Sports and Exercise* 12 (1980): 262–267.

Colker, C.M. "Immune Status of Elite Athletes: Role of Whey Protein Concentrate: A Review." *Medicine and Science in Sports and Exercise* 30 (1998): S17.

Conzolazio, C. Frank, Herman L. Johnson, Richard A. Nelson, et al. "Protein Metabolism during Intensive Physical Training in the Young Adult." *American Journal of Clinical Nutrition* 28 (1975): 29–35.

Cook, James D., and Elaine R. Monsen. "Vitamin C, the Common Cold, and Iron Absorption." *American Journal of Clinical Nutrition* 30(2) (Feb 1977): 235–241.

Copinschi, Georges, Laurence C. Wegienka, Satoshi Hane, et al. "Effect of Arginine on Serum Levels of Insulin and Growth Hormone in Obese Subjects." *Metabolism* 16 (1967): 485–491.

Cossack, Zafrallah T., Ananda Prasad. "Effect of Protein Source on the Bioavailability of Zinc in Human Subjects." *Nutrition Research* 3 (1983): 23–31.

Costill, D.L., R. Bowers, et al. "Muscle Glycogen Utilization during Prolonged Exercise on Successive Days." *Journal of Applied Physiology* 31 (1971): 834–838.

Costill, D.L., and M. Hargreaves. "Carbohydrate Nutrition and Fatigue." *Sports Medicine* 13(1992): 86.

Costill, D.L., W. M. Sherman, et al. "The Role of Dietary Carbohydrate in Muscle Glycogen Synthesis after Strenuous Running." *American Journal of Clinical Nutrition* 34 (1981): 1834–1836.

Coyle, Edward F., and Andrew R. Coggan. "Effectiveness of Carbohydrate Feeding in Delaying Fatigue during Pro-longed Exercise." *Sports Medicine* 1(6) (Nov–Dec 1984): 446–458.

Davies, Kelvin J. A., Alexandre T. Quintanilha, et al. "Free Radicals and Tissue Damage Produced by Exercise." *Biochemical and Biophysical Research Communications* 107, no. 4 (1982): 1198–1205.

Despres, J. P., C. Bouchard, and R. Savard, et al. "Level of Physical Fitness and Adipocyte Lipolysis in Humans." *The American Physiological Society* (1984): 1157–1161.

"Diets Containing Less than 42% Carbohydrates Do Not Meet the Energy Demands or Provide Adequate Glycogen Stores for Bodybuilders and Their Intense Workouts." *Strength and Conditioning Journal* 24(2002):42–53

DiPrampero, P. Enrico. "Energetics of Muscular Exercise." *Biochemical Pharmacology* 89 (1981): 143–209.

Dohm, G. Lynis, George J. Kasperek, and Edward B. Tapscott, et al. "Effect of Exercise on Synthesis and Degradation of Muscle Protein." *Biochemical Journal* 188 (1980): 255–262.

Dray, F. "Role of Prostaglandins in Growth Hormone Secretion." *Advanced Prostaglandin and Thromboxane Research* 8 (1980): 1321.

"Effects of Branched Chain Amino Acid Supplementation Before and After Training." *Medicina Dello Sport* 50 (1997):293–303.

Ehn, Lars, Bjorn Carlmark, and Sverker Hoglund. "Iron Status in Athletes Involved in Intense Physical Activity." *Medicine and Science in Sports and Exercise* 12, no. 1 (1980): 61–64.

Engelhandt, M., G. Neumann, A. Berbalk, et al. "Creatine Supplementation in Endurance Sports." *Medicine and Science in Sports and Exercise* 30 (1998): 1123–1129.

Erling, T.A. "Pilot Study With the Aim of Studying the Efficacy and Tolerability of CLA (Tonalin) on the Body Composition in Humans." Liilestrom, Norway: Medstat Research Ltd, 1997.

"Fatigue and Underperformance in Athletes." *British Journal of Sports Nutrition* 32 (1998): 107–110.

Ferreira, M., R. Kreider, M. Wilson, et al. "Effects of Conjugated Linoleic Acid (CLA) Supplementation during Resistance Training on Body Composition and Strength." *Journal of Strength and Conditioning Research* 11 (1997): 280.

Food and Agriculture Organization of the United Nations. *The Amino Acid Content of Foods and Biological Data on Proteins. Nutritional Study #24. Rome* Lanham, MD: UNIPUB, 1970.

Food and Nutrition Board. *Recommended Dietary Allowances,* 9th Edition. Washington, D.C.: National Academy of Sciences, 1980.

Forbes, Gilbert B. "Growth of the Lean Body Mass in Man." *Growth* 36 (1972): 325–338.

———. "Body Composition as Affected by Physical Activity and Nutrition." *Metabolic and Nutritional Aspects of Physical Exercise: Federation Proceedings* 44, no. 2 (1985): 334–352.

Forbes, Richard M., and John W. Erdman, Jr. "Bioavailability of Trace Mineral Elements." *Annual Reviews of Nutrition* 3 (1983): 213–231.

Friedman, J.E., et al. "Regulation of Glycogen Resynthesis Following Exercise." *Sports Medicine* 11 (1991): 232.

Galton, David J., and George A. Bray. "Studies on Lipolysis in Human Adipose Cells." *Journal of Clinical Investigation* 46, no. 4 (1967): 621–629.

Gao, J.P., D.I. Costill, C.A. Horswill, et al. "Sodium Bicarbonate Ingestion Improves Performance in Interval Swimming." *European Journal of Applied Physiology* 58 (1988): 171–174.

Garza, C., N.S. Scrimshaw, and V.R. Young. "Human Protein Requirements: The Effect of Variations in Energy Intake within the Maintenance Range." *American Journal of Clinical Nutrition* 29 (1976): 280–287.

Gastelu, D.L. "Developing State-of-the-Art Amino Acids." *Muscle Magazine International* (May 1989): 58–64.

————. *The Complete Nutritional Supplements Buyer's Guide.* NY: Random House, 2000.

Gastelu, Daniel, and Fred Hatfield. *Dynamic Nutrition for Maximum Performance.* Garden City Park, NY: Avery, 1997.

Gattas, V. "Protein-Energy Requirements of Prepubertal School-age Boys Determined by Using Nitrogen-Balance Mixed-Protein Diet." *American Journal of Clinical Nutrition* 52 (1990): 1037–42.

Gleeson, M., et al. "Effect of Low- and High-Carbohydrate Diets on the Plasma Glutamine and Circulating Leukocyte Responses to Exercise." *International Journal of Sports Nutrition* 8 (1998): 49–59.

Goldberg, Alfred L., Joseph D. Etlinger, David F. Goldspink, et al. "Mechanism of Work-Induced Hypertrophy of Skeletal Muscle." *Medicine and Science in Sports* 7, no. 3 (1975): 185–198.

Goldspink, David F. "The Influence of Activity on Muscle Size and Protein Turnover." *Journal of Physiology* 264 (1976): 283–296.

Gollnick, Philip D. "Metabolism of Substrates: Energy Substrate Metabolism during Exercise and as Modified by Training." *Metabolic and Nutritional Aspects of Physical Exercise: Federation Proceedings* 44, no. 2 (1985): 353–368.

Gontzea, I., P. Sutzescu, and S. Dumitrache. "The Influence of Muscular Activity on Nitrogen Balance and on the Need of Man for Proteins." *Nutrition Reports International* 10 (1974): 35–43.

Gotshalk L.A., J.S. Volek, R.S. Staron, et al. "Creatine Supplementation Improves Muscular Performance in Older Men." *Medicine & Science in Sports & Exercise* 34, no. 3 (March 2002):537–43.

Green A.L., E. Hultman, I.A. Macdonald, et al. "Carbohydrate Ingestion Augments Skeletal Muscle Creatine Accumulation during Creatine Supplementation in Humans." *Am J Physiol.* 271, no. 5, Pt 1 (1996): E821–6.

Green A.L., Simpson E.J., Littlewood J.J., et al. "Carbohydrate Ingestion Augments Creatine Retention during Creatine Feeding in Humans." *Acta Physiol Scand.* 158, no. 2 (1996):195–202.

Greenhaff, P., et al. "Effect of Oral Creatine Supplementation on Skeletal Muscle Phosphocreatine Resynthesis." *American Journal of Physiology,* 266 (1994): E725–E730.

Haff, G.G. "Roundtable Discussion: Low Carbohydrate Diets and Anaerobic Athletes." *Strength and Conditioning Journal* 23, no. 3 (2001): 42–61.

Hagerman, F.C., et al. "Effects of High-Intensity Resistance Training on Untrained Older Men. I. Strength, Cardiovascular, and Metabolic Responses." *Journal of Gerontology Series A Biological Sciences Medical Sciences* 55, no. 7 (2000): B336–346.

Hamilton K.L., M.C. Meyers, W.A. Skelly, et al. "Oral Creatine Supplementation and Upper Extremity Anaerobic Response in Females." *International Journal of Sport Nutrition and Exercise Metabolism* 10, no. 3 (2000):277–89.

Haralambie, G., and A. Berg. "Serum Urea and Amino Nitrogen Changes with Exercise Duration." *European Journal of Applied Physiology* (1976): 39–48.

Hartog, M., R.J. Havel, G. Copinschi, et al. "The Relationship Between Changes in Serum Levels of Growth Hormone and Mobilization of Fat During Exercise in Man." *Quarterly Journal of Experimental Physiology* 52 (1967): 86–96.

Heeker, A.L., and K.B. Wheeler. "Protein: A Misunderstood Nutrient for the Athlete." *National Strength and Conditioning Association Journal* 7 (1985): 28–29.

Helie, R., J.-M. Lavoie, and D. Cousineau. "Effects of a 24-Hour Carbohydrate-Poor Diet on Metabolic and Hormonal Responses during Glucose-Infused Leg Exercise." *European Journal of Applied Physiology* 54 (1985): 420–426.

Henneman, Dorothy, and Philip H. Henneman. "Effects of Human Growth Hormone on Levels of Blood and Urinary Carbohydrate and Fat Metabolites in Man." *Journal of Clinical Investigation* 39 (1960): 1239–1245.

Hermansen, Lars, Eric Hultman, and Bengt Saltin. "Muscle Glycogen during Prolonged Severe Exercise." *Acta Physiolgica Scandinavica* 71 (1967): 129–139.

Heymsfield, Steven B., Carlos Arteaga, Clifford McManus, et al. "Measurement of Muscle Mass in Humans: Validity of the 24-Hour Urinary Creatinine Method." *American Journal of Clinical Nutrition* 37 (1983): 478–494.

Hofman, Z., et al. "Glucose and Insulin Responses After Commonly Used Sport Feedings Before and After a 1-Hour Training Session." *International Journal of Sport Nutrition* 5 (1995): 194–205.

Holloszy, John O. "Adaptation of Skeletal Muscle to Endurance Exercise." *Medicine and Science in Sports* 7, no. 3 (1975): 155–164.

Hubbard, R., et al. "Apparent skeletal muscle loss related to dietary trans fatty acids in a mixed group of omnivores and vegetarians." *Nutrition Research* 23 (2003): 651–658.

Institute of Medicine. "Military Strategies for Sustainment of Nutrition and Immune Function in the Field," Robert O. Nesheim, ed. A Report of the Committe on Military Nurition Research, Food and Nutrition Board. Washington, D.C.: National Academy Press, 1999.

Izquierdo M., J. Ibanez, J.J. Gonzalez-Badillo, et al. "Effects of Creatine Supplementation on Muscle Power, Endurance, and Sprint Performance." *Medicine & Science in Sports & Exercise* 34, no. 2 (2002):332–43.

Jakeman, P., and S. Maxwell. "Effect of Antioxidant Vitamin Supplementation on Muscle Function after Eccentric Exercise." *European Journal of Applied Physiology* 67 (1993): 426.

James, M.J., R.A. Gibson, L.G. Cleland. "Dietary Polyunsaturated Fatty Acids and Inflammatory Mediator Production." *American Journal of Clinical Nutrition* 71 (suppl) (2002): 3435, 3485.

Jequier, E. "Thermogenesis Induced by Nutrient Administration in Man." *Infusionsther Klin Ernahr* 11: (1984):184–189

Jezova, D., M. Vigas, P. Tatar, et al. "Plasma Testosterone and Catecholamine Responses to Physical Exercise of Different Intensities in Men." *European Journal of Applied Physiology* 54 (1985): 62–66.

Kanter, M. "Free Radicals, Exercise, and Antioxidant Supplementation." *International Journal of Sports Nutrition* 4 (1994): 205.

Karagiorgos, Athanase, Joseph F. Garcia, and George A. Brooks. "Growth Hormone Response to Continuous and Intermittent Exercise." *Medicine and Science in Sports* 11, no. 3 (1979): 302–307.

Karlsson, Jan, and Bengt Saltin. "Lactate, ATP, and CP in Working Muscles during Exhaustive Exercise in Man." *Journal of Applied Physiology* 29, no. 5 (1970): 598–602.

Karlsson, Jan, Lars-Olof Nordesjo, and Bengt Saltin. "Muscle Glycogen Utilization during Exercise after Physical Training." *Acta Physiolgica Scandinavica* 90 (1974): 210–217.

Kasai, Kikuo, Hitoshi Suzuki, Tsutomu Nakamura, et al. "Glycine Stimulates Growth Hormone Release in Man." *Acta Endocronologica* 90 (1980): 283-286.

Kasai, Kikuo, Masami Kobayashi, and Shin-Ichi Shimoda. "Stimulatory Effect of Glycine on Human Growth Hormone Secretion." *Metabolism* 27 (1978): 201–208.

Kasperek, George J., and Rebecca D. Snider. "Increased Protein Degradation after Eccentric Exercise." *European Journal of Applied Physiology* 54 (1985): 30–34.

Katch, Victor L., Frank I. Katch, Robert Moffatt, et al. "Muscular Development and Lean Body Weight in Body Builders and Weight Lifters." *Medicine and Science in Sports and Exercise* 12, no. 5 (1980): 340–344.

Kellis, J.T., and L.E. Vickery. "Inhibition of Estrogen Synthetase (Aromatase) by Flavones." *Science* 225 (1984): 1032–1033.

Kelly, V.G., and D.G. Jenkins. "Effect of Oral Creatine Supplementation on Near-Maximal Strength and Repeated Sets of High-Intensity Bench Press Exercise." *Journal of Strength and Conditioning Research* 12 (1998): 109–115.

Kies, C.V., and J.A. Driskell. *Sports Nutrition: Minerals and Electrolytes.* Boca Raton, FL: CRC, 1995.

Klatz, Ronald, and Robert Goldman. *The New Anti-Aging Revolution.* North Bergen, NJ: Basci Health Publications, Inc., 2003.

Knopf, R.F., J.W. Conn, S.S. Fajans, et al. "Plasma Growth Hormone Response to Intravenous Administration of Amino Acids." *Journal of Clinical Endocrinology* 25 (1965): 1140–1144.

Koeslag, J.H. "Post-Exercise Ketosis and the Hormone Response to Exercise: A Review." *Medicine and Science in Sports and Exercise* 14, no. 5 (1982): 327–334.

Kreider, R. "Which Protein Is Best for Sports Performance?" *Functional Foods and Nutraceuticals* (Sept. 2002).

Kreider, R.B., "Effects of Creatine Supplementation on Performance and Training Adaptations." *Molecular and Cellular Biochemistry* 244 (1–2) (Feb 2003): 89–94.

Kreider, R.B., et al. "Effects of Creatine Supplementation on Body Composition, Strength, and Sprint Performance." *Medicine and Science in Sports and Exercise* 30 (1998): 73–82.

Krieger, D.R., P.A Daly, A.G. Dulloo, et al. "Ephedrine, Caffeine and Aspirin Promote Weight Loss in Obese Subjects." *Trans. Assoc. Am. Physicians* 103 (1990): 307–312.

Lemon, P.W. "Effects of Exercise on Dietary Protein Requirements." *International Journal of Sport Nutrition* 8, no. 4 (1998): 426–447.

———. "Beyond the Zone: Protein Needs of Active Individuals." *Journal of the American College Nutrition* 19, no. 5, Suppl. (2000): 513S–521S.

Lemon, P.W.R., et al. "Protein Requirements and Muscle Mass/Strength Changes During Intensive Training in Novice Bodybuilders." *Journal of Applied Physiology* 73 (1992): 767–775.

Lemon, P.W., J.M. Berardi, and E.E. Noreen. "The Role of Protein and Amino Acid Supplements in the Athlete's Diet: Does Type or Timing of Ingestion Matter?" *Current Sports Medicine Reports* 1, no. 4 (2002): 214–21.

Lemon, P.W.R., and J. P. Mullin. "Effect of Initial Muscle Glycogen Levels on Protein Catabolism during Exercise." *The American Physiological Society* (1980): 624–629.

Lemon, P.W.R., and F. J. Nagle. "Effects of Exercise on Protein and Amino Acid Metabolism." *Medicine and Science in Sports and Exercise* 13, no. 3 (1981): 141–149.

Lemon, P.W.R., and D. Proctor. "Protein Intake and Athletic Performance." *Sports Medicine* 12, no. 5 (1991): 313.

Linderman, J., and T.D. Fahey. "Sodium Bicarbonate Ingestion and Exercise Performance." *Sports Medicine* 11, no. 9 (1991): 71.

Lucke, Christoph, and Seymour Glick. "Experimental Modification of the Sleep-Induced Peak of Growth Hormone Secretion." *Journal of Clinical Endocrinology and Metabolism* 32 (1971): 729–736.

MacLean, William C., Jr., and George G. Graham. "The Effect of Level of Protein Intake in Isoenergetic Diets on Energy Utilization." *American Journal of Clinical Nutrition* 32(7) (Jul 1979): 1381–1387.

Manore, M. "Vitamin B_6 and Exercise." *International Journal of Sports Nutrition* 4 (1994): 89.

Marable, N.L., J.F. Hickson Jr., M.K. Korslund, et al. "Urinary Nitrogen Excretion as Influenced by a Muscle-Building Exercise Program and Protein Intake Variation." *Nutrition Reports International* 19, no. 6 (1979): 795–805.

Marriott, B. *Food Components to Enhance Performance*. Washington, D.C.: National Academy Press, 1994.

Maughan, Ronald. "Creatine Supplementation and Exercise Performance." *International Journal of Sport Nutrition* 5(2) (Jun 1995): 94–101.

Mayer, Jean, Roy Purnima, and Kamakhya Prasad Mitra. "Relation Between Caloric Intake, Body Weight, and Physical Work: Studies in an Industrial Male Population in West Bengal." *American Journal of Clinical Nutrition* 4, no. 2 (1956): 169–175.

McBride, J.M., et al. "Effect of Resistance Exercise on Free Radical Production." *Medicine and Science in Sports and Exercise* 30 (1998): 67–72.

Mercola, Joseph. "Reduce Grains and Sugar to Lose Weight and Improve Health." *Cancer Comfort* 18 (July 30, 2003).

Merimee, T.J., D. Rabinowitz, and S.E. Fineberg. "Arginine-Initiated Release of Human Growth Hormone." *New England Journal of Medicine* 26(26) (Jun 1969): 1434–1438.

Merimee, Thomas J., David Rabinowitz, Lamar Riggs, et al. "Plasma Growth Hormone after Arginine Infusion." *New England Journal of Medicine* 23 (1967): 434–438.

Mitchell, J.B., D.L. Costill, J.A. Houmard, et al. "Effects of Carbohydrate Ingestion on Gastric Emptying and Exercise Performance." *Medicine and Science in Sports and Exercise* 20, no. 2 (1988): 110–115.

Mittleman, K.D., M.R. Ricci, and S.P. Bailey. "Branched-Chain Amino Acids Prolong Exercise During Heat Stress in Men and Women." *Medicine and Science in Sports and Exercise* 30 (1998): 83–91.

Mosoni L., and P.P. Mirand. "Type and Timing of Protein Feeding to Optimize Anabolism." *Current Opinions in Clinical Nutrition and Metabolic Care* 6, no. 3 (2003): 301–306.

Murphy, T., et al. "Performance Enhancing Ration Components Project: U.S. Army." Abstract. Presented at the 11th Annual Symposium of Sports and Cardiovascular Nutritionists. Atlanta, Georgia (April 1994): 22-24.

Pavlou, Konstantin N., William P. Steffee, Robert H. Lerman, et al. "Effects of Dieting and Exercise on Lean Body Mass, Oxygen Uptake, and Strength." *Medicine and Science in Sports and Exercise* 17, no. 4 (1974): 466–471.

Piehl, Karin. "Time Course for Refilling of Glycogen Stores in Human Muscle Fibres Following Exercise-Induced Glycogen Depletion." *Acta Physiologica Scandinavica* 90 (1974): 297–302.

Pizza, F., et al. "A Carbohydrate Loading Regimen Improves High Intensity, Short Duration Exercise Performance." *International Journal of Sport Science* (1995): 110–116.

Prasad, Ananda S. "Role of Trace Elements in Growth and Development." *Nutrition Research* (1985): 295–299.

Preuss H.G., D. DiFerdinando, M. Bagchi, D., et al. "Citrus Aurantium as a Thermogenic, Weight-Reduction Replacement for Ephedra: An Overview." *Journal of Medicine* 33, nos. 1–4 (2002):247–64.

Rassmusen, B.B., K.D. Tipton. "An Oral Essential Amino Acid-Carbohydrate Supplement Enhances Muscle Protein Anabolism After Exercise." *Journal of Applied Physiology* 88, No. 2 (Feb 2000): 386–392.

Rawson, E.S., and J.S. Volek. "Effects of Creatine Supplementation and Resistance Training on Muscle Strength and Weightlifting Performance." *Journal of Strength and Conditioning Research* 17, no. 4 (2003): 822–31.

Rossi, A., R.A. DiSilvestro, A. Blostein-Fujii. "Effects of Soy Consumption on Exercise-Induced Acute Muscle Damage and Oxidative Stress in Young Adult Males." *FASEB Journal* (1998): A653.

Rudman, D., et al. "Effects of Human Growth Hormone in Men over 60 Years Old." *New England Journal of Medicine* 323 (July 5, 1990): 1–6.

Satabin, Pascale, Pierre Portero, Gilles Defer, et al. "Metabolic and Hormonal Responses to Lipid and Carbohydrate Diets during Exercise in Man." *Medicine and Science in Sports and Exercise* 19, no. 3 (1987): 218–223.

Schalch, Don S. "The Influence of Physical Stress and Exercise on Growth Hormone and Insulin Secretion in Man." *Journal of Laboratory and Clinical Medicine* 69, no. 2 (1967): 256–267.

Schwartz, J.M., Y. Schulz, V. Piolino, et al. "Thermogenesis in Men and Women Induced by Fructose vs. Glucose Added to a Meal." *American Journal of Clinical Nutrition* 49 (1989): 667–674.

Spiller, G.A., C.D. Jensen, T.S. Pattison, et al. "Effect of Protein Dose on Serum Glucose and Insulin Response to Sugars." *American Journal of Clinical Nutrition* 46 (1987): 474–480.

Tarnopolsky, M.A., and D.P. MacLennan. "Creatine Monohydrate Supplementation Enhances High-Intensity Exercise Performance in Males and Females." *International Journal of Sport Nutrition and Exercise Metabolism* 10, no. 4 (2000): 452–63.

Tesch, Per, et al. "Skeletal Muscle Glycogen Loss Evoked by Resistance Exercise." *Journal of Strength and Conditioning Research* 12 (1998): 67–73.

Thomas, D., et al. "Plasma Glucose Levels after Prolonged Strenuous Exercise Correlate Inversely with Glycemic Response to Food Consumed before Exercise." *International Journal of Sport Nutrition* 4 (1994): 361.

Tipton, K.D., and Wolfe, R.R. "Exercise, Protein Metabolism, and Muscle Growth." *International Journal of Sport Nutrition and Exercise Metabolism* 11 (2001): 109–132.

Todd, Karen S., Gail E. Butterfield, and Doris Howes Calloway. "Nitrogen Balance in Men with Adequate and Deficient Energy Intake at Three Levels of Work." *Journal of Nutrition* 114 (1984): 2107–2118.

Tokmakidis, S.P. "The Effects of Ibuprofen on Delayed Muscle Soreness and Muscle Performance after Eccentric Exercise." *Journal of Strength and Conditioning Research,* 17 (February 2003): 53–59.

Tsintzas, K. and C. Williams. "Human Muscle Glycogen Metabolism during Exercise. Effect of Carbohydrate Supplementation." *Sports Medicine* 25 (1998): 7–23.

Valeriani, A. "The Need for Carbohydrate Intake During Endurance Exercise." *Sports Medicine* 12, no. 6 (1991): 349.

Walberg, Janet L., V. Karina Ruiz, Sandra L. Tarlton, et al. "Exercise Capacity and Nitrogen Loss during a High or Low Carbohydrate Diet." *Medicine and Science in Sports and Exercise* 20 (1986): 34–43.

Warber, J.P., W.J. Tharion, J.F. Patton, et al. "The Effect of Creatine Monohydrate Supplementation on Obstacle Course and Multiple Bench Press Performance." *Journal of Strength and Conditioning Research* 16, no. 4 (2002): 500–8.

Ward, P.S., and D.C.L. Savage. "Growth Hormone Responses to Sleep, Insulin Hypoglycemia and Arginine Infusion." *Hormone Research* 22 (1985): 7–11.

Welbourne, I.C. "Increases in Plasma Bicarbonate and Growth Hormone After an Oral Glutamin Load." *American Journal of Clinication Nutrition* 61 (1995): 1058–1061.

Weltman, Arthur, Sharleen Matter, and Bryant A. Stamford. "Caloric Restriction and/or Mild Exercise: Effects on Serum Lipids and Body Composition." *American Journal of Clinical Nutrition* 33 (1980): 1002–1009.

West, D. "Reduced Body Fat With Conjugated Linoleic Acid Feeding in the Mouse." *Federation of American Societies of Experimental Biology Journal* 11 (1997): A599.

Wilcox, Anthony R. "The Effects of Caffeine and Exercise on Body Weight, Fat-Pad Weight, and Fat-Cell Size." *Medicine and Science in Sports and Exercise* 14 (1981): 317–321.

Williams, M.H. "Vitamin Supplementation and Athletic Performance." *International Journal of Vitamin and Nutrition Research* 30 (1989): 163.

Wolfe, R.R. "Protein Supplements and Exercise." *American Journal of Clinical Nutrition* 72 Suppl. (2000): 551S–557S.

Wolinsky, I., and J. Hickson. *Nutrition in Exercise and Sport.* 2nd ed. Boca Raton, FL: CRC Press, 1994.

Wright, J. "Tribulus: A Natural Wonder." *Muscle and Fitness* 224 (September 1996): 140–142.

Yan, W., et al. "Steroidal Saponins from Fruits of Tribulus Terrestris." *Phytochemistry* 42, no. 5 (1996): 1417–1422.

Young, K., and C.T.M. Davies. "Effect of Diet on Human Muscle Weakness Following Prolonged Exercise." *European Journal of Applied Physiology* 53 (1984): 81–85.

Young, Vernon R., and Peter L. Pellett. "Protein Intake and Requirements with Reference to Diet and Health." *American Journal of Clinical Nutrition* 45 (1987): 1323–1343.

Zawadzki, K.M., B.B. Yaspelkis, and J.L. Ivy. "Carbohydrate-Protein Complex Increases the Rate of Muscle Glycogen Storage after Exercise." *Journal of Applied Physiology* 72 (1992): 1854–1859.

Macrobolic Nutrition Chart References

Y. Boirie, M. Dangin, P. Gachon, et al., "Slow and Fast Dietary Proteins Differently Modulate Postprandial Protein Accretion," *Proceedings of the National Academy of Science U.S.A.* 94 (1997): 14930–14935.

Céline Morens, Cécile Bos, Maria E. Pueyo, et al., "Increasing Habitual Protein Intake Accentuates Differences in Postprandial Dietary Nitrogen Utilization between Protein Sources in Humans," *Journal of Nutrition* 133 (2003): 2733–2740.

Index

About the Authors

Gerard Dente has over fifteen years of experience in bodybuilding and nutrition. He is a former top-ranked national bodybuilder who has now dedicated his life to sports enhancement through nutrition and supplementation. He is the founder and president of one of the leading sports nutrition companies, Maximum Human Performance. He also serves as a nutritional consultant to many professional athletes and bodybuilders.

Kevin Hopkins attended Rutgers University College of Pharmacy and took a position with one of the nation's largest compounding pharmacies. Shortly thereafter, he started a business that integrated the use of nutritional supplements with prescription medications and nutrition. He also works with MHP's research and development team in designing cutting-edge supplements. He owns Gibson's Gym in Washington, New Jersey, and is continuing to compete recreationally as a bodybuilder in the NPC.